MATH PUZZLES & GAMES

DORSET PRESS

Illustrations by Pat Hickman

This edition published by Dorset Press,
a division of Barnes & Noble, Inc.,
by arrangement with Michael Holt.

1992 Dorset Press

ISBN 0-88029-948-7

Printed and bound in the United States of America

M 9 8 7 6 5 4

VOLUME ONE

MATH PUZZLES & GAMES

BY MICHAEL HOLT

CONTENTS

INTRODUCTION

A word of advice on solving puzzles. If you really get stuck, don't give up—or you'll spoil the fun. Put the sticky puzzle aside, and perhaps the next day a new line of attack may suddenly strike you. Or you can try to solve an easier puzzle similar to the sticky one. Or again you can guess trial answers just to see if they make sense. Who knows, you might be lucky and hit on the right answer. Of course, a pure fluke is not as satisfying as working the puzzle out logically.

As a last resort you can always look up the answer, but only glance over the first few lines. This may give you the clue you need without giving the game away. As you will see, I have written very complete answers to the harder puzzles or to those needing several steps to solve.

But most of the puzzles call for straightforward arithmetic or simple reasoning. Almost all of them need no algebra to speak of; the couple that do can be solved, as I show, by trial and error or cunning.

The puzzles are not graded but are simply grouped by type; however, within each type you will find the easier ones at the start and the harder ones at the end. Practically all the puzzles are mathematical, but I have included a few word puzzles where they have an unusual slant or are totally different from crosswords, acrostics, and the general run of word puzzles.

As a slight departure from some puzzle books, I have included some easy-to-do mathematical tricks. Most of them I have performed myself either on stage or on television in Britain. Follow the instructions carefully, and with a little practice you should be able to amaze an audience with your mathematical powers. I should add that all the tricks work automatically: the magic is in the mathematics and does not require any sleight-of-hand skill on your part. I have ended the book with a group of puzzles about physics—that is, problems you can solve by experiment, if you prefer, about monkeys on ropes, moving belts, magnets, and the like.

In this collection of puzzles you will find, I hope you will agree, a happy mixture of puzzles of all kinds suitable for the entire family. Some are easy, some hard; some are versions of classical puzzles, and a few are truly brand-new ones. I find that today the Russians are the best puzzle-makers, although nobody has outdone the colorful story puzzles of America's greatest puzzlist, Sam Loyd, or his life-long British rival, Henry Dudeney. Both men worked toward the end of the nineteenth century. To them and to ***Moscow Puzzles: Three Hundred Fifty-nine Mathematical Recreations*** (Scribners), I am particularly indebted. Where I have adapted a Loyd or Dudeney puzzle, I have invariably had to simplify it for a younger—and more modern—audience. For some puzzle ideas I have drawn from mathematical research in education.

But far and away the most original "idea-men" are the children I have known, including my own son and daughter. To all of them I owe a lot.

1. Number Problems

Here is a wide selection of problems and puzzles that you can solve with only the simplest arithmetic; a few you could do by algebra, but as the answers show, this is not essential. The main problem is to wrest the actual "sum" from the words of the puzzle. The sum itself should present little or no difficulty—especially if you have a pocket calculator handy.

All the Fun of the Fair

Our picture shows one of the booths at a fair. You can have as many throws as you like, but you must score exactly 50. How do you do so? That is, what toys will you be able to win?

Chessboard Problem

How many squares are there on an eight-by-eight chessboard? For a start the answer's *not* 64. There are all the bigger squares (multiples of the smaller ones) to take into account. Here is a method that may ease the problem and reduce it from sheer impossibility to simple slog! Think of how many seven-by-seven squares there are. Draw one on an eight-by-eight board. As you see, you can slide it up one square or across one square. That's two positions up and two positions across, allowing it 2 X 2 different positions. Thus there are 2 X 2 different seven-by-seven squares on the board. Now what about the six-by-six squares? Draw a six-by-six square on your chessboard picture. You will find you can slide it up two places and across two places. So, including the original position, that gives . . . well, how many positions in all? Got the hang of it? (Don't forget there is just *one* eight-by-eight square.)

Cat and Mice

Puss had taken a catnap. He dreamed that there were five mice sitting in a circle around him, four gray mice and one white mouse. In his dream Master says: "Go on, Puss, you can eat them up. But you can only eat each fifth mouse, going around in a clockwise direction. The last mouse you eat must be the white mouse."

HINT: Number the mice in a circle from 1 to 5. Pretend that Puss starts on the mouse at position 1. At what number must the white mouse be?

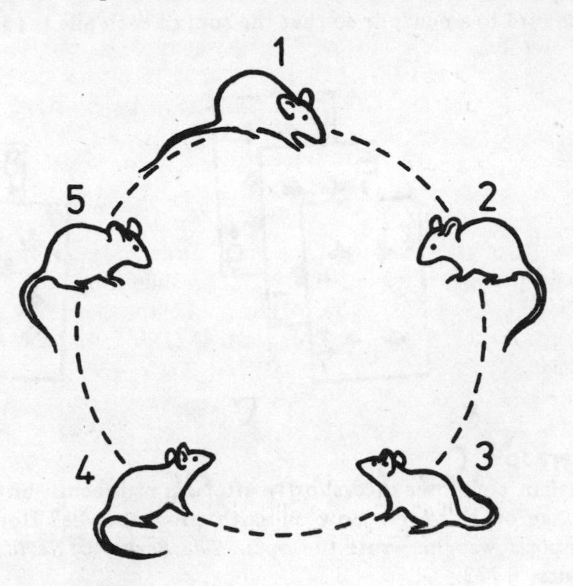

A Question of Ages

Two youngsters are chatting about their ages. Sam is just three times as old as May. But in two years' time he will only be twice as old as she is. How old is each youngster?

Another Question of Ages

In a film the actor Charles Coburn plays an elderly "uncle" character who is accused of marrying a girl when he is three times her age. He wittily replies: "Ah, but in twenty years' time I shall only be twice her age!" How old is the "uncle" and the girl?

Teen-Age Problem

Sam is four years younger than Jo. But in five years' time Jo will be twice Sam's age now. How old are they now?

CLUE: One of them is a teen-ager.

15 Shuffle

Move just one card to a new pile so that the sum of each pile is 15.

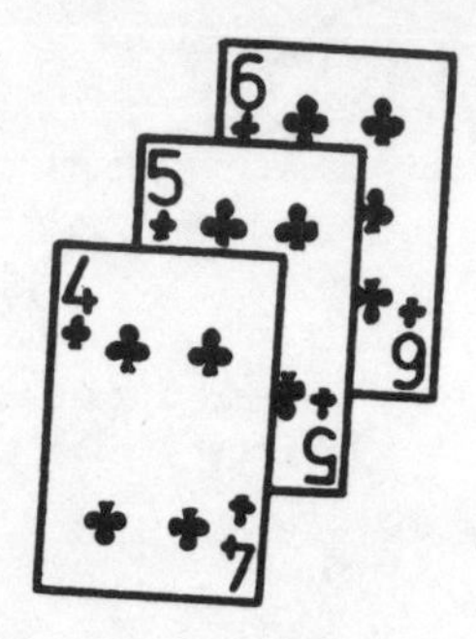

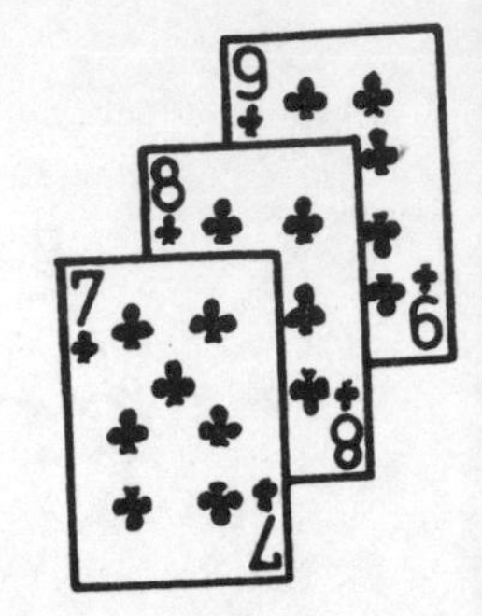

Birthday Paradox

A famous Italian composer died shortly after his eighteenth birthday—at the ripe old age of 76 years! How on earth could that be? Don't worry who the composer was; he wrote the opera *The Barber of Seville.* He was born in February 1792.

Word Sums

In word sums or letter sums letters stand for digits. What you have to do is find the digits that fit the sums. Trial and error and some sound reasoning will be needed. Here's a simple one to set you off:

$$\begin{array}{r} \text{T W O} \\ +\ \text{T W O} \\ \hline \text{F I V E} \end{array}$$

Each letter O stands for 4. There are several solutions possible.

Easy as ABC?

In these two sums, each letter stands for a different digit. What are the digits?

$$\begin{array}{r} \text{A A A} \\ \text{B B B} \\ +\ \text{C C C} \\ \hline \text{F G H I} \end{array} \qquad \begin{array}{r} \text{A A A} \\ \text{D D D} \\ +\ \text{E E E} \\ \hline \text{F G H I} \end{array}$$

To start off, remember that the biggest number you can get from adding three single-digit numbers is three 9s, or 27. Since *B* and *C* must be different from A, then the most they add up to is $9 + 8 + 7 = 24$. But the "carry" number must be different in the tens place and also in the hundreds place. So $A + B + C$ must equal 19. You're on your own.

The Missing Dollar

Three college girls want to buy a $30 radio they see in the local store. They each chip in $10 and buy it. The manager tells the saleslady she should have sold it for $25, since it was a sale. The very next day when the girls are passing the store, the saleslady beckons them in. She explains that she has made a mistake over the price and she owes each of them $1. She has taken $5 from the till, and out of it she gives each girl $1—so each paid $9, not $10. The saleslady secretly pockets the other $2. The girls have paid three lots of $9, or $27 in all, and the saleslady has made $2 on the sly. But $27 and $2 is $29. So where has the other dollar gone?

Merchants' Finger Figuring

In the Middle Ages merchants used to multiply on their fingers. They used this finger figuring only for numbers between 5 and 10. You can use it if ever your memory of your multiplaction tables fails you.

This is how the merchants multiplied 6 by 9. First show 9 on one hand by putting up five fingers, closing your fist, and then lifting four more fingers one by one: 6-7-8-9. So you have four fingers up. To show 6 on the other hand, put up five fingers, close your fist, then lift one finger, your thumb; you've put up six fingers in all.

You multiply the numbers like this. Add the fingers sticking up and multiply those bent down. Using the picture, this means you add 1 (the thumb) to 4 (the four fingers) to give 5; this is the number of tens, or 50. Multiply the bent fingers: $4 \times 1 = 4$ ones $= 4$. Total the two answers: $50 + 4 = 54$, which is 6×9. Try it out on other multiplications. There is, of course, no answer given.

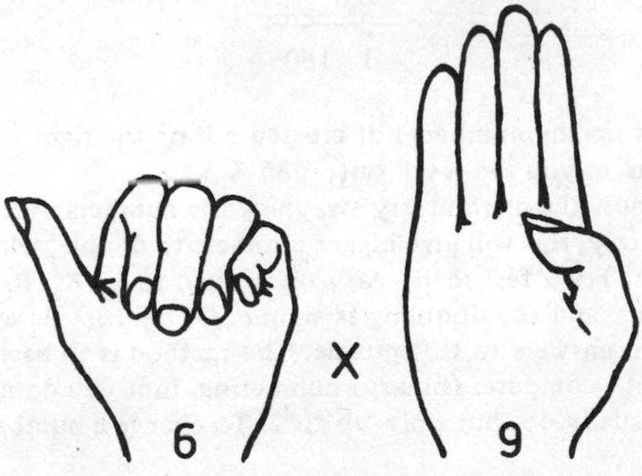

6 X 9

You Can't Take It (All) with You

Suppose a millionaire offered you all the dollar bills you could take away with you, but you would have to count them nonstop! You can take what you count until you stop. We'll say you count at one bill a second. How many do you think you could really take?

Peasants' Multiplying

The oldest dodge for multiplying is based only on doubling and halving. This method was certainly used by the Egyptians. Here is how to multiply 35 by 5.

First halve the left side each time and double the number on the right, like this:

35 ×	5
17	10
8	20
4	40
2	80
1	160

Happily, ignore remainders. So you write half of 35 as 17, not as 17½. This is why the method is so easy to use. Go on halving till you get to 1 on the left.

The next step is to cross off all the *even* numbers on the left side together with their partners on the right:

35 ×	5
17	10
~~8~~	~~20~~
~~4~~	~~40~~
~~2~~	~~80~~
1	160

Finally, add up the numbers not crossed out on the right side: 5 + 10 + 160 = 175. This, as you can work out, is 35 × 5.

To get to know the method, try swapping the numbers over: that is, try 5 × 35. Obviously, this will give bigger numbers to double, which makes it harder for you. Try a few really easy ones, such as 13 × 10. The answer (130) is obvious, and the doubling is simple. Or try 13 × 1: even simpler!

There are no answers to this puzzle. The method is all based on changing numbers into computer (binary) numbering. In it you do not count up to 10, as we usually do, but only up to 2. To change a number to binary, you divide by 2 again and again and note down the remainders. We won't turn this into a lecture; we'll simply leave it at that.

Tear 'n' Stack

Here is a puzzle to demonstrate the power of doubling. Take a sheet of paper and tear it across the middle. Put the 2 halves together and tear them in half to get 4 pieces of paper. Stack them and tear in half to get 8 pieces. Stack and tear again to get 16 pieces. Continue doing this 47 times. You can't, of course, as you can quickly discover. How high a stack would you get if you could? As high as your table? the roof of a house? the top of the Empire State Building? nearly to the moon? Say a sheet is one thousandth of an inch (known as a thou) thick; so a stack of 1,000 sheets will be one inch high.

Grains of Wheat

Long ago in India the grand vizier Sissa Ben Dahir invented the game of chess for King Shirham. The king was so delighted with the game, he offered the grand vizier any boon he desired. The clever vizier seemed very modest in his desire, saying to the king: "Majesty, give me a grain of wheat to put on the first square of the chessboard, and two grains to put on the second square, and four grains to put on the third, and eight grains to put on the fourth. And so, O King, doubling the number of grains of wheat on each square that follows, give me enough wheat to cover all sixty-four squares of the board."

What a fool! the King thought to himself. Then he said aloud: "Your boon is granted, Grand Vizier."

But easier said than done! The king sent for a sack of wheat to be brought to the throne. When the grains were counted out, the sack was emptied before they had counted out the twentieth square. Can you say, then, roughly how many grains of wheat were in a sack? Choose from:

100,000	1,000,000	10,000

How many grains of wheat were needed to cover the chessboard in the grand vizier's way? Choose from:

about 18 million million million grains
today's annual world wheat production for two thousand years
18,446,744,073,709,551,615 grains
the number of grains of sand on the beach at Coney Island

A Sweet Problem

Can you put ten sugar lumps into three cups so there is an *odd* number of lumps in each cup?

Stock Taking

A cunning farmer, asked how many sheep he had, replied: "A third of my sheep are in the barn. A fifth are out to pasture. Three times the difference of these two numbers are newborn. And one is my daughter's pet. But there's less than twenty in all." How many sheep had the farmer?

Slobodian Coin Puzzle

In Slobodia they only have two coins, a one-slob coin and a two-slob coin. How many ways can a Slobodian pay a sum of one slob? Simple. One way. How many ways for a sum of two slobs? Two ways—with two one-slob coins or with one two-slob coin. Can you tell how many ways a Slobodian can pay a sum of six slobs?

Tug of War

In a tug of war four boys can tug as hard as five girls.

And two girls and one boy can tug as hard as one dog.

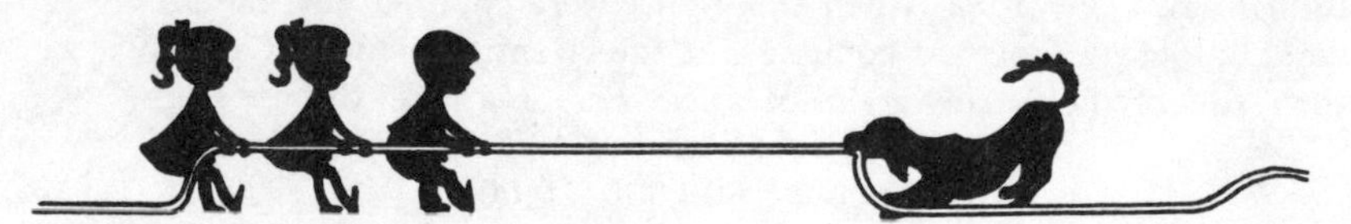

The dog and three girls tug against four boys.

Which side will win the last tug of war?

Check-out Check

In the store Gus said to the check-out person: "I bought two sticks of chewing gum at ten cents and three bars of chocolate. But I can't remember how much the chocolate cost." "That'll be $2.20," said the checker. Gus said: "But you've made a mistake!" The checker checked again and agreed with Gus. How did Gus spot the error?

CLUE: It's all to do with dividing one number into another.

Puzzle Triangles

Six discs are joined by one-way arrows and two-way links, as shown in our picture. Each arrow means you add 4 to the number the arrow begins on and then divide the result by 6 and keep the remainder and put *that* in the disc the arrow points to. The puzzle is to give each disc its number, from 0 up to 6. For example, you begin at 0, already marked. Add 4 and the result is 4; divide by 6 and keep the remainder, 4, and put that in the disc the arrow points to. Also, on the inner triangle, beginning on 3 (already marked), the disc pointed to is 1 because (3 + 4)/6 leaves a remainder of 1. The difference between the numbers on the discs at either end of each two-way link is 3. See if you can fill in all the discs.

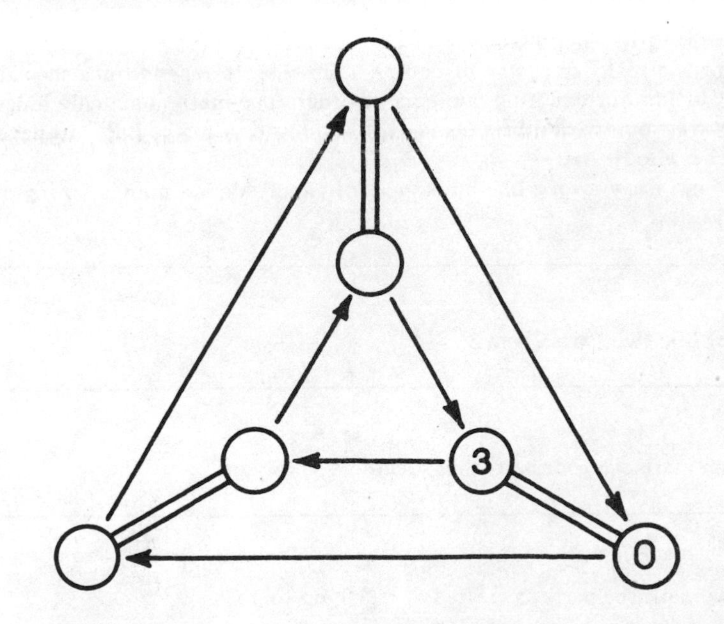

Nice Work If You Can Get It!

A college girl applied for a job advertised in her local newspaper. The boss, who interviewed her, had a mathematical turn of mind. He offered her two pay rates: a straight ten dollars a day; or one cent the first day, two cents the second day, four cents the third day, eight cents the fourth day, and so on, the pay doubling each day. The girl chose the second pay rate. The boss hired her. Why?

CLUE: He *actually* paid her a different rate!

12 Days' Gifts

On the twelfth day of Christmas my true love sent to me
12 drummers drumming, 11 pipers piping,
10 lords aleaping, 9 ladies dancing,
8 maids amilking, 7 swans aswimming,
6 geese alaying, 5 gold rings,
4 calling birds, 3 French hens,
2 turtledoves, and a partridge in a pear tree.

How many things did my true love send to me?

Dividing-the-Line Code

Here is a really new way of coding a message. It depends on a special way of putting our counting numbers in order. The method actually hinges on the way binary numbers (as used in computers) work. But you need not bother about that.

First draw a long line on a sheet of paper. Mark a point near its middle and call it 1.

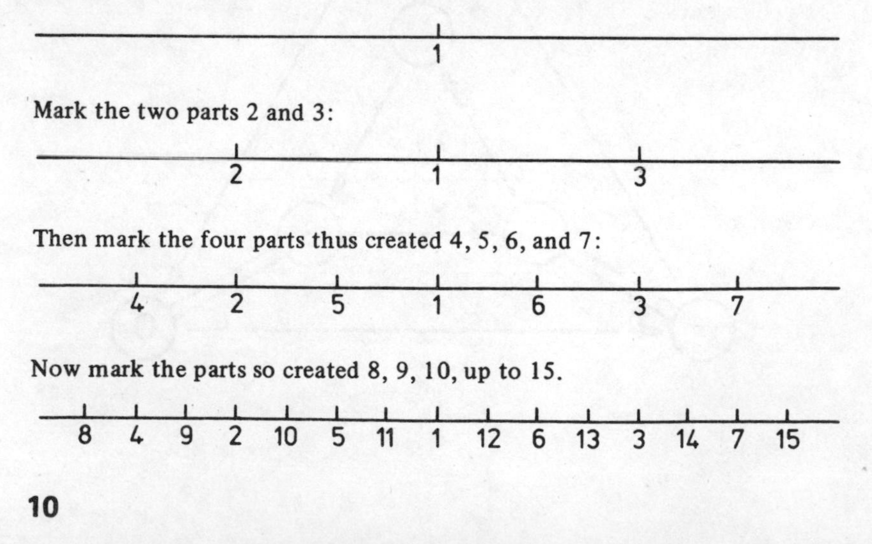

Now divide the line once more so the last number is 31.

Now for the code. Suppose you want to put this little message into code: MEET ME AT THE HAUNTED HOUSE. Number off the letters in the order they come in the message:

1 2 3 4 5 6 7 8
M E E T M E A T

You see we run the words together, for it is usually possible to unravel words in a message once you have all the letters, provided you have enough words (as the eight letters show!). Having numbered your letters serially, now write them above your prepared number line. So the first eight letters come out like this:

T T E M M E E A
8 4 2 5 1 6 3 7

I have given you a line that will take only 31-letter messages. If you want to send a longer message, then all you have to do is divide the parts of the line once more and put in the numbers above the marks, from 32 up to 63.

Can you see the pattern of each new set of numbers you write in? Just to remind you, the number of parts the line is divided into is part of the following series: 2, 4, 8 . . . With your coded message you can send the key number, here 16; this tells the person who receives the message how many parts he must divide his line into to decode the message. But it doesn't matter if you don't put in the 16. Can you see why?

Holiday Message

Copy this picture of a ruler. On it write each letter above its correct mark shown in the box. The letter *D* has been done for you. Some of the letters appear twice and so go above two marks. Can you find the holiday message?

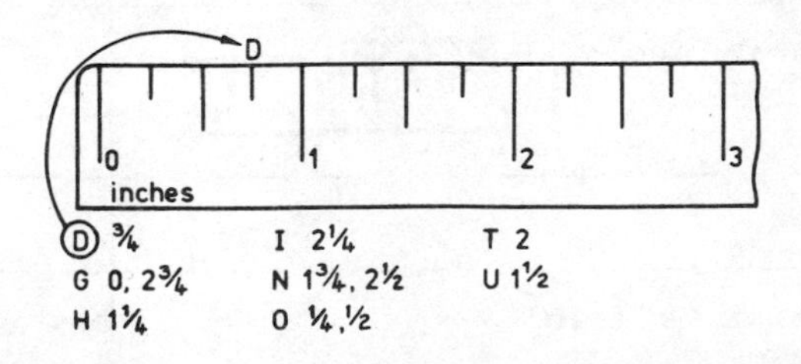

Bottle and Cork

A bottle costs three cents more than a cork. (Both are returnable!) Together they cost five cents. How much does each cost? Too easy? Then try the next puzzle.

Juggling and Balancing

In picture *A* the jug on the left pan balances the bottle on the right pan. In *B* the jug alone balances a mug and a plate. In *C* three of these plates balance two bottles. How many mugs will balance a jug?

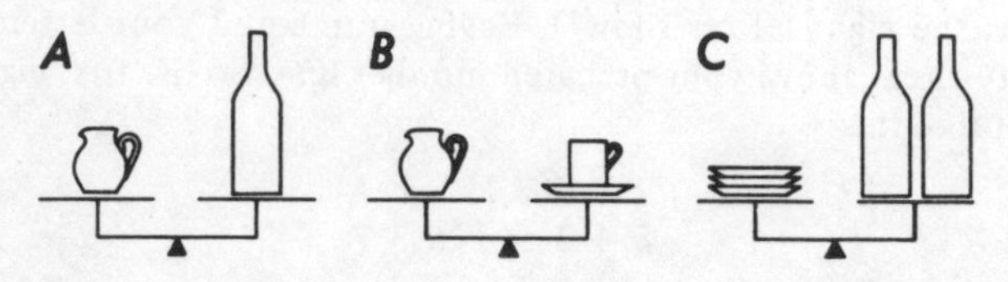

Hidden Animal

The idea in this code is to find the hidden animal. What you do is work out each little problem. The answer will be a number. You change this number to its letter in the alphabet, 1 to *A*, 2 to *B*, 3 to *C*, and so on. The completed letters spell a well-known animal. For example, suppose the problem was: *How many in a dozen?* The answer is 12. The twelfth letter of the alphabet is *L*. So you would write *L*.

Copy and fill in a table like this:

	Number	*Letter*
How many square feet in a rug three feet by four feet?		
How many dimes in half a dollar?		
Half the number of days that are in September		
4 squared equals . . .		
How long is the grey rod?		
2 X 3 X 3 =		
This number times itself is 16:		

CLUE: It cannot change its spots.

Pictures by Numbers

You know the game of Battleships, I expect, where you name squares in a grid by calling two numbers. For instance, in the bit of grid shown here there are three shaded squares: *A, B,* and *C.* To name a square, you call the *across* number first, then the *up* number. So for square *A* you call 1, 2; for *B,* 2, 1. The order of the numbers makes all the difference! The little arrow in the corner of the grid may remind you of this order. Square *C* is 2, 2.

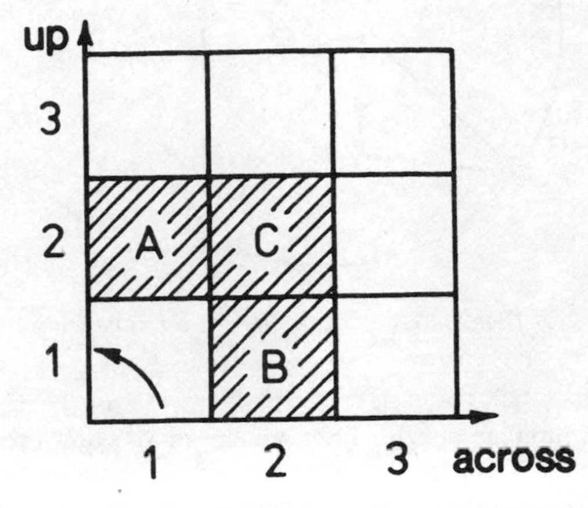

As in Battleships, we can shade in a picture on a grid by calling out number pairs. For fun we can code the number pairs by using a cunning device, a mapping. This is how we put the numbers for the shaded squares into code:

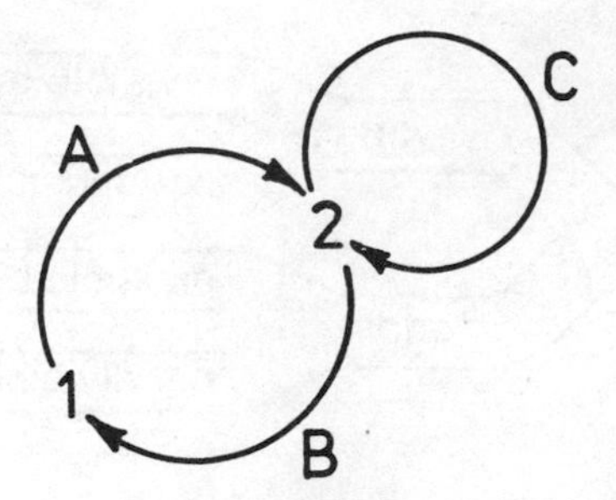

The *1*-to-*2* arrow means you shade the square *A* (1, 2), *2*-to-*1* means you shade square *B* (2, 1), and the arrow looping back on *2* means shade square *C* (2, 2).

All set? Then try your hand at drawing the picture from the mapping shown here. You'll need an eight-by-eight grid to draw it on.

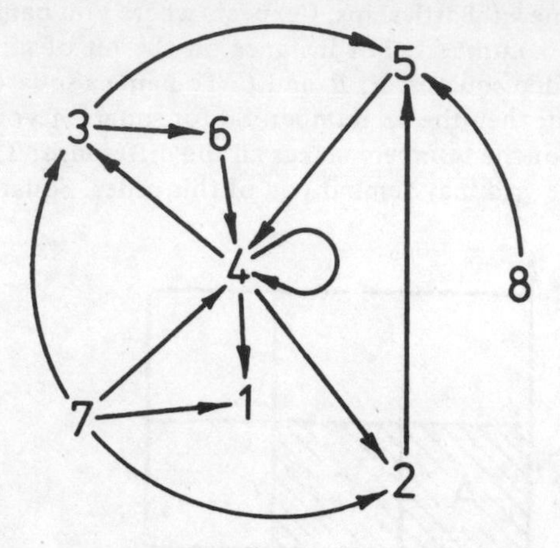

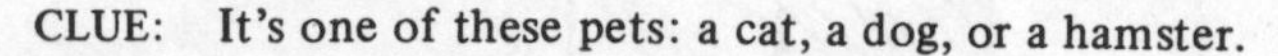

CLUE: It's one of these pets: a cat, a dog, or a hamster.

Number Tracks

Here's a novel number puzzle. First you need to copy the tracks if this book is not yours. Then jot down where each of the numbers 1 to 20 end up—at *A*, *B*, *C*, or *D*—after you have sent them along their tracks. For example, 1 must take the lower odds track at the first fork because it is an odd number; 2, an even number, takes the upper track. At the next fork 1 takes the lower track because it is not divisible by 3. So 1 ends up in *D;* 2 ends up in *B*, 3 in *C*, and 6 in *A*. See if you can sort out the other numbers waiting at the starting gate. Spot anything special about all the numbers that end up in *A?*

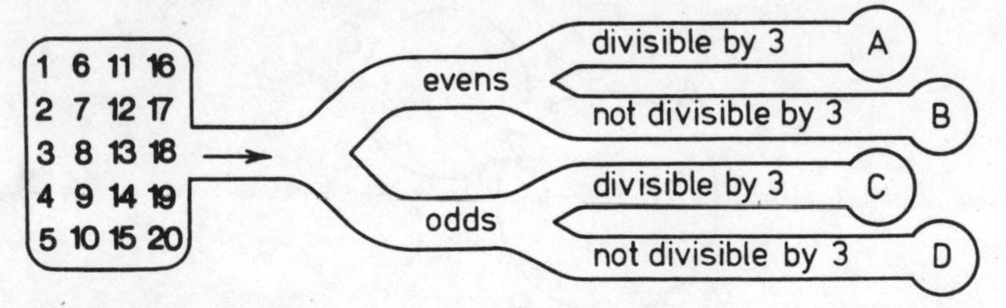

Number Fo*u*rte!

Think of a number—any number will do. Write it out in full as a word. Count the number of letters in the word and write down that number too as a word; again count the number of letters and spell that number out, and so on. Go on as far as you can, but we bet you will always finish up with the word *four.* Here is an example:

FIFTY-THREE ⟶ TEN ⟶ THREE ⟶ FIVE ⟶ FOUR
(ten letters) (three letters) (five letters) (four letters) (four letters)

The chain of numbers ends at four and stays there. You can bet a friend that whatever number he thinks of, provided it is spelled properly, the chain will always end up at FOUR. Try a few numbers yourself first to see.

Solve It in Your Head

If you've done equations, you can surely solve these with pencil and paper:

$$7x + 3y = 27$$
$$3x + 7y = 23$$

But can you solve them together in your head? You might multiply the first equation by 3 and the second by 7 in your head. Better still, use another, simpler method.

HINT: Add the equations; then take them away.

Movie Times

At his neighborhood movie theater George checks on the time of the films showing that day. He sees that some of the numerals have fallen off the display board:

Carry On UFOs	2:30	5:30	
The Reel Life	3:30		8:30
The Impossible Triangle	3:45		

Can you say when the second showing of *The Reel Life* begins? When does the film *The Impossible Triangle* end?

Time, Please

Tell me quickly: What time is it when it's 60 minutes to 2?

Picture and Frame

A portrait of your favorite TV star costs half a dollar more than the frame to go around it. Together they cost two dollars. How much does each cost?

Idle Ivan and the Devil

An old Russian tale tells how Idle Ivan was fooling about by a river. He sighed to himself: "Everybody tells me to get a job or go to the devil. But I don't 'xpect even he could help me get rich."

No sooner had he said this than the devil himself was standing before him. "You want to make money, Ivan?" asked the devil. Ivan nodded, lazily. "Then," the devil went on, "you see that bridge over there? All you have to do is cross it. And every time you do, the money in your pocket will double." Ivan was about to make for the bridge when the devil stopped him. "One moment," said the devil foxily. "Seeing that I'm so generous, I think you ought to give me a little for my pains. Will you give me eight rubles every time you cross the bridge?"

Idle Ivan readily agreed. He crossed the bridge and put his hand in his pocket. As if by magic the money *had* doubled! He lobbed eight rubles over the river to the devil and crossed again. Again his money doubled; he paid another eight rubles to the devil and crossed a third time. Once more his money doubled. But when he counted it, he found he had only eight rubles in his pocket, which he threw to the devil, leaving him with no money in his pocket to double.

The devil laughed and vanished.

PUZZLE: How much money did Idle Ivan start with in his pocket?

Happy Landing

Gary takes off from La Guardia Airport, New York, at 10:00 in the morning. In Anchorage, Alaska, the time is exactly 5:00 in the morning. Gary's flight takes just seven hours. Can you tell what time he should land in Anchorage by *Anchorage time?*

Cracked-Clock Problem

How can you split the clockface in two so that the sum of the numbers on the two halves are the same?

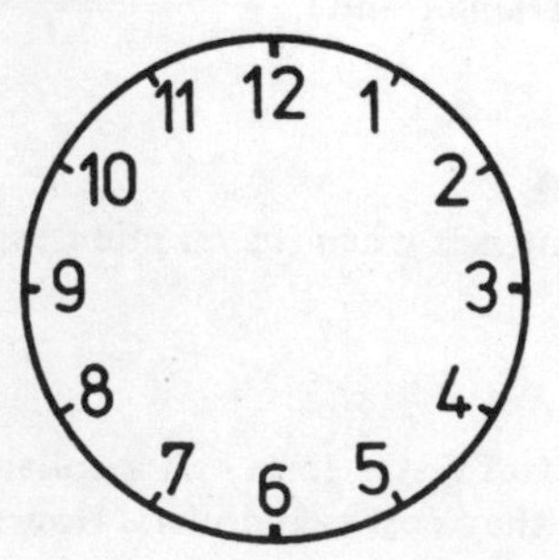

Stamp-Strip Puzzle

Here is a pretty puzzle to try next time you buy a strip of stamps. No reason why you shouldn't use a strip of ordinary paper. Look at the strip of two stamps, which the artist has labeled *a* and *b*. The puzzle is: How many ways of folding the stamps are there if you don't break the strip? Well, obviously, just one, *ab*. Now take a strip of three stamps. How many different ways of folding the stamps are there now? As the picture shows, there are two ways, *abc* and *acb*. How many different ways are there of folding a strip of four stamps? To start you off, we show you the first two ways, *abcd* and *abdc*. Look at the pictures and see if you can write down the other three ways.

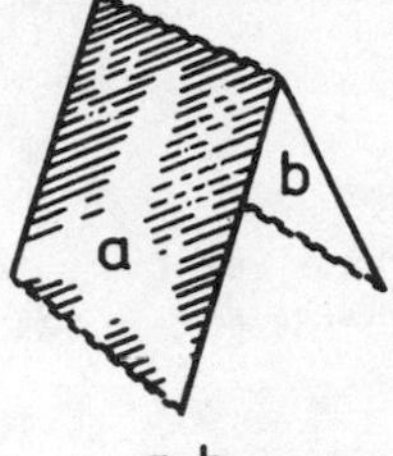

a b

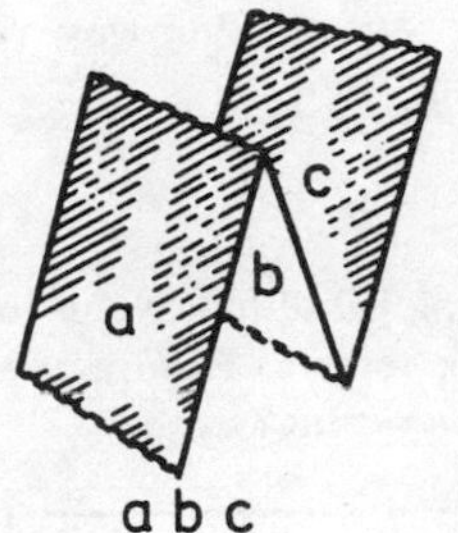

a b c

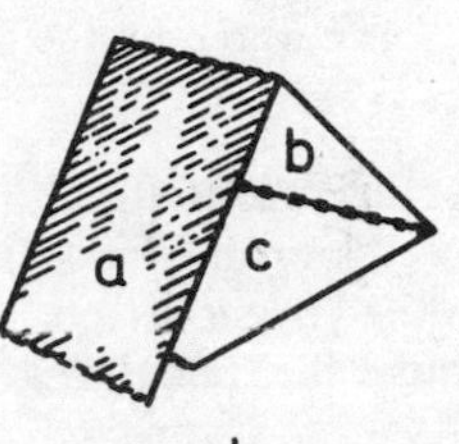

a c b

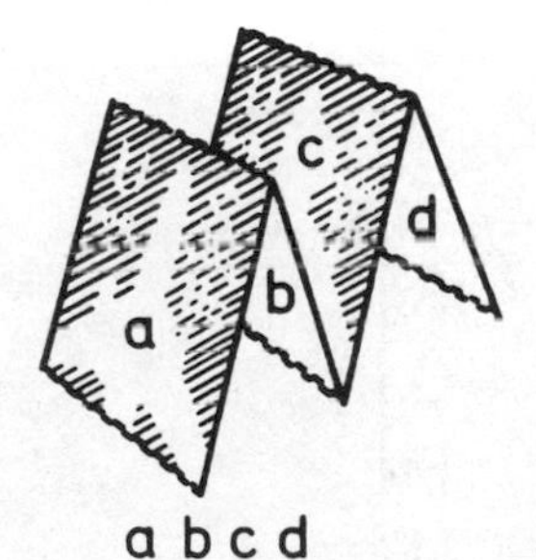

a b c d

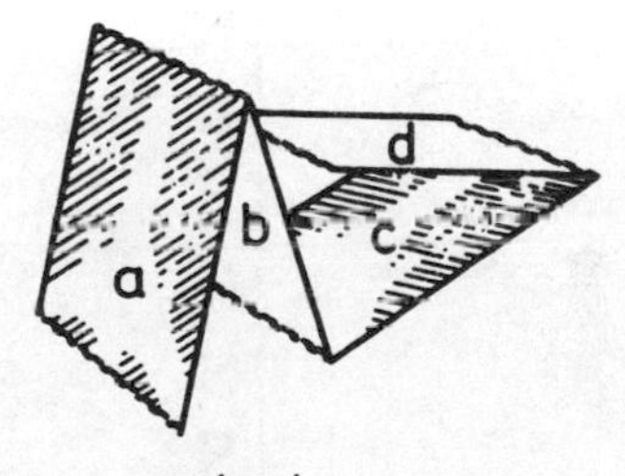

a b d c

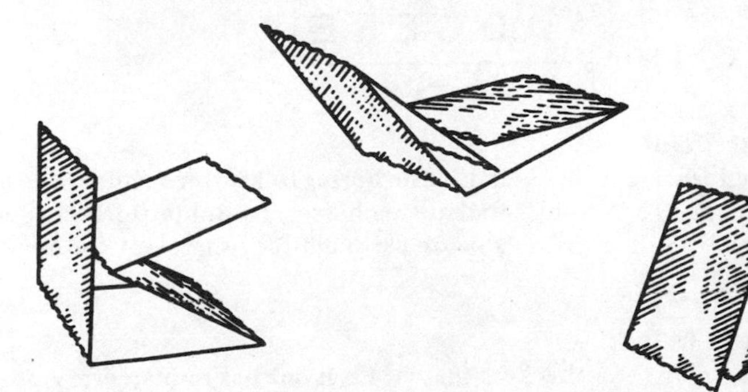

The Smallest Flock

A farmer had a very large flock of sheep. He discovered something very odd about their number: When he counted them in 2s he had 1 left over; he also had 1 left over when he counted them in 3s, 4s, 5s, and so on up to 10s. The problem is: What was the *smallest* size of flock he must have had?

HINT: If this is too hard, pretend that he counted the flock in 2s, 3s, and 4s only, 1 over each time. What is the smallest size flock then? It is not $2 \times 3 \times 4 + 1$, or 25, because that is not the *smallest* flock possible. Remember 2 goes into 4, so if the flock is divisible by 4 with 1 left over, it is also divisible by 2 with 1 left over. So the smallest size of flock is $3 \times 4 + 1$, or 13. If you like to think of it another way, remember that the dividing by 2 is covered by the dividing by 4.

Letter Frame-up

A well-known (almost!) saying is hidden in this letter frame. See if you can read it. Begin at one of the letters. Reading every other letter, go twice around the frame. What is the saying?

```
L S I M N U G C
R             S
L             H
E             T
O             S
H             O
R             P
T             N
A A D G E E E
```

The Farmer's Will

A farmer died leaving in his will 17 fine horses to his three children, Ann, Bob, and Charlie. To Ann he left half his horses, to Bob a third of them, and to Charlie a ninth of them. How on earth did they share out the horses?

The Checkers Match

Five children enter for a checkers match. Each one has to play every other one. How many games must they play?

The Spelling Bee

The picture shows where the rare Spelling bee lives: in a letter comb. It was, as you recall, named for the famous Dr. Spelling, the noted "bee-all-and-end-all-ologist." How many ways can the bee move down the honeycomb from cell *R* and spell out the word *rat?* As Dr. Spelling discovered, once started, he—the bee, not the noted bee- . . . -ologist—will never go back up again. Not hard, you'll agree, to see there are just four ways. So can you say how many ways the bee can spell out Lewis Carroll's word *rath,* and then *raths?* You should find a number pattern to your answers. You'll find the word *raths* in Lewis Carroll's poem "Jabberwocky," in which occurs this line: "And the mome raths outgrabe." Carroll tells us the word *mome* comes from *solemome,* or *solemn,* and means "grave"; *rath* is a kind of land turtle; and *grabe* means "squeaked." See if you can translate the line into *our* English, yours and mine.

Number Oddity

Make a number out of all the digits 1 to 9 leaving out 8: 12,345,679. Now multiply it first by *any* single-digit number—5, say—and then multiply the product by 9. You should get your single-digit number back ninefold.

12,345,679	Now complete:	12,345,679
X 5		X 7
________		________
61,728,395		
X 9		
________		________
555,555,555		X 9
		________
		________

Check that it works for the other single-digit numbers. Why does it work?

Six 1s are 24?

Write six 1s and three plus signs in a row in such a way that they add up to 24.

Pairing Puzzle

How do you pair off these numbers so that the sum of each of the four pairs adds up to the same number?

1 2 3 4 5 6 7 8

Diamonds of Marbles

Ned was playing solitaire one day. He put some black and some white marbles in four of the hollows to form a diamond. He started making different patterns with them. He began with one black bead at the top corner and three white in the other corners, as shown in the picture. Another pattern was with the black marble at the bottom of the diamond; another was four black marbles, one in each corner of the diamond. How many *different* patterns could he make altogether?

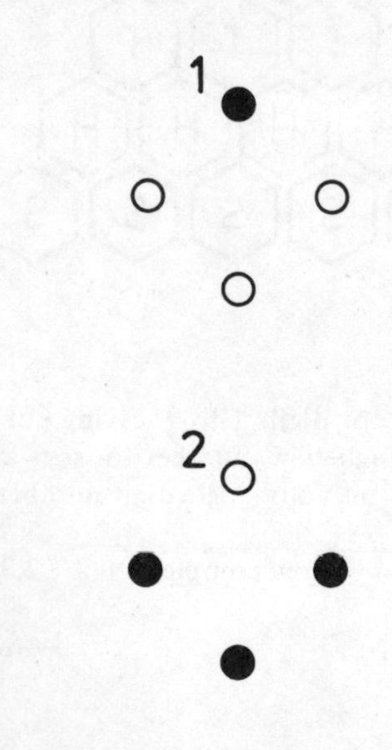

2. Number Patterns

All the next set of puzzles depends on curious and beautiful number patterns. From number crystals that grow before your very eyes to that classic of the IQ test, missing numbers in a series, you will find some, I hope, intriguing patterns to look at and play with.

Puzzle Boards

Jot down any four numbers on a board, like this:

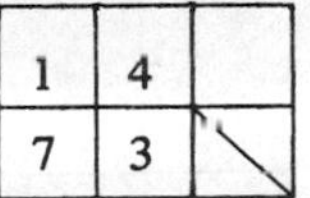

Write their differences. This means there will be no negative (minus) numbers at the end. For example, 4 and 1 gives 3, and so does 1 and 4.

1	4	4 − 1 = 3
7	3	7 − 3 = 4
7 − 1 = 6	4 − 3 = 1	

Your table looks like this:

1	4	3
7	3	4
6	1	

Take differences from the answers 3, 4 and 6, 1 and put them in the corner triangles:

4 − 3 = 1

6 − 1 = 5

1	4	3
7	3	4
6	1	**1** / **5**

PUZZLE: Can you make up boards like this that give the *same corner numbers?* Can you find a rule for making them?

1	4	3
3	7	4
2	3	**1** / **1**

Sum of the Whole Numbers

The sum of the numbers 1 through 10 is 55, as you can easily check. The sum of the numbers 1 through 100 is 5,050. Now can you write down from the pattern the sum for the numbers 1 through 1,000?

Sum 1 through 10 = 55
Sum 1 through 100 = 5,050
Sum 1 through 1,000 = ?

Number Crystals

A. Can you make this number pattern grow like a crystal by writing two more lines:

16 = 4 X 4
1,156 = 34 X 34
111,556 = 334 X 334

B. To grow this number crystal, keep adding 1 on the left and add 8 to the right half of the number, like this:

09 = 3 X 3
1,089 = 33 X 33
110,889 = 333 X 333

Can you write the next line of the crystal?

C. Grow this number crystal by writing one more line:

36 = 6 X 6
4,356 = 66 X 66

Number Carousel

Take the number 142,857 and multiply it by these numbers in turn: 1, 5, 6, 2, and 3. You should be able to check the lines from the growing pattern!

142,857 X 1 = 142,857
X 5 = 714,285 and so on

Now multiply by 8: 142,857 X 8 = 1,142,856

The pattern appears to be broken until you add the 1 on the left to the digit on the far right:

1,142,856 ⟶ 142,857

See if this pattern continues when you multiply by 9, 10, and 11.

Take-away Number Squares

This is just like the Take-away number triangle puzzle. Only this time you start with four numbers, one at each corner of a square. Here I have used 1, 5, 8, and 9.

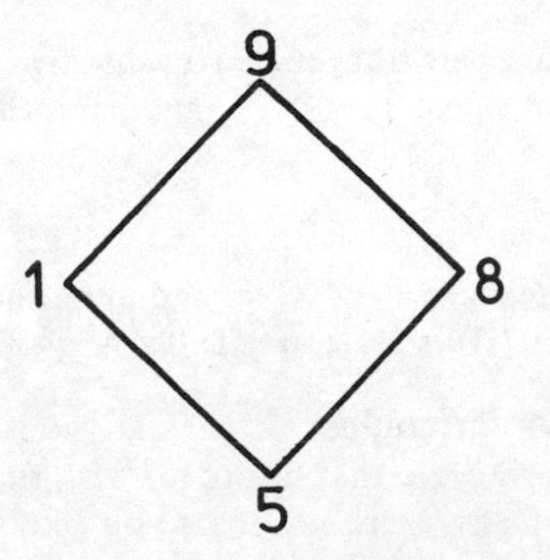

Draw a square around this one to go through its corners. At each corner of this larger square put the difference of the numbers at the next-door corners of the small square: 4 (from 5 − 1), 3 (from 8 − 5), 1 from (9 − 8), and 8 (from 9 − 1):

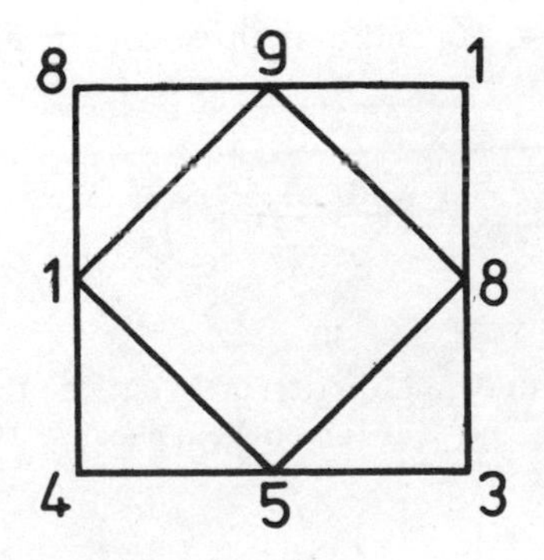

Repeat the process until you come to a pattern of four numbers that does not change. What is this pattern? You should find the same pattern whatever four numbers you start with. Do you?

Take Any Three-Digit Number

Take any three-digit number with each digit different—say, 123. Now write the same three digits again to make a six-digit number; 123 becomes

123,123. Now divide by 7, then by 11, finally by 13, and I predict you will have the first three digits you began with. It works for *any* three digits. Can you say why it works?

Five 2s

Can you write the numbers 0 through 10 using five figure 2s, no more and no less, and the usual signs: +, −, ×, ÷, and parentheses? To start you off: $0 = 2 - 2/2 - 2/2$.

Four 4s

Using four 4s and the signs +, −, ×, ÷, and parentheses, can you write the numbers 1 through 10? To start you off: $0 = 4 - 4 + 4 - 4$.

Take-away Number Triangles

This is a new number puzzle that has to do with finding a number pattern for taking away. Put any three numbers you like at the corners of a triangle, like this:

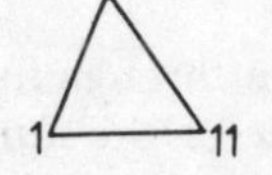

I have used 1, 5, and 11.

Now find the differences between next-door corners: $5 - 1 = 4$ and $11 - 1 = 10$ and $11 - 5 = 6$. Draw a larger triangle to go through these corners and put the differences 4, 10, and 6 at three corners of this new outside triangle, like this:

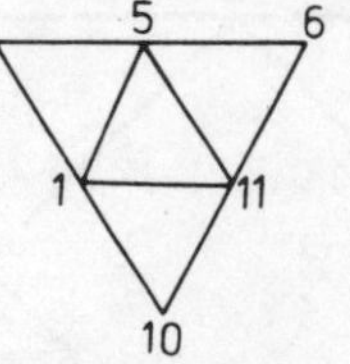

Repeat the process: draw another triangle outside the last one and put the new differences 6, 4, and 2 at the corners because $10 - 4 = 6$ and $10 - 6 = 4$ and $6 - 4 = 2$.

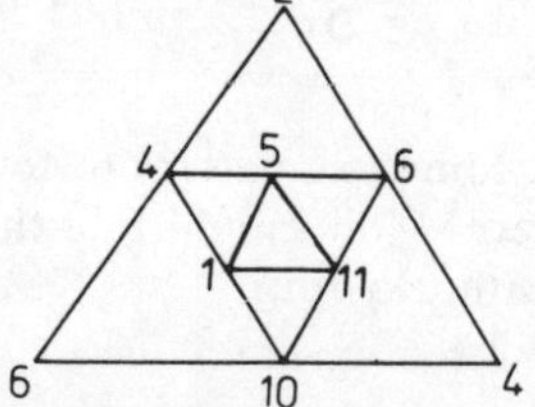

Now do this again two more times and you should finish up with a pattern of three numbers that does not change however many times you go on. What is this pattern? Begin with three other numbers and carry on taking away. Do you find you end up with the same pattern? The answer section will tell you what the pattern is.

Missing Numbers

Find the missing number in each pattern. These puzzles are very popular in IQ tests.

a. 2 5 ___ 11 14 17

b. 2 4 6 8 ___ 12

c. 2 7 12 17 22 ___ 32

d. 3 1 4 2 5 ___ 6

e. 1 4 9 16 25 ___ 49 64

f. 2 4 8 16 ___ 64 128

g. 0 2 6 14 30 62 ___ 254

h. 5 9 16 29 54 ___ 200

Sums in the Head

You should be able to do these sums in your head:

A. Multiply 999 by 3.

B. Group these three-digit numbers in pairs and add them quickly:

```
  645
  221
  301
  355
  779
+ 696
-----
```

C. Copy these numbers and beneath them put a third six-digit number. At once write (from left to right) the grand total:

```
604,253
283,012
```

We rule out 000,000, of course!

D. Which is easier to add, the sum on the left or the sum on the right?

```
  123,456,789            1
   12,345,678           12
    1,234,567          123
      123,456        1,234
       12,345       12,345
        1,234      123,456
          123    1,234,567
           12   12,345,678
+           1 + 123,456,789
-------------  ------------
```

9 in Ten Digits

The number 9 can be written as a fraction using all ten digits 1 through 9, like this:

$$9 = \frac{95{,}823}{10{,}647}$$

Can you find another way? There are actually six ways.

HINT: Try shuffling the same digits around.

Number Patterns

See if you can find the next two lines in this number pattern:

$$1 \times 2 \times 3 \times 4 + 1 = 5 \times 5$$
$$2 \times 3 \times 4 \times 5 + 1 = 11 \times 11$$
$$3 \times 4 \times 5 \times 6 + 1 = 19 \times 19$$

Check that both sides are equal.

Another Number Pattern

Finish the first three lines. Can you finish the last two lines?

$$37 \times (3 + 7) = 3^3 + 7^3 = ?$$
$$48 \times (4 + 8) = 4^3 + 8^3 = ?$$
$$111 \times (11 + 1) = 11^3 + 1^3 = ?$$
$$147 \times \underline{\qquad} \quad \underline{\qquad}$$
$$148 \times \underline{\qquad} \quad \underline{\qquad}$$

The little 3 above a number means you should multiply that number times itself three times. Thus $3^3 = 3 \times 3 \times 3$, and $7^3 = 7 \times 7 \times 7$.

Do the patterns multiply out correctly?

Reverse Sums

The sum $9 + 9 = 18$ gives the reverse answer when the numbers are multiplied: $9 \times 9 = 81$. Find two more reversals, beginning 24 + . . . and 47 + ...

Palindromes in Numbers

A palindrome is a word that spells the same forward and backward, such as *pip*, *radar*, and *rotator*. An example of a number that is a palindrome is

121. Here is how to arrive at one. Add to any number its reverse; then add to the sum the sums reverse. Carry on until you reach a palindrome, like this:

$$\begin{array}{r} 38 \\ +\,83 \\ \hline 121 \end{array}$$

Now begin with the number 139.

The Next Palindromic Year

The last palindromic year was 1881—it reads the same forward or backward. What is the next palindromic year?

Corridors of Numbers

See how this number table is made up:

1	3	5	7	9	11
1	4	7	10	13	16
1	5	9	13	17	21
1	6	11	16	21	26
1	7	13	19	25	31
1	8	15	22	29	36

Each row starts with 1 on the left. The numbers in the first row go up by 2 each time, in the second row by 3, in the third row by 4, and so on. The table continues to the right and downward as far as you like. Now add the numbers in each ⅃-shaped corridor. The sum of the top left-hand corridor comes to 1 alone, which equals $1 \times 1 \times 1$ or 1^3. The sum of the second corridor is $1 + 4 + 3 = 8 = 2 \times 2 \times 2$ or 2^3. See if this pattern continues for the next few corridors shown.

What are the numbers along the diagonal from the top left to the bottom right? Take any section of this diagonal. The sum of all the numbers in a square built around that section is a square number. For example, take the section 9, 16, 25. The numbers in the square with that as diagonal are:

$$\begin{array}{l} 9 + 13 + 17 \\ + 11 + 16 + 21 = 144 = 12 \times 12 = 12^2 \\ + 13 + 19 + 25 \end{array}$$

Try this for the section 4, 9, 16.

Multiplying Equals Adding?!

Take two numbers and multiply them together. Now add the numbers. The two answers are the same. What are the two numbers? Well, they could both be 2, for $2 \times 2 = 2 + 2$. The puzzle is: How many other pairs of numbers work in this way?

CLUE: To start you off, try 1½ and a whole number less than 5.

Curious Centuries

Can you make 100, a century, out of the numbers 1 through 9, using the usual signs +, −, ×, ÷, and parentheses? To start you off, here is how four centuries begin:

$$\begin{aligned} 100 &= 1 + 2 + 3 + \ldots \\ &= 123 - 45 \ldots \\ &= 123 - 4 - 5 \ldots \\ &= 1/2 + 6/4 + \ldots \end{aligned}$$

Times-Table Triangle

Here is an unusually simple number triangle. It's easy to build up. Yet it packs a mathematical punch! It's a multiplication ("times") table as well!

1

2 3 4

5 6 7 8 9

10 11 12 13 14 15 16

17 18 19 20 21 22 23 24 25

26 27 28 29 30 31 32 33 34 35 36

37 38 39 40 41 42 43 44 45 46 47 48 49

50 51 52 53 54 55 56 57 58 59 60 61 62 63 64

A. What do you see about the numbers on the right-hand sloping side? (Hint: They are all a special kind of number.)

B. Now for the mathematical punch. Pick any two numbers from one of the columns on adjacent rows. To start with, pick them near the top—say, 5 and 11. What is 5×11? The table will tell you. Look five rows down from the 5 and you find the answer, 55. Start with the smaller number and look down. Another example: What's 4×8? Find 4 and look four rows down to the answer, 32. We can write this briefly:

$$\begin{array}{r} 4 \\ \times\ 8 \\ \hline 32 \end{array}$$

(which is four rows down from the 4)

Copy the triangle, then add four or more rows. Then try these:

$$\begin{array}{r} 2 \\ \times\ 6 \\ \hline \end{array} \quad \begin{array}{r} 3 \\ \times\ 7 \\ \hline \end{array} \quad \begin{array}{r} 6 \\ \times\ 12 \\ \hline \end{array} \quad \begin{array}{r} 7 \\ \times\ 13 \\ \hline \end{array}$$

Of course, the triangle doesn't give *all* the multiplication tables.

3. Magic and Party Tricks with Numbers

I have described these tricks fully so that you can perform them for yourself in front of friends or a larger audience. I have tried to indicate the likely pitfalls and the sort of pattern to get you over the "tricky" parts. In fact, only one of the tricks requires any mental agility. The others either rely on the spectator's arithmetic skill or they work like a charm, purely from the (concealed) arithmetic underlying the trick. I hope you have fun trying thom out.

Dial-a-Number Trick

I have performed this impressive but simple number trick with great effect on stage and for television. It depends upon the same idea as that used in "Fiddling by Numbers" on page 34. To present the trick, make a board of nine "Secret Signs" like the one shown here. You'll also need a blackboard

for your chosen spectator to write on. A sheet of paper clipped to a board will do as well. Invite the spectator to step up to the board. Now you turn your back and give the following instructions:

You say: "Write the last three digits of your telephone number on the board. Make sure the digits are all different, that's all. If they aren't, invent a three-digit number." Stress to your audience that you cannot possibly know what the digits are. (Indeed, you do not need to know.) It is as well to ask the audience to check that the subtracting and adding are being done correctly. "Write the digits in reverse order to form a new number," you say. "Then write the smaller of the two three-digit numbers beneath the larger." So if the digits were 376, he would write near it 673 and then put the 376 under it. "Take the smaller number from the larger," you say.

$$\begin{array}{r} 673 \\ -376 \\ \hline 297 \end{array}$$

"Then add the individual digits of the result." He does so and gets 18 $(2 + 9 + 7)$, which he must not tell you.

You invite him over to the Chart of Secret Signs. Now you can face him. You ask him to count around clockwise on the chart, starting at the top as 1. Let him start counting to make sure he understands what to do and to build up tension. Then stop him, saying: "Now you agree that I cannot know your number. Yet I can predict you'll finish on the moon sign." Sure enough, if he did his sums correctly, he will count twice around the circle and land on the moon.

The trick depends on the fact that the sum of the digits will always be a multiple of 9; in this case it will come to 18. To heighten the effect, you can color the Secret Signs. Suppose the moon is green. Then select someone from your audience wearing something green. Then, at the Secret Sign Chart, predict *wrongly* that he will end on the red star, say. Then draw the audience's attention to the green in your "victim's" dress and appear to change your mind and say, "The green moon." With a little practice you can work up a most effective presentation of the trick.

The mathematics behind the trick is explained in the answer section.

Conjurer's Forces

Did you know conjurers can make you say a number? It's called "forcing" a number. You can try it on your friends. It goes like this:

You ask a friend for a number—any number—between 1 and 5. You'll find most people reply 3. Or ask for a number between 1 and 10 and most will say 7. You say to a friend: "Think of a number between one and fifty, but both figures have to be odd but not the same. For example, eleven won't do." Previously you have written 37 on a scrap of paper and handed it folded to the friend. The prompt of "eleven" is part of the act. When you say that, most people move on to the 30s. Now 33 will not do, and as 7 is the most popular number between 1 and 10, most answer 37. Your friend will be surprised to read 37 on the paper.

Here are several good tricks for guessing someone's age. They have an added advantage: They are very easy to perform in front of an audience; they do not depend on sleight of hand or great calculating skill.

How Old Are You?

"You won't tell me? All right, simply tell me the result of this little sum: Multiply your age by ten. From that take away nine times any single-digit number, such as one, two, three, up to nine itself. Done it? Tell me the result. . . . Now I know your age!"

Use this trick on your friends older than 9. For example, say your friend's age is 15, which times 10 is 150, and he chooses 4 for his digit. Product 4 X 9 = 36. He does this subtraction in his head: 150 − 36 = 114. He calls out 114. This is what you do. Remove the last digit of the number he called out and add it to what remains. Here, 114 without the 4 is 11, and 11 + 4 = 15. And this is his age. Perhaps, however, you had better check with the answer to see why the trick works before you use it.

For Someone Over 10 Years Old

Tell your friend to add 90 to his age, cross off the first digit of the result, and add it to the two digits left. Ask him for his answer. You then merely add 9 and tell him his age.

Suppose your friend is:	17
He adds 90:	+90
	107

He crosses off the first digit and adds it:

$$\begin{array}{r} \not{1}07 \\ +\;\;1 \\ \hline 8 \end{array}$$

He tells you 8. You add on 9 and tell him he is 17.

Fiddling by Numbers

Here's an unusual mathematical joke. Did you hear of the boy whose violin playing was the despair of his parents? The squeaks and screeches he made on the instrument drove them mad. But his uncle was a kindly man and a mathematician. "The trouble is," the boy told him, "I can't get a note out of my violin. It never sings." At this his uncle's face lit up: "Ah, I think I know what's needed. Let's do it by numbers. As you say, it *never sings.*" So saying, he scribbled on a scrap of paper these words and numbers:

N E V E R S I N G S
0 1 2 3 4 5 6 7 8 9

"Now choose any two numbers from *SINGS* and one from *NEVER*. Write them as a three-digit number," his uncle instructed. The boy chose, 8, 6, and 3. His uncle wrote the number 863. "Now reverse the figures and subtract the smaller number from the larger."

```
  863
− 368 (same digits in reverse order)
  495
```

His uncle turned the answer back into letters: "*R-S-S* . . . Nope, that doesn't seem to have done the trick. Reverse them again. And you'd better *add* this time." So the boy wrote the reversed number underneath and added: + 594

The uncle went on: "If fiddling is to be your *forte,* as musicians say, you'd better multiply by 40, hadn't you?" This the boy did: × 40

"Now decode those numbers," the uncle said with a knowing look, "and I think you'll know what your violin needs to make it sing." The boy turned the numbers back into letters, and found that what he needed was _____. Can you work it out?

"The strange thing is, it works whatever pair of numbers you pick from *SINGS* and whatever single number you choose from *NEVER*. One thing, though. In the first number you write, the first digit must be at least 2 more than the last—564 won't work, for example, because 5 is only 1 more than 4. But if you try it on a friend, all you have to do is write 954 instead. You can write the first two numbers chosen in either order.

It also works for one number chosen from *SINGS* and two from *NEVER*. More surprisingly, it works for a pair of numbers chosen from *SINGS* and a pair from *NEVER* to make a four-digit number. Now see the answer to this puzzle.

Magic Matrix Force

This breathtaking stunt depends on nothing more advanced th n a simple addition table. I have used it on stage and in clubs. A *matrix,* by the way, is simply a square array of numbers. And a "force" is what magicians use to make a chosen number reappear. The trick goes very like "The Calendar Trick."

You, the magician, ask for a number from your audience, between 30 and 100. We'll say it is 56. You now predict that you will give that number back by making up a magic square of numbers. You then proceed to fill in *very rapidly* and apparently in scrambled order a table with four numbers on a side, beginning with the numbers 6, 7, 8, and 9, as shown below left:

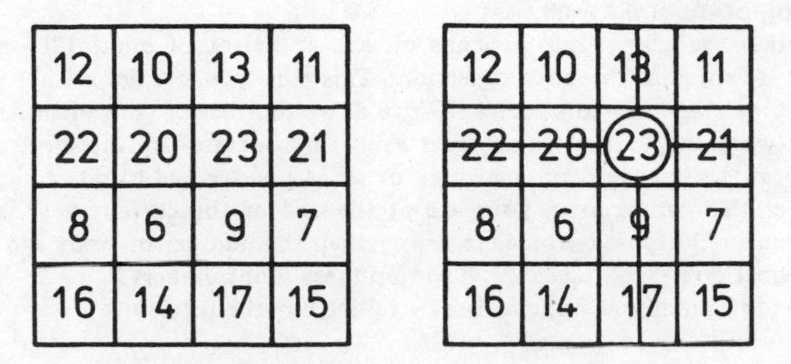

Next you ask for any number in the table to be selected. Suppose it is 23. You ask for a spectator to circle it and cross out the rest of the row and column it is in, as shown above right. If he continues in this fashion, the board might be completed as shown below leaving one number (7), which has to be circled: There's then no choice. Now you invite your audience to add up the four circled numbers–23, 12, 14, and finally 7, giving 56. This was the number your audience supplied and your matrix has "forced."

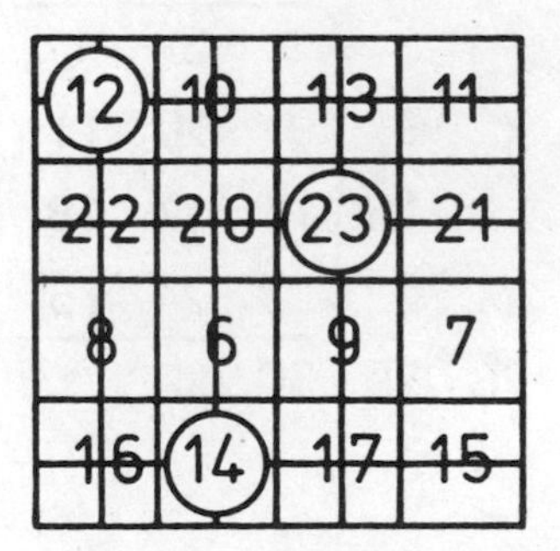

Filling in the table is the hardest part of the trick. With a little practice and no little nerve you will master it. You subtract 30 from the number supplied; then divide by 4 and note the remainder. For 56, you get 26 and then 6 with a remainder 2. Then 6 is the first number you put down in the table. You continue writing the numbers 7, 8, 9, and so on, keeping exactly to the same order of squares in each row. In our example we used middle left square, far right, far left, then middle right square. But in filling up the last line you do not put 18 above the 6; instead you add on the remainder of 2, making 20. Then you write the last three numbers in the same order. Write the numbers quickly, and your audience will believe you are writing them in scrambled order.

Using Someone's Age

Another age-telling trick depends on a neat sleight of mind. I'll explain how it works in the answer section. This time you predict a total using someone's age. Say to a friend: "Write down the year of your birth. Under that write the year of some great event in your life—for instance, when you saved someone from drowning or when you learned to ride a bicycle. Under that write down your age at the end of the current year, as of December thirty-first. Under that jot down the number of years ago that the great event took place. Now add up these four numbers."

At this point you surprise him by telling him the total.

The Calendar Trick

This prediction trick was invented by the mathematician Mel Stover. Find an old calendar. On it a spectator blocks off any square of numbers, four numbers on a side, that he chooses, as shown:

Su	M	Tu	W	Th	F	Sa
		1	2	3	4	5
6	7	8	9	10	11	12
13	14	15	16	17	18	19
20	21	22	23	24	25	26
27	28	29	30			

Turn away from your audience so that they think you need to hide your proceedings. At this point you hand a folded slip of paper to someone in the audience, with instructions not to open it until you say so.

With your back to the audience you say to your subject something along these lines: "Circle one of the dates in the blocked-off square." Unknown to you he circles, say, 11. "Cross out all the other dates in the row and column the circled date is in." The calendar now looks like this:

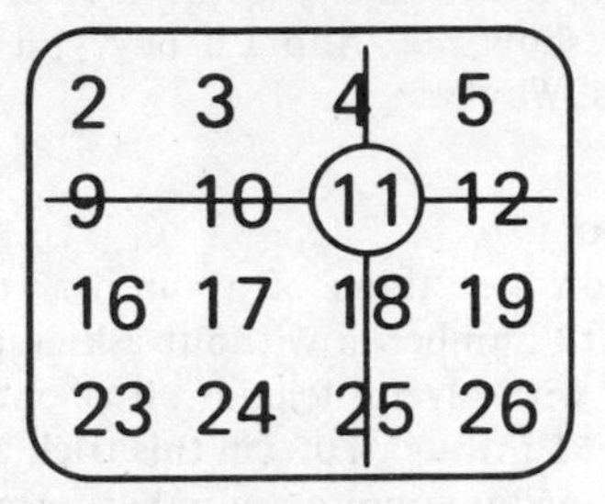

At your request he secretly circles another date (19) and crosses out the horizontal and vertical dates, as shown in the picture on the left, and then he repeats the process with yet another date (23), as shown in the picture on the right.

Only one date is left which is not circled or crossed out. Have him circle this date (3) and then add up all four dates circled. You ask the audience member to read aloud the number on the folded slip of paper. Everyone is amazed that the number, 56, is the same as the sum of the dates.

How did you manage to predict it? You add either two opposite corner dates (23 + 5 or 2 + 26 = 28) and then double the result. For an explanation, see "Magic Matrix Force."

Hundred Dollars for Five

I do a mathematical-magical stage routine in which I put this apparently attractive bet to my audience (I have changed the money to dollars here, although in England I work in pounds):

"I'll pay a hundred dollars to anybody who can give me five dollars in ten coins—half-dollars, quarters, and dimes only. You have to use at least one of each. One hundred for five. Any takers?" The audience usually says nothing. Some scribble on the backs of cigarette packs. But nobody has yet taken me up on this bet.

"Perhaps," I go on, "you haven't any small change? That's O.K. Just jot down on a scrap of paper how many coins of each kind–halves, quarters, and dimes–you must show me. And I'll pay you one hundred dollars." There can be no takers. Why?

No Questions Asked

This is a clever twist on the "think of a number" trick. In this trick you say what the "thought" number is without asking a single question. You can perform the trick with several friends all at once. Each friend picks a thought number from 51 through 100 (in this trick each can be different!). You are the magician, and you write a number from 1 through 50 and put it in an envelope.

In your mind subtract your "envelope" number from 99. Say the result aloud; then tell the friends that each must add it to his number, cross out the first digit of the sum, and add that same digit to the result. He must then take away the answer from his thought number to get his final answer. Your friends don't know it, but their final answers are all the same. Each in turn looks in the envelope to read his final answer. You could also write numbers in several separate envelopes–one for each friend.

How is the trick done? See the answers at the end of the book.

Lightning Sums

Here is a way to impress your friends as a lightning calculator. Ask a friend to pick any two numbers–2 and 5, say. Then he must write one under the other like this: 2
5

But he mustn't show you the list. Add the two numbers and write the sum (7) beneath them. Add the bottom two numbers, 5 and 7, and put their sum below (12). Repeat the process until there are ten numbers, as shown.

2
5
7
12
19
31
50
81
131
212

You ask to glance at the list; then quickly turn your back. You ask your friend to total the ten numbers. Long before he has finished, you announce the total: 550. How is it done?

When you quickly glanced at the list, you noted the fourth number up from the bottom—that is, 50. You multiply it by 11. This is easily done if you mentally see the number set out like this:

$$\begin{array}{r} 50 \\ +\ 50 \\ \hline \end{array}$$

Magic Year Number

Suppose the year is 1980. Say to a friend: "Write your shoe size. Ignore half sizes. Now multiply your shoe size by two, add five, and then multiply the result by fifty. Add the Magic Year Number—twelve hundred and thirty. Then take away the year of your birth. You have a four-digit number. The last two digits give your age." (The Magic Year Number changes from year to year: In 1979 it is 1,229; in 1980 it is 1,230; in 1981 it is 1,231; and so on.)

Actually, only the last two digits of the Magic Year Number matter. So you could use either 1,230 or simply 30, but using either might *j-u-s-t* give the trick away. See the answer section for the reason.

Suppose your friend's shoe size is 7½. She is 12 years old; so, since this is 1980, she was born in 1968. The shoe size, after the fraction is dropped, is 7. When she multiplies this by 2, she gets 14. Adding 5, she gets 19. After she multiplies this by 50 (or she could multiply by 100 and divide the result by 2), she gets 950. Adding the Magic Year Number for 1980 (1,230) yields 2,180. Subtracting the birth year (1968) yields 212. The last two digits reveal her age—12.

4. Magic Squares and Sliding-Block Puzzles

These puzzles date back to early China, where legend says Lo Shu found a 3-by-3 magic square scratched on the shell of a tortoise. We only show 3-by-3 and 4-by-4 magic squares. The magic of the squares is simply this: whether you add across, down, or along each diagonal, all the numbers in a row add up to the same magic number.

Magic Squares

See if you can recreate the Chinese magic in a large square made up of three squares on a side, using the numbers 1 through 9. When you have filled in the squares, or cells, the numbers across each row, up and down each column, and along each of its two main diagonals must all come to the same number—the magic number 15.

In this three-by-three "magic" the magic number is always 3 times the central cell. When you have filled in your "magic," you will find there are actually eight different large squares. You can turn it around in four different positions, and each position has a mirror image, giving a total of eight different "magics."

See the answers for an easy way to remember how.

Cross Sums

Arrange the consecutive numbers 1 through 9 in a cross like the one shown. But the across row must add up to the same sum as the down row. Can you do it?

		1		
		2		
6	7	3	8	9
		4		
		5		

A Number Square

Put the numbers 1, 2, 3, 4, 5, 6, 7, 8, 9 into the cells of a square like the one shown so that the sum of the two outer numbers less the number in the middle comes to 5. This must work for all four directions through the middle square—across, up and down, and along the two diagonals. Ignore the cases where all the squares are on the outside. For example, the diagonal of numbers shown in the second picture is correct.

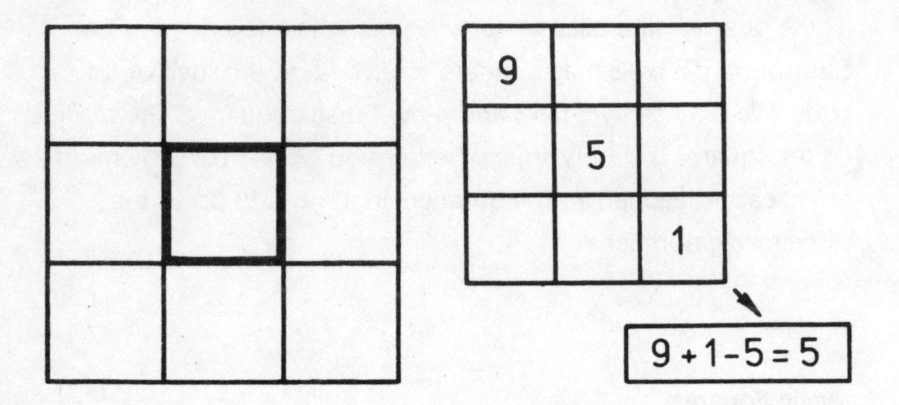

A Triangle of Numbers

Can you put the numbers 1 through 9 into these discs so that each side of the triangle adds up to 20?

HINT: The corner discs add up to 15. So one of them must be 5.

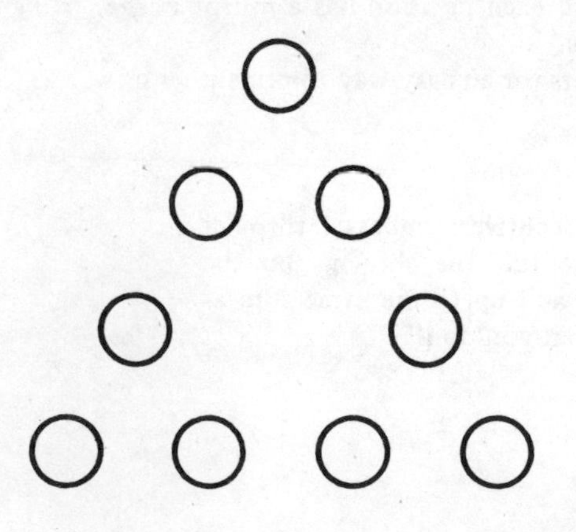

Star of David

Can you put the numbers from 1 through 12 in the discs on this star so that the sum of each of the six rows comes to 26?

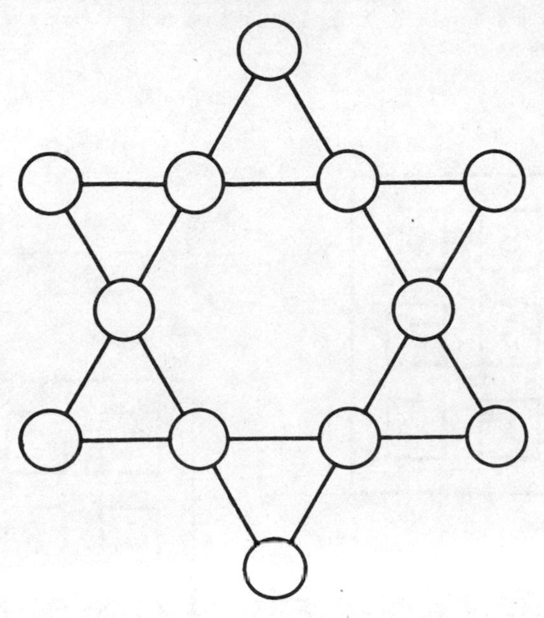

Number Rows

Use each number from 1 through 7 once only. Can you arrange them so that each row adds up to 12?

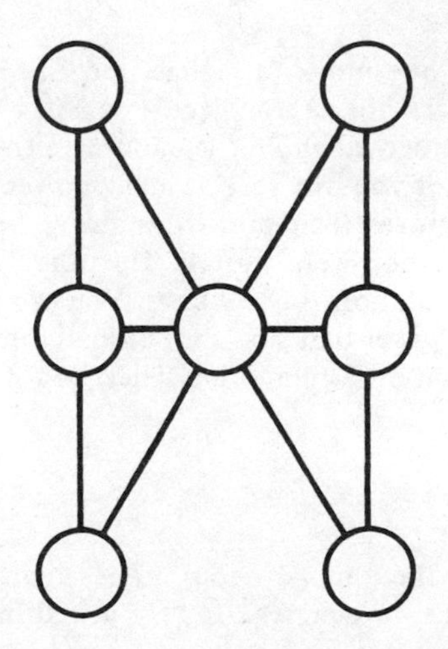

The Eight-Block Puzzle

Here is a reminder of the famous 15-block puzzle—a plastic puzzle you can buy in stores—where you have to slide numbered blocks about in a box. Eight blocks are numbered from 1 through 8 and put into a box, as shown in the picture on the left.

You can only move one block at a time into an empty space. No block may be lifted out of the box. The object is to shift the blocks around until you get them in the order shown in the picture on the right.

Well, it's not hard if you can have as many moves as you like. But see if you can do it in 22 moves. To record your moves, you only need note the numbers in the order they were shifted. Thus the first six moves are 2, 6, 5, 3, 1, and 2. This notation is quite clear. You can make your puzzle out of numbered slips of paper that you slide around on our picture. The same puzzle can be made out of lettered blocks, lettered *A* through *H*.

Four-Square Magic

The easiest way to make a four-by-four magic square is as follows: Draw a four-by-four grid with 16 squares. Lightly pencil in the numbers from 1 through 16. Now reverse the two main diagonals about the center. So 1 swaps places with 16, 6 with 11, 4 with 13, and 7 with 10:

1	2	3	4
5	6	7	8
9	10	11	12
13	14	15	16

16	2	3	13
5	11	10	8
9	7	6	12
4	14	15	1

That done, add up the numbers along each row across, each column, and each of the two main diagonals. What's the magic number?

Surprisingly, you can swap rows or columns, and the four-by-four square is still magic. Swap the two middle columns so the square looks like this:

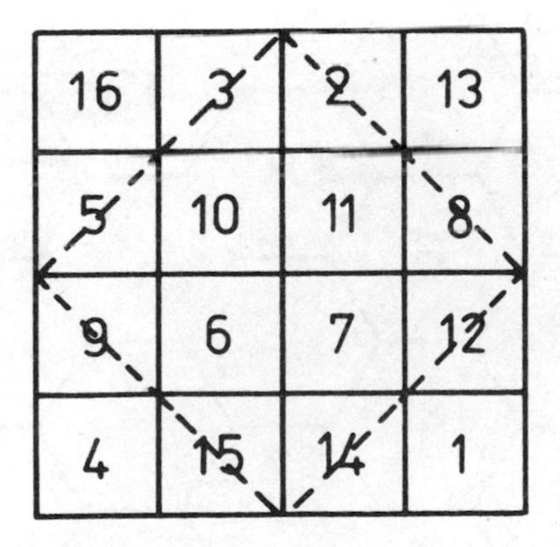

Check that it is still magic. Take pairs of opposite sides in the dotted square and add them: 3 + 5 + 12 + 14 and 2 + 8 + 9 + 15. Do you see anything? Now take the squares of these numbers: $3^2 + 5^2 + 12^2 + 14^2 = 9 + 25 + \ldots$ and $2^2 + 8^2 + 9^2 + 15^2 = 4 + 64 + \ldots$. Carrying on, what do you see?

Some more surprising things about a four-by-four "magic" are:

The corners add up to 34

The five two-by-two squares, in the corners and the center, all add up to 34

In each row one pair of adjacent numbers adds up to 15, and the other to 19

The painter Albrecht Dürer made an engraving called *Melancholia.* In it he shows a four-by-four magic square–just the second one shown here. If you look at the bottom of the middle columns you can tell the date he made the engraving. What was the date?

A Magic Honeycomb

Use the numbers from 1 through 19. Can you put them in the bee cells so that each arrowed row adds up to 38?

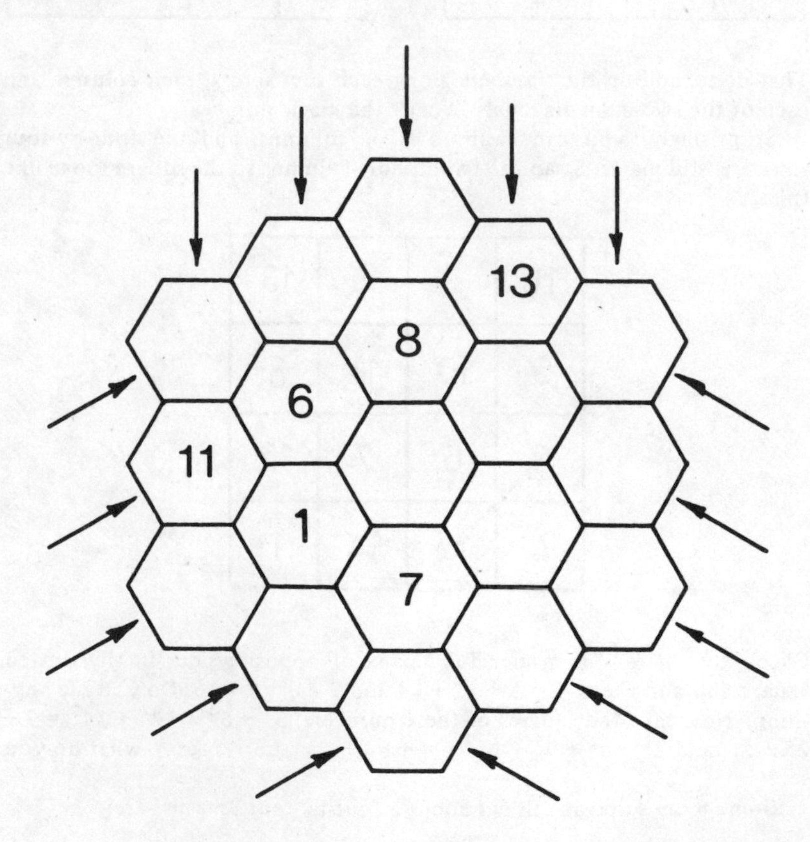

Multi-Magic Square

A multi-magic square is like an ordinary magic square except that you multiply numbers in each row instead of adding them. Each row, column, and diagonal multiply to the same number, the multi-magic number. Can you see what it is?

I have started you off on the smallest multi-magic square with the lowest numbers possible. You have to copy the square and fit in the numbers shown to the right of the square in their correct cells. There are four ways of doing this, but only one of them is right.

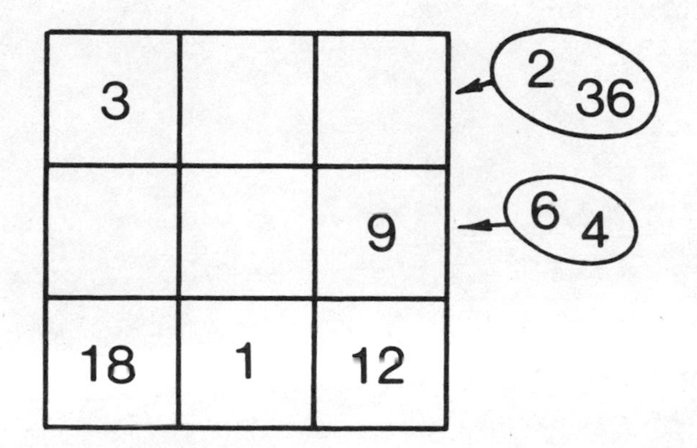

5. Illusions

Optical illusions are drawings that fool the eye. They are not only fascinating in themselves, but they provide the material for excellent puzzles. Seeing is believing, they say. But can you always believe what you see? The next batch of puzzles will test your belief. But I must let you into a secret. It is not only the eye that is fooled by the pictures that follow; the brain too takes part in the deception. We see what we have learned to see. So strong is this habit that we refuse to see the evidence before our eyes. Instead we see what fits in with our experience. I should also mention that you may not see all the illusions; not every illusion may work for you. It depends by and large on your seeing "habits." Most of the pictures should puzzle you. Don't look at the answers until you have checked the illusions with a ruler.

Illusive Lengths

Which is bigger, the length *AB* or *BC*?

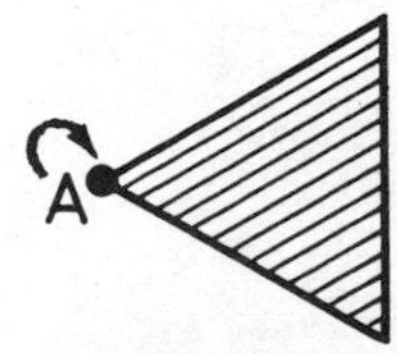

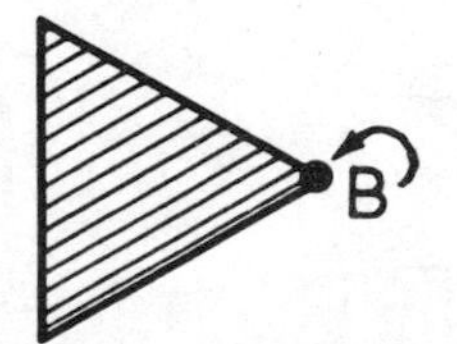

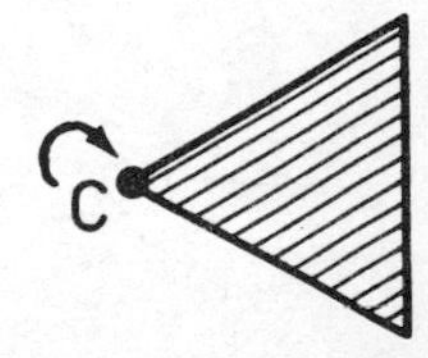

Diamond-Square Puzzle

Which is a diamond and which a square? And which is the larger?

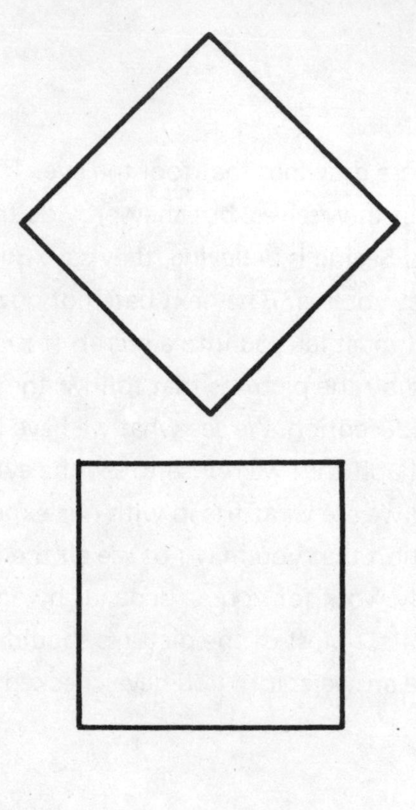

Candle Flicker

Which candle is bigger?

The Three Streetlamps

Cities used to have attractive streetlamps to light the sidewalks at night. Which of the lamps shown here is the tallest?

Railroad Track

This is a very famous illusion. Which of the two horizontal lines—that is, the ties between the tracks—is the longer?

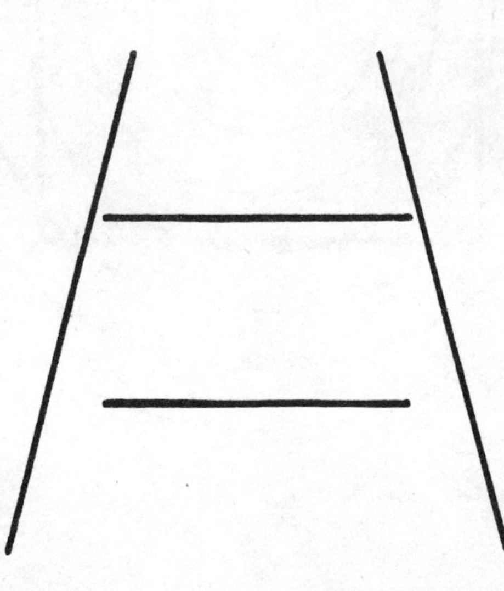

Target Square

The target circles look true enough. But what about the square?

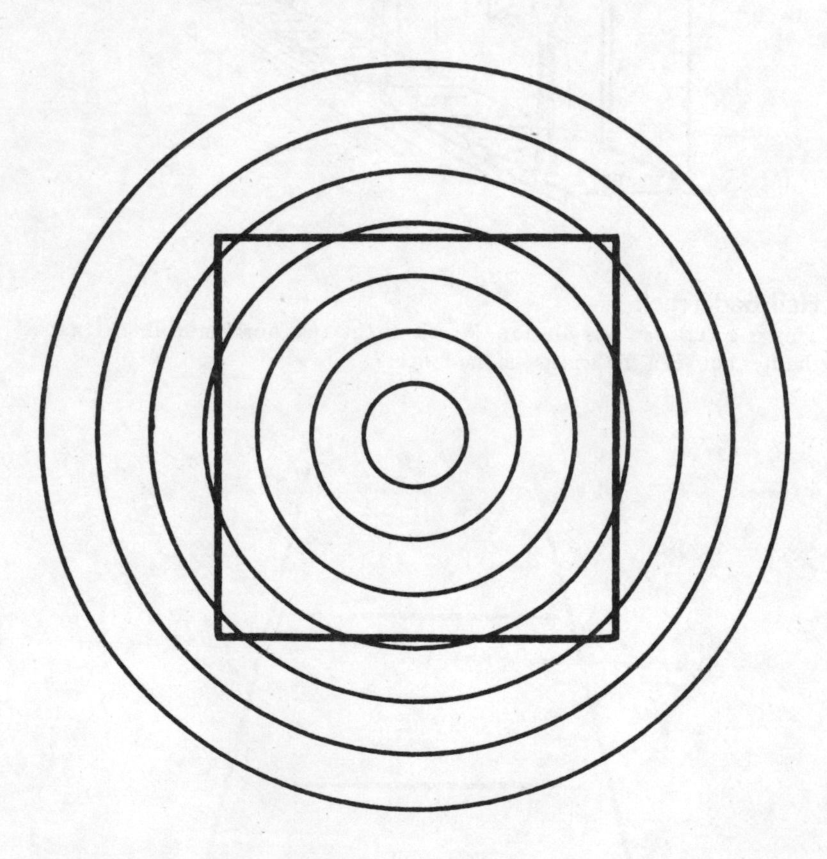

Squaring the Circles

Which of the two circles is bigger?

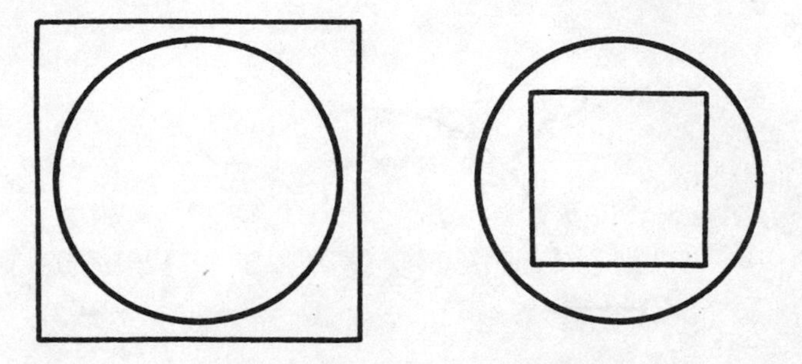

The Flap Tabletop

You know those tables with flaps on two sides. The picture shows three flap tables. Which tabletop is the longest?

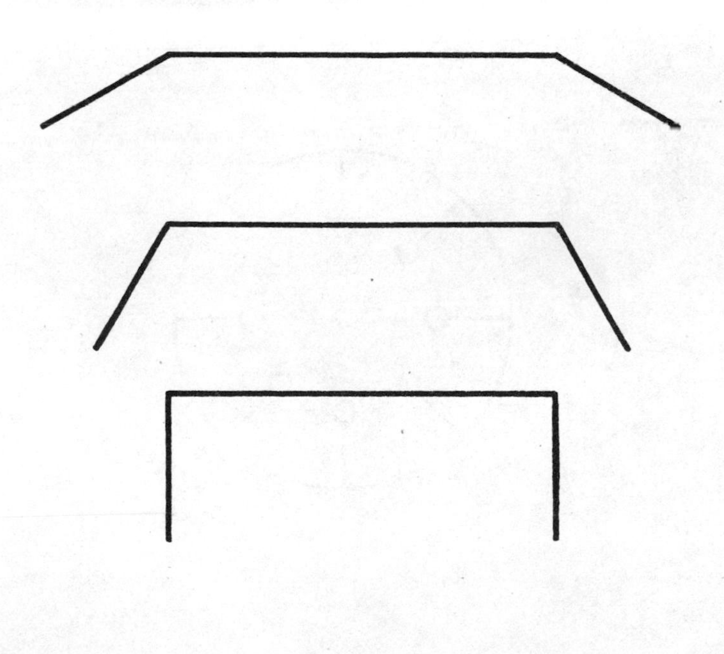

Run Rings Around You?

Which of the large circles is bigger?

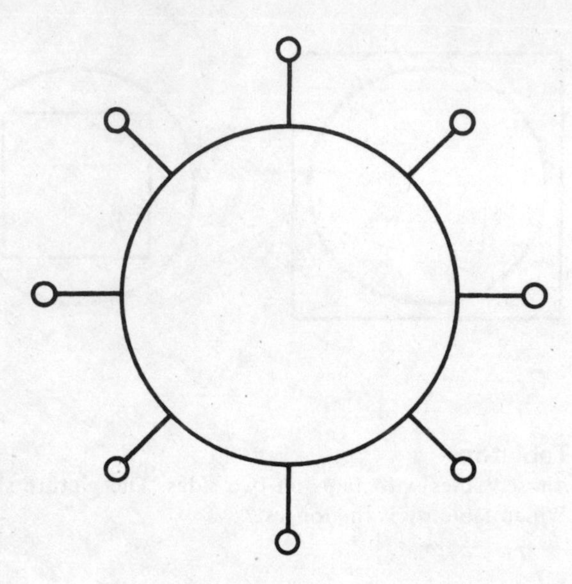

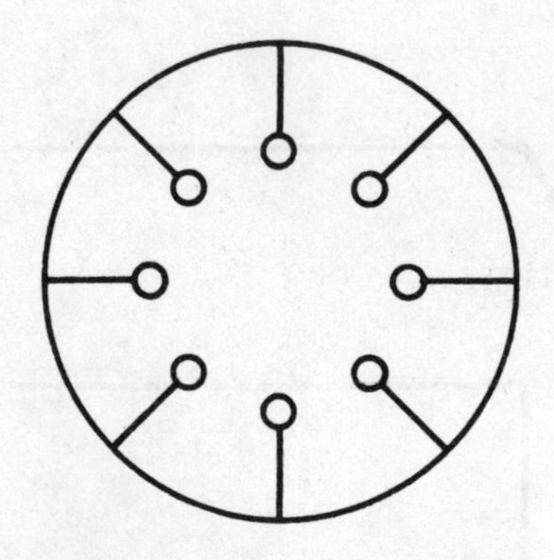

Circle Counting

How many circles are there here?

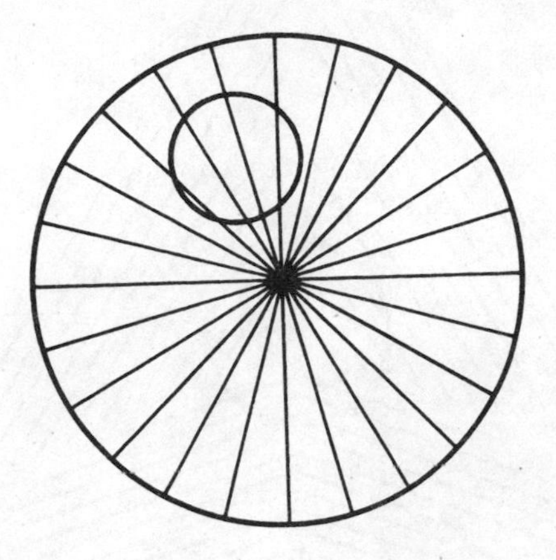

Bull's-eye and Ring

Which has the greater area, the bull's-eye or the outer ring?

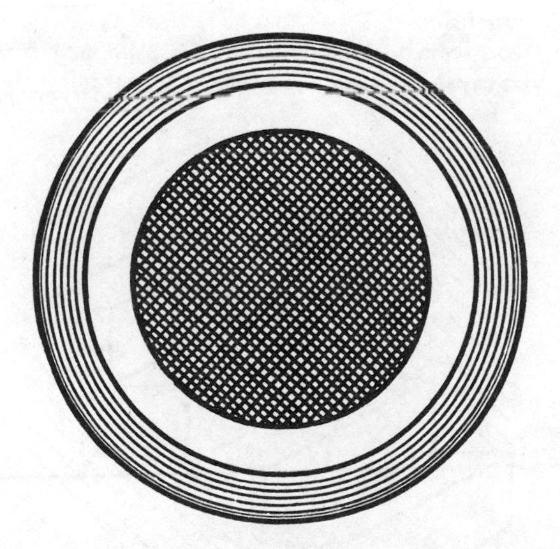

Circle Sorcery

Something has happened to the circle here. How much is bent?

Upstairs, Downstairs

One moment you seem to be looking upstairs, the next downstairs. Can you believe your eyes? There is no answer to this puzzle.

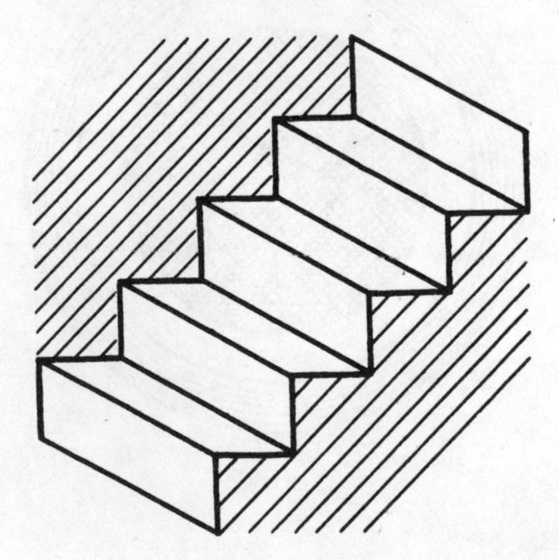

The Tricky Tower

Try to fix this figure before your eyes. You cannot: It shifts as if one moment you are looking down on it, the next under it. There is no answer.

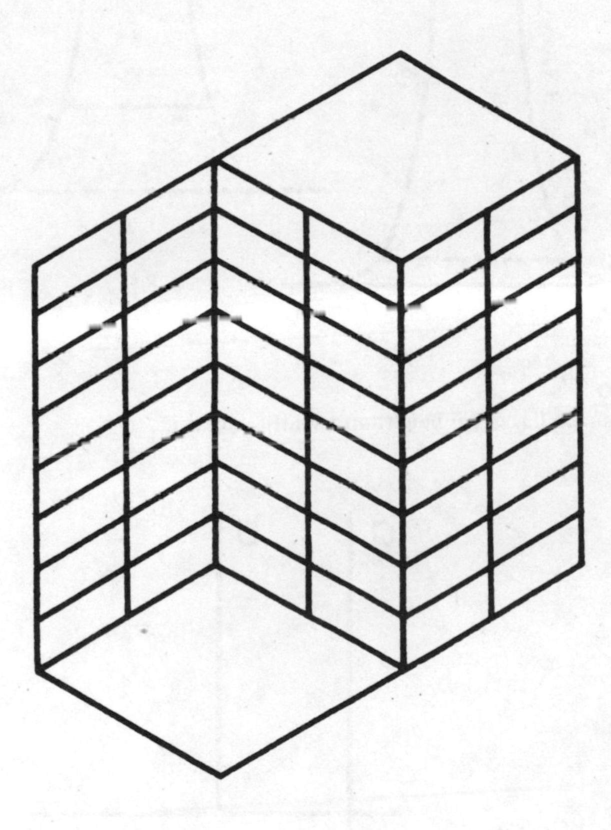

Two Tall Hats

Look at the top lines of the hatbands on the two hats here. Which line is half the width of its brim?

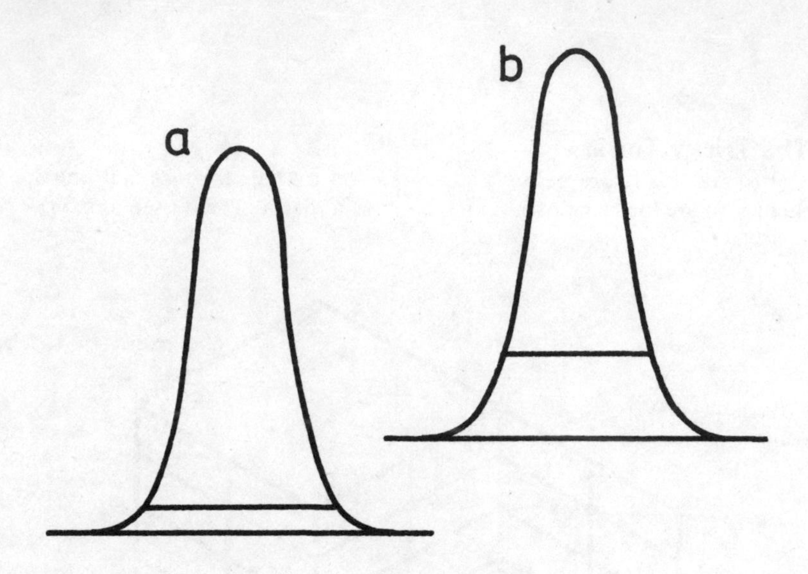

The Two T's

Which T shape has equal height and width, *a* or *b*?

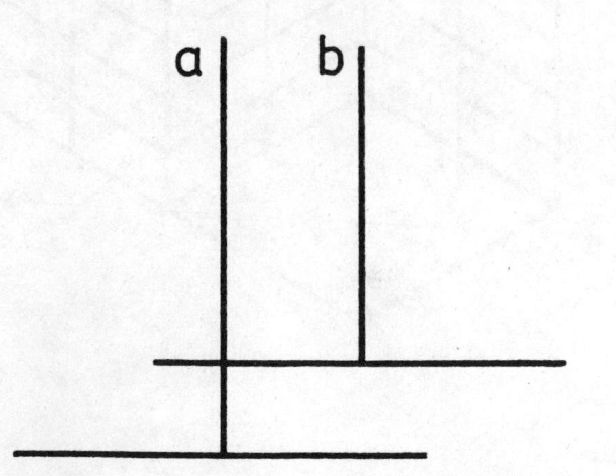

Impossible Triangle

This has to be the most famous illusion invented this century. Two psychologists, both called Penrose, dreamed it up. There is no answer. It is used in many works of modern art to fool the eye of the beholder.

The Herringbone Pattern

The four heavy lines are meant to be straight. Are they?

The Blinking Squares

Stare at this grid of squares, and I bet you will see gray patches come and go in the white crossings. And yet, as you can see, there is no gray printed on the paper. There is no answer.

The Bamboozle Box

Actually, this is called the Necker cube after the scientist who noticed the effect. The box seems to flip in and out before your very eyes. There is no answer.

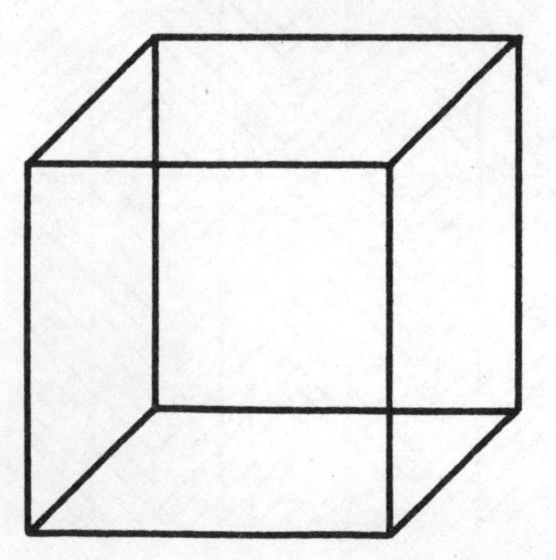

The Picture Frame

You'd better check the frame. It doesn't look square.

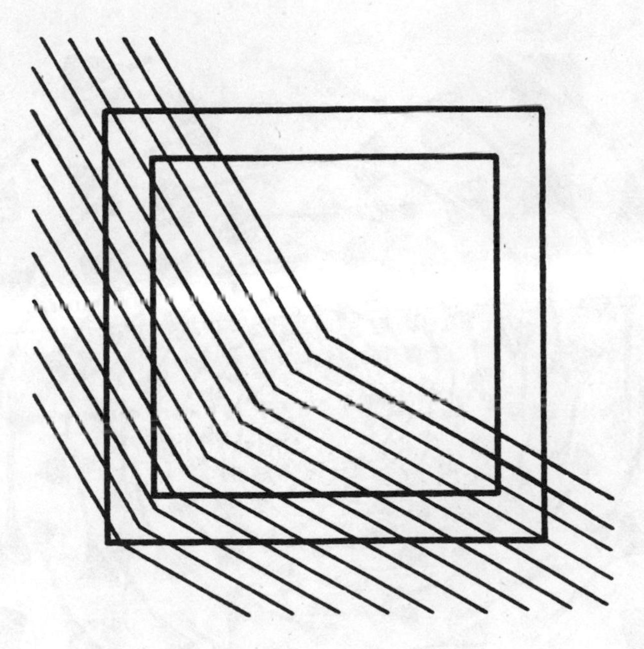

The Fraser Spiral

Here's another very famous illusion. Just follow around the whorls of the spiral and what do you see?

The Swollen Ruler

What's happened to the ruler? Has it swollen?

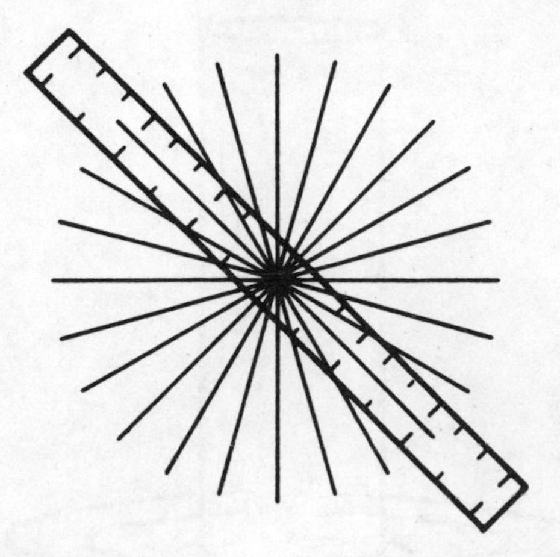

Zooming Lenses

Look at the surfaces of these three lenses. Which do you think is most curved, the little lens or the big lens?

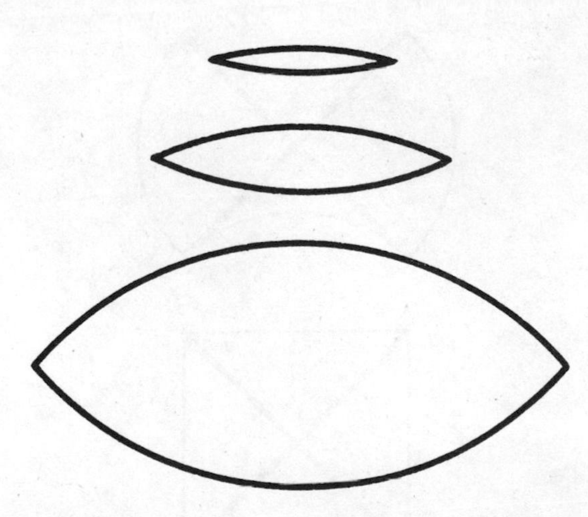

The Long Glass

Well, the long glass is rather taller than the plate it rests on is wide, isn't it? Guess by how much, then check with a ruler.

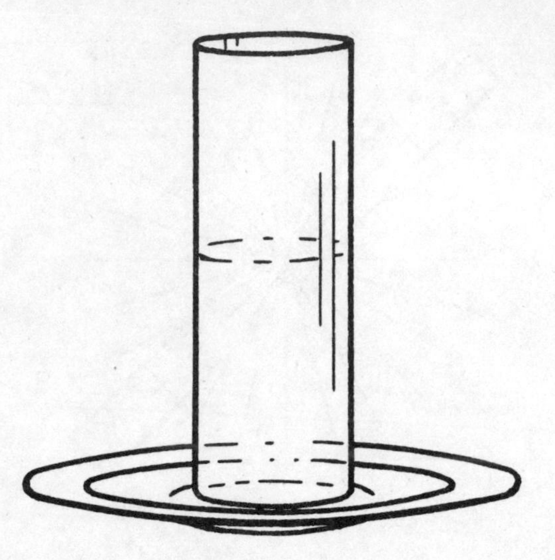

The Black Crosses

How much smaller is the black cross in the square than the black cross in the top figure?

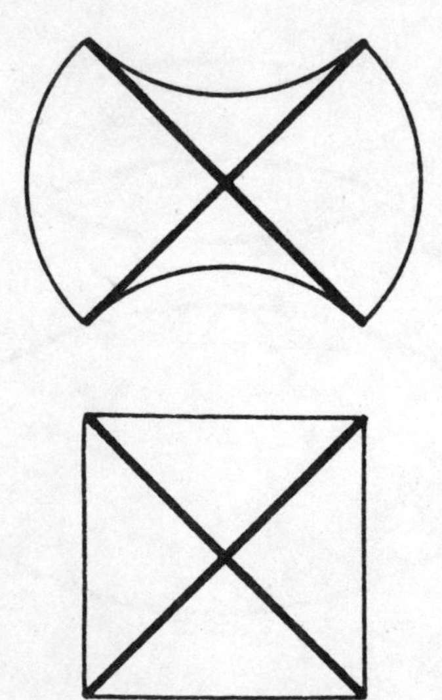

The Blacker Squares

Which of the two blacker squares shown here is the larger?

Lampshade and Flowerpot

Look at the heavy lines in the two drawings. Which do you think is longer?

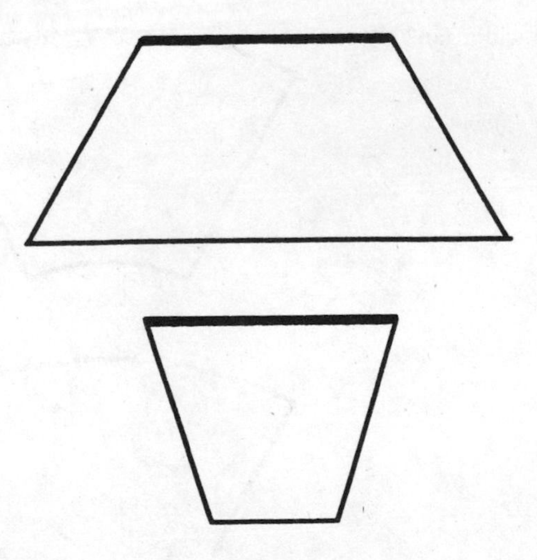

The Top Hats

I can tell you that the height and width of one of the hats shown here are equal. The question is, which hat, *a* or *b*?

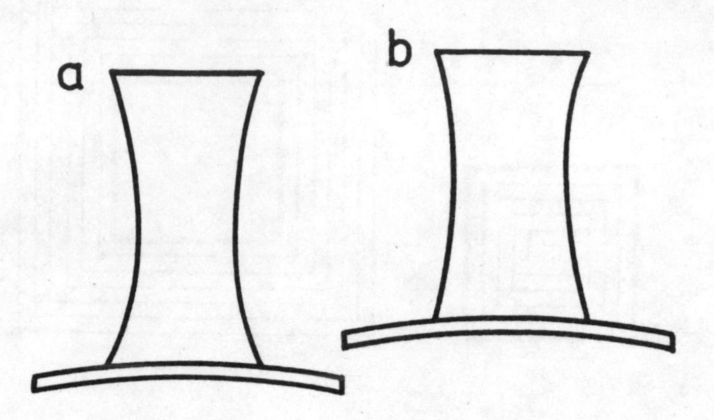

The Fans

Which is the wider fan?

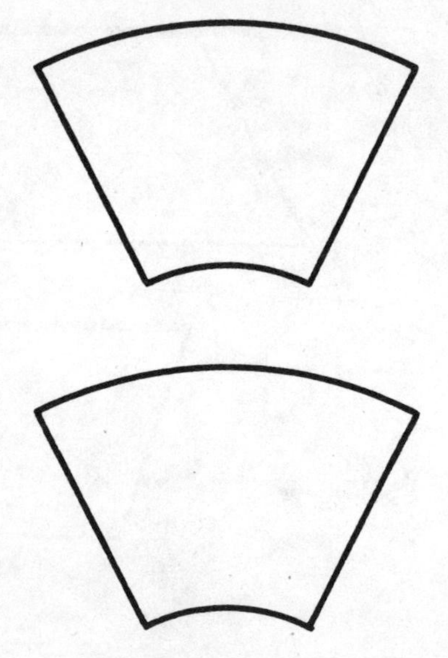

The Long and Short of It

Is the middle line half as long as the longer ones?

The Artful Arrows

A very well-known illusion. Obviously, the double-headed arrow is shorter than the other figure. But by how much?

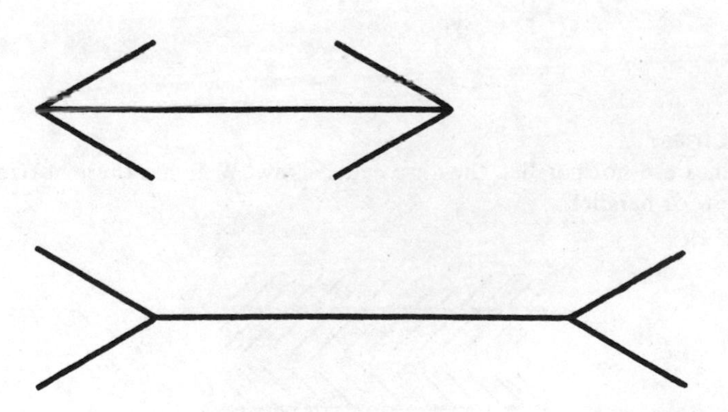

Straight As an Arrow

Run your eye along line *x*. Think of it as an arrow passing through a door, the two vertical lines. Which line, *p* or *q*, is the continuation of the arrow?

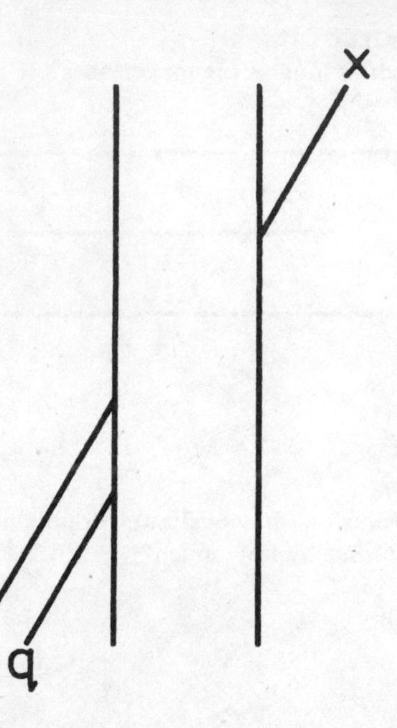

Skew Lines?

When lines are not parallel, they are called skew. Well, are these horizontal lines skew or parallel?

Stars and Diamonds

Look at the distance between a tip of the star and the tip of the nearest diamond. Is the length of a diamond the same as this distance?

Circles Before Your Eyes

Look at the center circles in each group. Which one is larger?

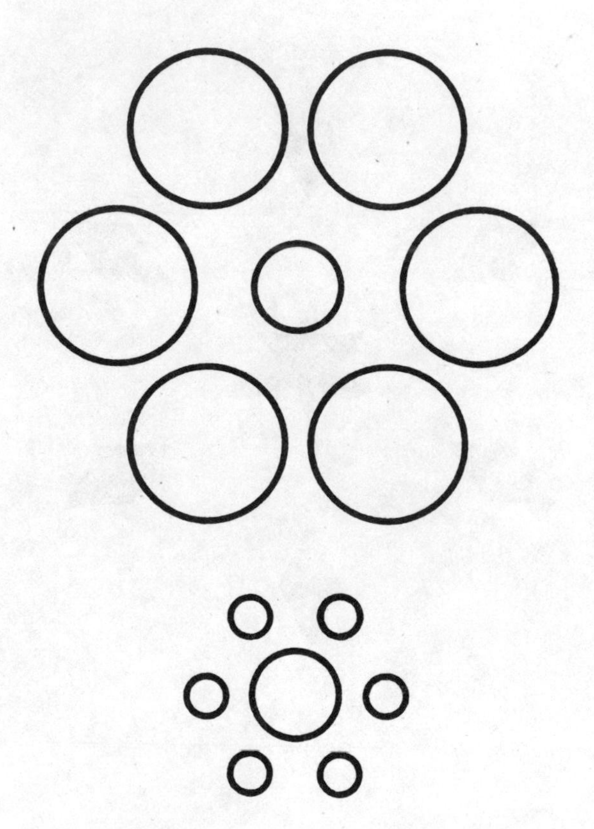

Arcs More or Less Curved

Which of the arcs shown is the most curved?

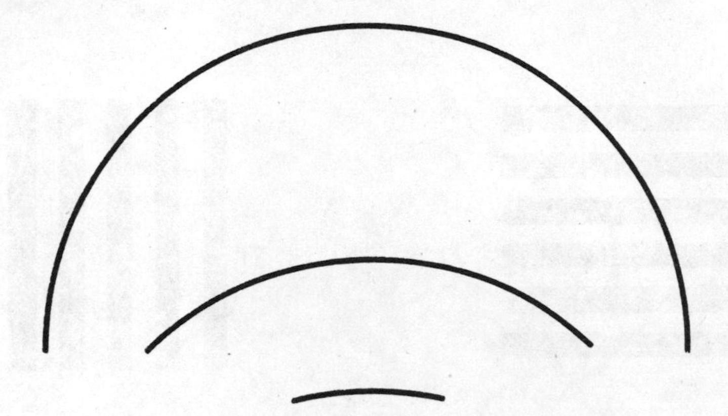

Funny Figure

Stare at this figure and you'll be able to see it in eight different ways.

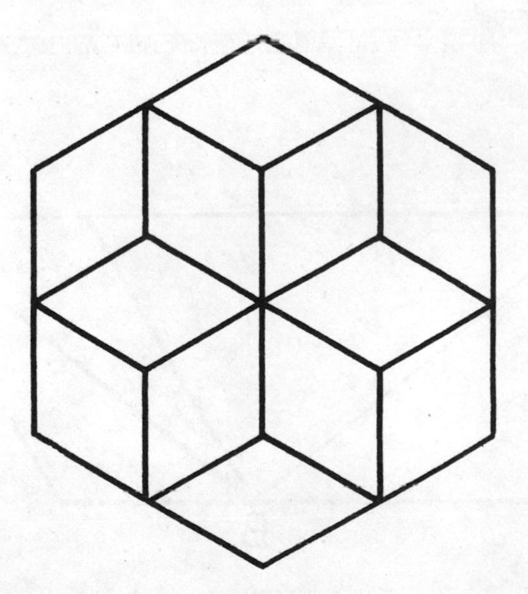

Hickman's Squares

This illusion was created by the artist who drew all the pictures in this book, Pat Hickman. Can you tell which of these figures is not a square? Or are they both squares?

Devilish Diagonals

Which is longer, *AB* or *BC*? Guess first, then measure and see for yourself.

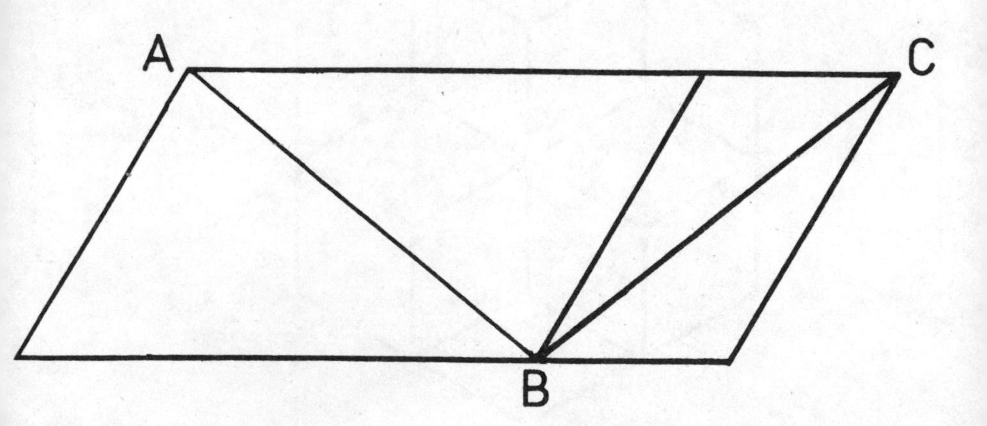

The Extra Cube

Here is a well-known optical illusion. Look hard at these six cubes. Can you see by any chance an extra cube?

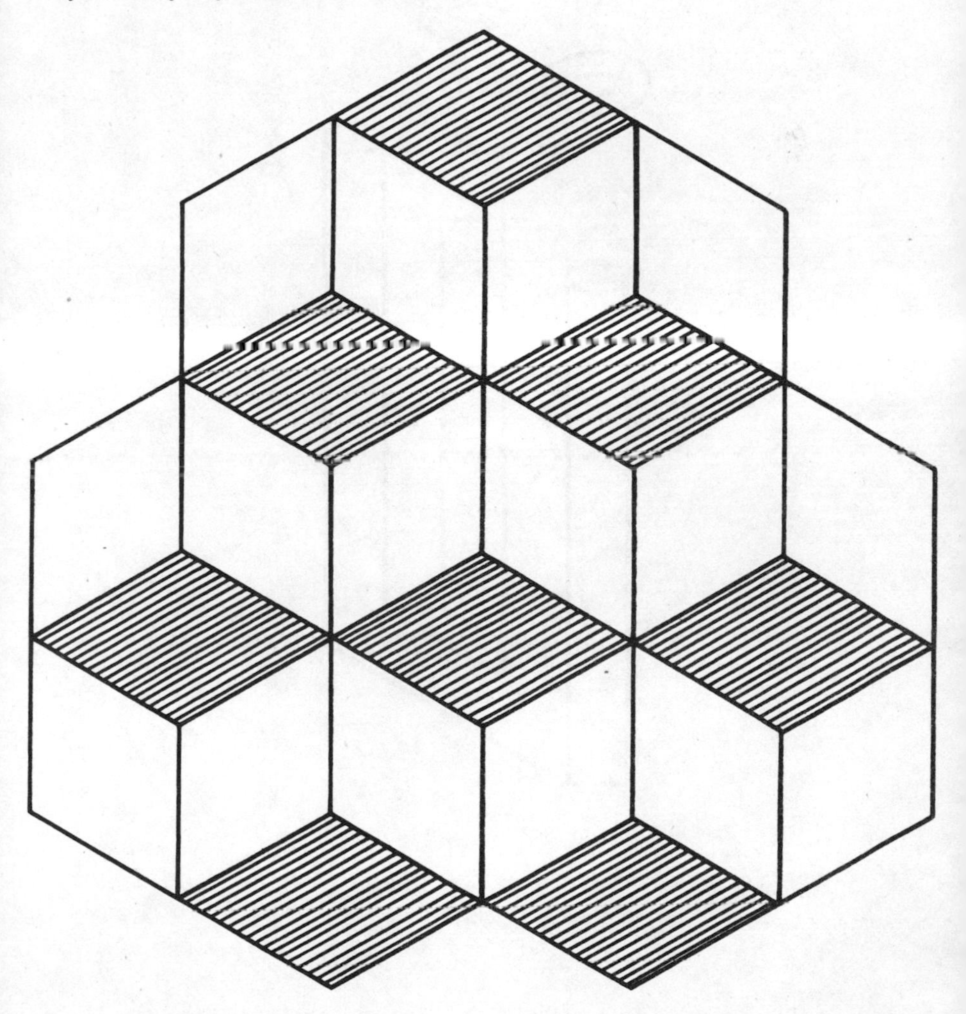

Rods and Rings

This illusion depends upon the same principle as the impossible triangle. There are three rings about to slip onto three rods. First you see it, then you don't! There is no answer.

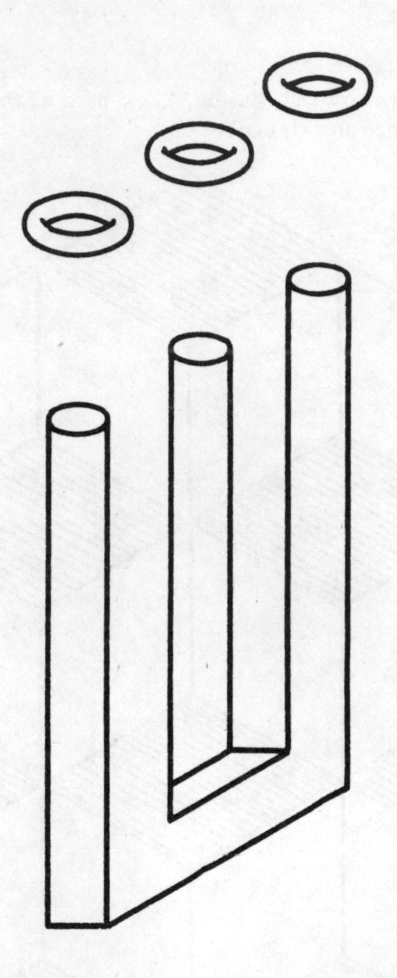

6. Dominoes and Dice

The next batch of puzzles is about dominoes and dice. Dice, as you probably know, are small cubes with six sides that are numbered by dots from one to six, so placed that the sums of the dots on a side and the opposite side equal seven. Dice is probably one of the oldest of all games. They have been found in ancient Egyptian tombs and the ruins of Babylon.

Dominoes are derived, in remote times, from dice. They are oblong tiles, usually known as bones, marked in two squares, with from zero up to six dots on each square. It is the only parlor game to use the number 0. Dominoes are marked with all possible combinations of numbers that can be rolled with two dice. There are 21 combinations. The number 0 is always added in the form of a blank, making 28 bones in all, as shown in the picture below.

The basic rule of play is: You add to a chain of dominoes by playing a bone with its end matching an end of the chain. So you play a 6 against a 6, a 5 against a 5, a blank against a blank, and so on.

A domino on which both squares have the same number of dots is called a doublet. The bone at the top left of the picture on the next page is a doublet.

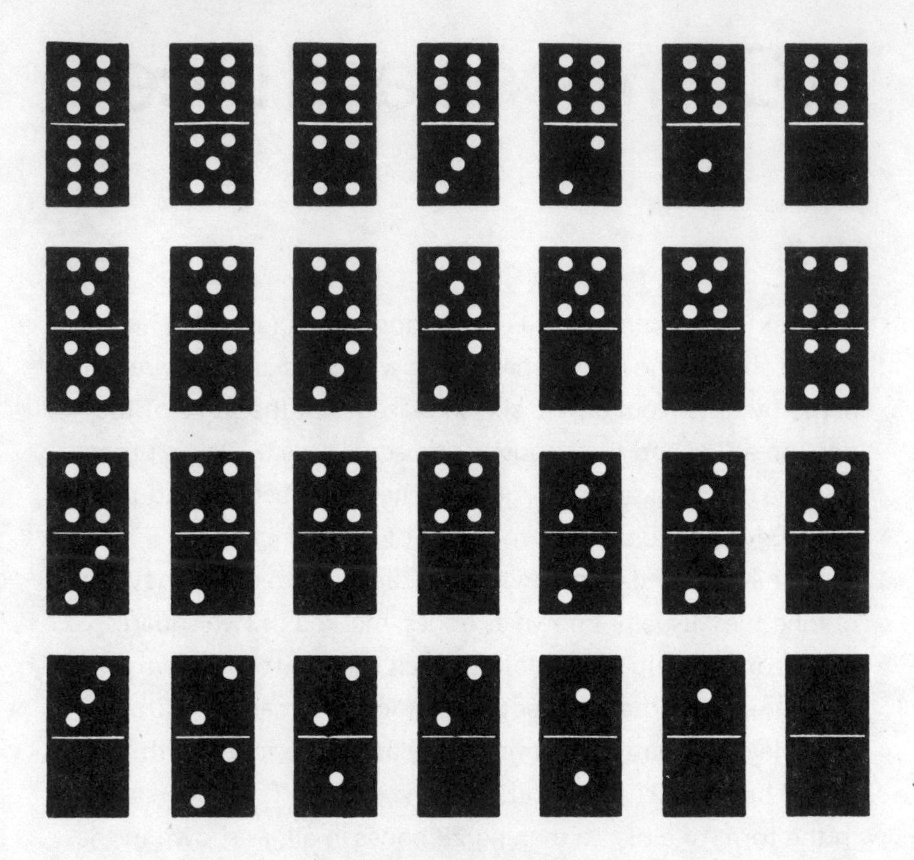

Dominoes—with a Difference

Try playing dominoes where you put down a tile whose numbers do *not* match at either end of the chain. A good rule is: The difference between numbers on adjacent tiles must be 1. Can you form closed chains this way?

Or play to this rule: The sum of the numbers on adjacent tiles must be 7. Thus, next to 3 you play 4, next to 6 a 1, and so on. This way you can make closed chains.

The Dot's Trick

Empty a box of dominoes on the table and spread them out. Put them in a chain according to the usual domino rule: Ends next to each other must match. Say 3 is at one end of the chain. How many dots will be at the other end? Do it in your head. Then check with real dominoes. How is the trick done?

Domino Trick

Secretly pocket a domino. Make sure it is not a doublet, since this may make the trick too obvious. Ask a friend to make a chain of the remaining 27 dominoes, which he thinks are a full set. You predict what the numbers at the ends of the chain will be. They will be the very numbers on the bone you pocketed. How does it work? "The Dot's Trick" should tell you.

Magic Domino Squares

The first picture here shows a three-by-three magic square made out of dominoes instead of the usual nine numbers. You count the total value of both squares of a domino as the cell's number. For example, the top row reads 1 + 8 + 3; its sum is 12. What is the magic number for the square? Add up all the rows, columns, and both diagonals.

Look at the domino square on the next page. What is its magic number?

Party Trick

Put a box of dominoes face down in a row. You turn your back and ask a friend to move any number of bones, up to 12, from the *right* end of the row to the *left*. After he does this, you turn around and turn over a bone. The number of its dots is the number of bones moved! The trick is, you previously picked out all 13 bones with a 6 or a blank on them and then placed them face down as in our picture. Then you put the rest of the bones to their right. When you turn around, you turn over the thirteenth bone from the left. Why does it work?

Domino Fractions

From a box of dominoes take out all the doublets (double 6s, double 5s, and so forth) and any bones with a blank on them. That leaves fifteen bones to play with. You can consider them as fractions. For example:

$$= \frac{3}{6} + \frac{4}{6} = \frac{7}{6} = 1\frac{1}{6}$$

Put down the fifteen bones in three rows of five. Now, can you make the sum of each row come to 10?

Another Magic Square

Can you form a magic square from these nine bones with a magic number of 21?

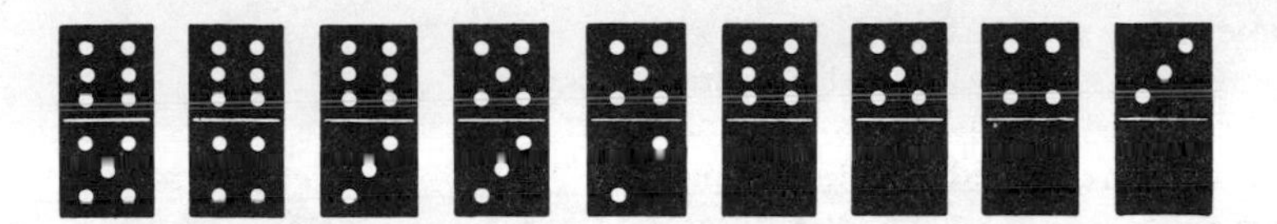

Domino Window

The picture shows a window formed by four dominoes. Count the dots along each side. What do the four sums each come to? Make up three more domino windows like this. The sums for the different windows need not be the same as this one, but in each window the sum of each side should be the same.

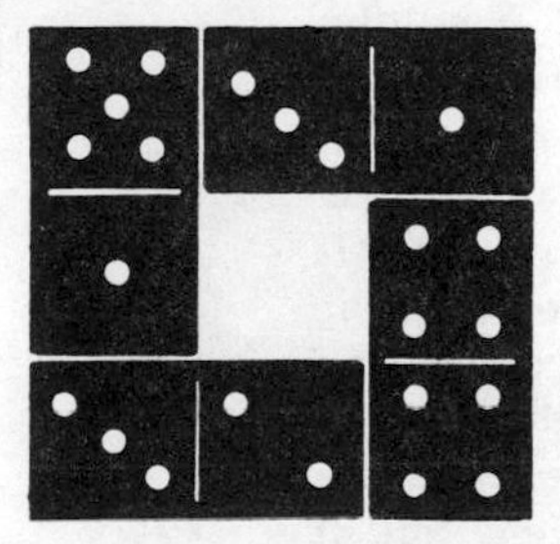

Reading the Bones

This trick is the same as giving back to somebody the two numbers he first thought of. Here the two numbers are read from the two squares of dots on a domino bone.

Ask a friend to secretly pick a domino. Tell him to multiply one of its numbers by 2, add 4 to the result, multiply the sum by 5, add in the other number on the bone, and tell you the answer. You then tell him the numbers on his domino.

How is it done? What you do is subtract 20 from the two-digit answer he gives you. So if he said 35, you subtract 20, leaving 15, which means he picked the bone 1-5. If he said 23, you take away 20, leaving just 3, which means the bone 0-3.

Suppose he chooses the bone 0-2. He multiplies 0 by 2, which gives 0; then he adds 4 to get 4. He multiplies 4 by 5, getting 20, and adds the other number 2 on the bone to get 22, which he tells you. You take away 20, leaving 2. You then tell him he chose the bone 0-2.

Do you know why it works?

Hidden Faces of Three Dice

Here is a very effective trick with dice, well known to most conjurers, which always seems to baffle the audience. I have used it with complete success—even on an audience of math teachers!

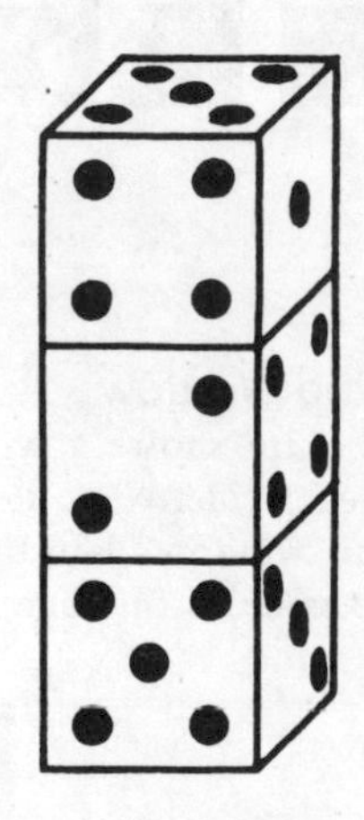

Take three dice and stack them in a pile. Explain to your subject that he is to stack the dice himself any way he likes and then add up the spots on the hidden faces—that is, the five hidden faces. (This means "not the top face," but on no account say this or you might give the trick away!) You turn your back, and he stacks the dice. You turn around and pretend to read the total in his mind. You can make play of certain numbers to heighten the audience's amazement. For example: If you work it out as 20, you ask if he has perfect vision; if it is 18, you might ask when he or she went to college; and so forth. The sum in the picture is 16. How do you work it out?

Three Dice in a Row

Another amazing trick you can do with three dice is this one: With your back turned, ask your subject to set the dice in a row and add up the spots on the three tops of the dice. Then he is to choose any one of the dice, pick it up, and add in the spots on the bottom face to the sum he has already got. Without putting that die down he is to toss it and note the spots on the top face and add them into the sum he has so far, and to remember the grand total (of the five faces). Instruct him to arrange the dice in a line. Then you say that you cannot possibly know which die he picked up and tossed, yet you will read his mind and tell him the grand total. How is it done?

CLUE: When you turn around, you quickly read off the sum of the spots on the top faces of the dice. Here are the dice at the end of this trick. The magician says the subject's grand total is 18. How does he know?

What Did the Dice Show?

Yet another dice trick. Give a friend a pencil and paper and two dice. (You can do this trick with three dice, but the working is lengthier.) Turn your back and ask him to arrange the dice in order so that he can read the spots on the top faces from left to right and make a two-digit number. For example, he would read 35 on the dice shown. Ask him to peek at the bottom faces and write what they show in the same left-to-right order and attach it to the first number to make up a four-digit number. He would write 42 with the dice in our picture (since opposite sides add up to 7) to make 3,542. Tell him to divide this number by 11 and give you the result. You then tell him what the top faces show.

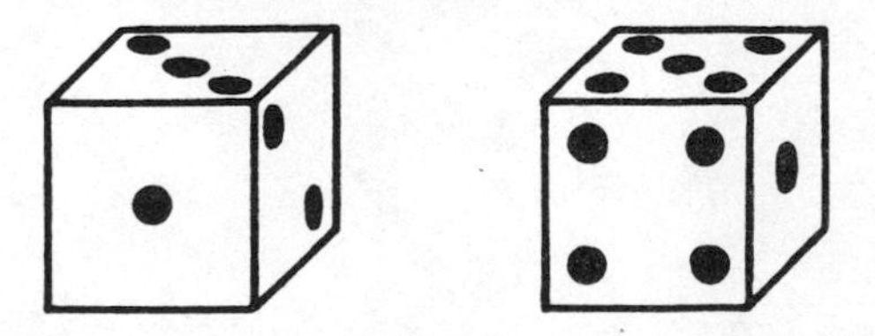

The method is: Take away 7 from the result he gives you, then divide by 9. In our example, 3,542 ÷ 11 = 322, which is the number he gives you. You take away 7: 322 − 7 = 315. Then you divide 9: 315 ÷ 35: the number on the top faces! Can you explain it?

7. Physics Puzzles

The next batch are all puzzles in physics—that is, the laws of nature. You can either solve them by scientific flair or, if you can rig up the experiments, by trial and error. My aim has been to astound or amuse you rather than to test your powers of reasoning. In other words, do not be put off if at first you can see no way to solve one of these puzzles. They have eluded the grasp of some of the greatest scientists who have ever lived, particularly the problems on chance and coin tossing. The puzzles on measuring water out of cans of different capacities can, however, be cracked by simply taking thought.

Ruler Rolling

Rest a ruler on two round pencils as shown here.

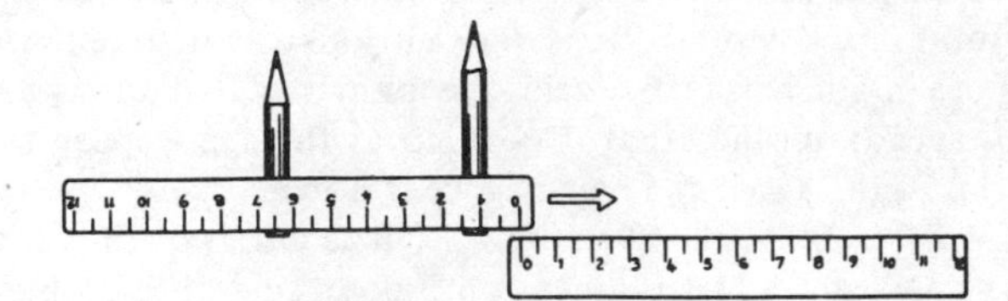

Slide the ruler forward, keeping it firmly pressed down on the pencils so it does not slip over them. When the pencils have rolled forward 2 inches, how far will the ruler have moved?

Dollar Bill for Free?

Balance a pile of about six or more coins on top of a dollar bill resting on the rim of a glass. Now bet a friend that he can't pull the bill free without toppling the coins or touching the glass.

The Coin-rolling Bet

Take two coins. Half-dollars will do. Place one coin tails up, the other next to it heads up and with the picture of the President's head as shown. Begin to roll the heads-up coin around the first, making sure there's no slipping.

Now bet a friend that the heads-up coin will end up with the President's head upside down, as shown. The friend is pretty sure to take your bet . . . and lose.

Why?

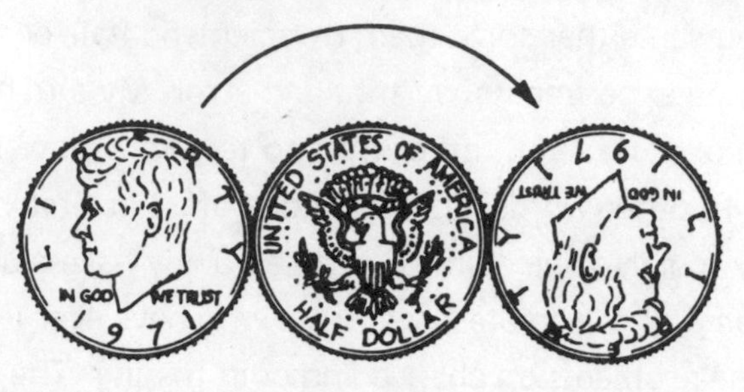

Monkey Puzzle

Lewis Carroll wrote, as you know, the famous Alice books. He was also, as you may not know, an Oxford professor of mathematics. One day he set himself this problem:

A rope passes over a free-running pulley—no friction at all! A bunch of bananas hanging from one end of the rope exactly balances a monkey clinging to the other end. The monkey begins to climb the rope. What happens to the bananas?

Don't be put off if you find this monkey business too much for you! As Carroll himself wrote: "It is very curious the different views taken by good mathematicians." One said the bunch of bananas goes up with increasing speed; another that it goes up at the same speed as the monkey does; while a third said the bananas went down.

Not only is the pulley frictionless, it is also weightless, and the rope, too, has no weight. (This is quite common in scientific problems.)

A Weighty Problem

A balance scale has only two weights, 1 ounce and 4 ounces. In only three weighings split 180 ounces of seed into two bags of 40 and 140 ounces.

Tug of War

Sam and Sally take separate ends of a rope in their hands. Sam pulls on his end with a force of 100 pounds. Sally tugs with a pull of 100 pounds. What is the tension of the rope?

Rolling Rouleau

Rouleau is a French word, pronounced "roo-loh." It means a roller, like a common, or garden, roller. But it is rather more unusual than that! It is really the strangest yet simplest invention of math you've ever seen. The curved figure shown here inside the square and outside the dotted triangle is a *rouleau.* It's easy enough to draw. Place the point of a compass on each of the corners of the triangle and draw an arc through the other two corners.

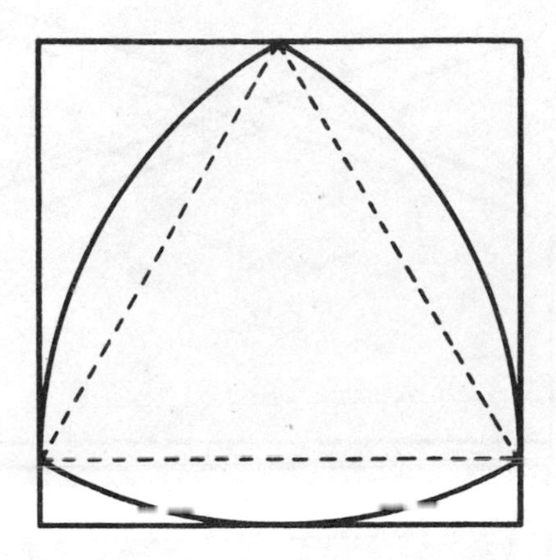

Cut this *rouleau* out of thick card or, better, plywood. Rest a ruler on the edge of it and push the ruler forward with no slipping. You'll be surprised to discover that the ruler moves smoothly along, without bobbing up and down.

If you put an axle in the middle of the *rouleau,* you'll find it works perfectly well as a wheel. How do you find its middle? It will be the center of the dotted triangle (an *equilateral* triangle). Join each corner to the middle of the opposite side with a line; these lines all cross at the triangle's center.

You can design *rouleaux* (plural of *rouleau*) with five or seven curved sides or more. The British 50-pence coin is a seven-sided *rouleau.* Rest a ruler on its edge, and the ruler will slide smoothly over it, just as it would over a round roller.

There is one more surprise. Look at the *rouleau* in our picture. It fits so snugly in the square box. Yet, believe it or not, it can turn inside the square. This is more than a mathematical curiosity. The *rouleau* shape is used in the revolutionary (pun intended!) Wankel engine named after its inventor. Where the everyday automobile has pistons that move up and down in a cylinder, the Wankel engine has a *rouleau*-shaped piston that turns in a square-shaped box.

(There is no answer.)

Belts

Wheels *A*, *B*, *C*, and *D* are connected by belts as shown. Wheel *A* turns clockwise, as the arrow shows. Can all four wheels turn without the belts slipping? If so, which way does each wheel turn, clockwise or counter-clockwise?

Now imagine all four belts are crossed. Can the wheels all turn now? What if one or three belts are crossed?

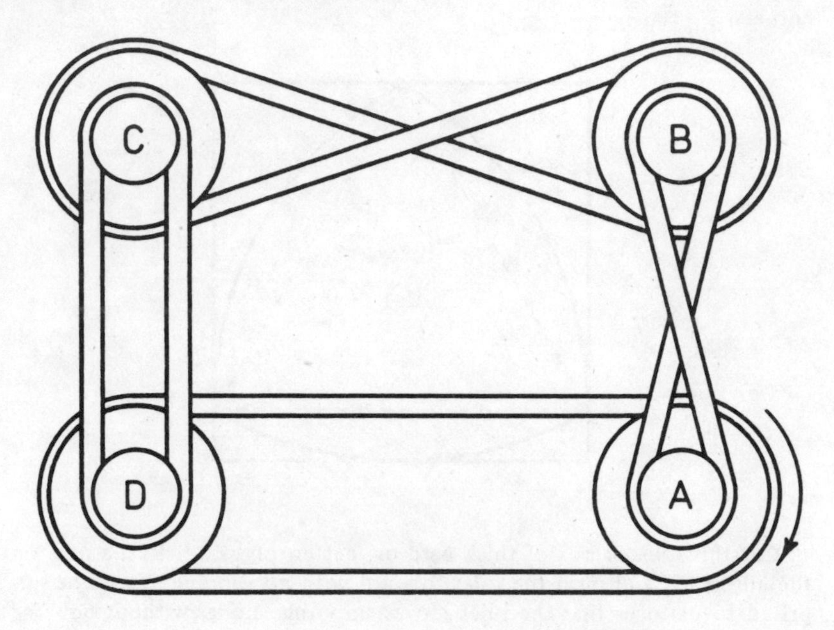

Magnetic Puzzle

You have two identical-looking bars of iron. One is a magnet, with north and south poles; the other is not. You don't know which is which. The puzzle is to find out. How can you tell just by pushing the bars around and seeing how each pulls (or pushes) the other? Try it out and see for yourself.

HINT: Remember, a magnet pulls iron things toward itself. An iron bar is magnetic (which means a magnet can pull it), but it is not necessarily a magnet (which would do the pulling).

Leaky Can

Imagine taking an empty can and punching three holes in its side—one near the top, one halfway up, and one near the bottom. Place the can in the sink. Fill the can with water from a faucet and keep it just topped up to the brim all the time. Water streams from the three holes in gentle curves known as parabolas and hits the sink floor a little way from the can.

PROBLEM: Does the water spurt out fastest from the can from the bottom, middle, or top hole?

Measuring Water by Cans

Jack wanted a quart of water. He only had two cans for measuring the water. One held five quarts and the other three. He found he could measure out a quart with the two cans. He filled the three-quart can and then poured the water into the five-quart can. What did he do next to measure out just one quart?

More Measuring

Jack wanted to measure out two quarts of water. He only had two cans, a five-quart and a three-quart can. How did he do it?

Yet More Measuring

Jack wanted to measure six pints using only a nine-pint can and a four-pint can. How did he to it?

Bottle in the Lake

A youngster plans to row at a steady speed in a straight line across a big lake from the boathouse to an island one-half mile away. As he sets off, the boathouse clock strikes noon. At that moment his bottle of soda, perched on the stern of the rowboat, falls into the lake. Thinking the bottle empty, he rows on blithely until he reaches the island, at 12:30. Then he remembers the bottle still had some ginger ale in it. (He's also conservation-minded.) So he turns the boat around instantly and rows back to the bottle at the same steady speed. As he fishes the bottle out of the water, the boathouse clock strikes 1. Well, how fast did the youngster row?

Birthday Match

Next time you are at a party ask if any two people, including yourself, have the same birthday. They don't have to be the same age. That is, the year of birth does not have to match. For instance, two partygoers might both have their birthday on May 23. What do you think the chances of a match-up would be among 23 people? Among 60 people? Remember, there are 365 days in a year, ignoring leap year. The answer will surprise you.

Tossing Two Coins

Toss two coins. What are the odds that two heads will turn up? This problem has puzzled some of the greatest minds. So don't worry if you don't get it right; if you get the wrong answer, it may be the same one as the great minds gave! Then you can say: "Great minds think alike."

Heads or Tails

Take a dime and toss it. What are the odds that it will fall heads up? Perhaps you know it is 50-50, or ½. There's a 50-50 chance, as they say, it will fall heads up and the same chance it will fall tails up. Say you tossed the dime and it fell heads up ten times in a row. What is the chance of it falling heads on the next throw? Do you think it is still ½? Or do you think it's more likely to fall tails to keep up the law of averages because it has had a long run of heads? Another "great minds think alike" problem!

ANSWERS

1. Number Problems

All the Fun of the Fair
19 + 6 + 25 = 50; teapot, doll, coconut.

Chessboard Problem
The answer is (1 X 1) + (2 X 2) + (3 X 3) + and so on up to 8 X 8, or 1 + 4 + 9 + . . . + 64 = 204 squares in all. (Algebra books give a formula for writing out what is called the sum of the squares.) For a six-by-six board it is 1 + 4 + 9 + . . . + 36 = 91.

Cat and Mice
Suppose Puss starts at mouse number 1, marked with a cross in the diagram. It will help if you draw one like this. Go around clockwise through positions 2, 3, 4, and 5, which you cross out. Crossing out each fifth dot goes in this order: 1, 2, 4, 5, 3. So the white mouse must be at position 3, if Puss starts at position 1 and moves clockwise. Or he could go counterclockwise from position 1; then the white mouse must be at position 4.

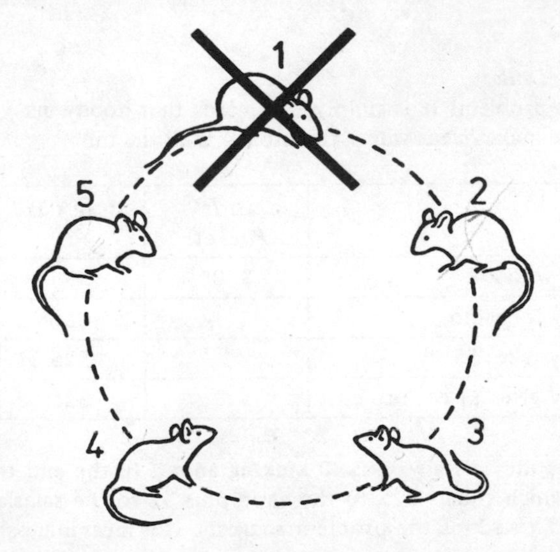

A Question of Ages
Sam 6 years, May 2 years.

Another Question of Ages
Uncle 60 years, girl 20 years.

Teen-Age Problem
Jo 13 years, Sam 9 years.

15 Shuffle
Move the 9 to the first pile: 9 + 1 + 2 + 3 = 15.

Birthday Paradox
He was born on February 29; 1792 was a leap year. So he only had a birthday every fourth year. (1800 was not a leap year.)

Word Sums

$$\begin{array}{r} 764 \\ +\ 764 \\ \hline 1{,}528 \end{array} \qquad \begin{array}{r} 534 \\ +\ 534 \\ \hline 1{,}068 \end{array}$$

Easy as ABC?

$$\begin{array}{r} 888 \\ 777 \\ +\ 444 \\ \hline 2{,}109 \end{array} \qquad \begin{array}{r} 888 \\ 666 \\ +\ 555 \\ \hline 2{,}109 \end{array}$$

The Missing Dollar
There *is* no problem! It is simply the words that hoodwink you. The following table makes clear where the money is all the time.

	Girls' Pockets	*Store's Till*	*Saleslady's Purse*
1. To start with	$30		
2. Girls pay for radio		$30	
3. Saleslady takes $5		$25	$ 5
4. Saleslady gives $1 each to girls	$ 3	$25	$ 2

As you see, there is always $30 kicking about. In the end the girls have paid $27, which equals $25 to the shop plus $2 to the saleslady. You do not add $27 to $2, as the problem suggests. It is meaningless! You would be adding what the girls have paid to what the saleslady has gained. But you could say: The girls' losses ($27) equals the saleslady's gain (an ill-gotten $2) plus the store's gain ($25). Or, to put it another way, the girls' losses plus the saleslady's loss equals the store's gain—that is, $27 + (− $2) = $25. But that − $2 may not appeal to you, in which case use the first way of putting it.

You Can't Take It (All) with You
To count $1 million would take 11 days 13 hours 46 minutes 39.9 seconds, or just over 11½ days. With no sleep—the counting was nonstop—this would be more than flesh and blood could stand! You *might* manage to count for 2½ days, bringing you $216,000.

Tear 'n' Stack
Believe it or calculate it, the answer is as high as the moon. The calculation goes like this: 1 tear makes a stack 2 sheets, or 2 thou, thick; 2 tears make 4 thou; 3 tears make 8 thou, or 2 × 2 × 2 thou. So 47 tears make a stack 2 × 2 × 2 × . . . (47 times) thou thick, or 140,737,488,355,328 thousandths of an inch high. Divide this by 1,000 to bring it to inches, then by 12 to give feet, then by 5,280 to give miles. The result is about 221 million miles, which is about the distance to the moon (actually 250 million miles).

Grains of Wheat
A sack of wheat held about a million grains of wheat. To finish covering the first 20 squares a total of 1,048,575 grains was needed. The first three answers in the second box are all about right! The last answer *might* be!! But nobody has counted the grains of sand, so far as I know.

A Sweet Problem
Five lumps in one cup, two lumps in the second cup, and three lumps in the third cup. Then sit the third cup in the second cup so the second cup now has in it five lumps!

Stock Taking
15 sheep.

Slobodian Coin Puzzle
There are four ways. Break it down like this. First way: 1 + 1 + 1 + 1 + 1 + 1; second way: 1 + 1 + 1 + 1 + 2; third way: 1 + 1 + 2 + 2; fourth way: 2 + 2 + 2 + 2.

Tug of War
In the last event you can replace the dog by two girls and a boy because, as the second tug of war showed, they are equally matched. The last tug of

war then becomes a contest between five girls and a boy on the left against four boys on the right. But the first event showed that five girls are as strong as four boys—that is, a boy is stronger than a girl. The tug of war comes down to a contest between five boys on the left and five girls on the right. So the left-hand team will win. This all supposes that each girl pulls as hard as the next, and similarly for the boys. If you are clever you could also solve the puzzle by algebra.

Check-out Check
Take away the 20 cents for the two sticks of gum. Then the three bars must have cost $2.00, or 200 cents. But 200 cannot be divided by 3 to leave a whole number of cents.

Puzzle Triangles

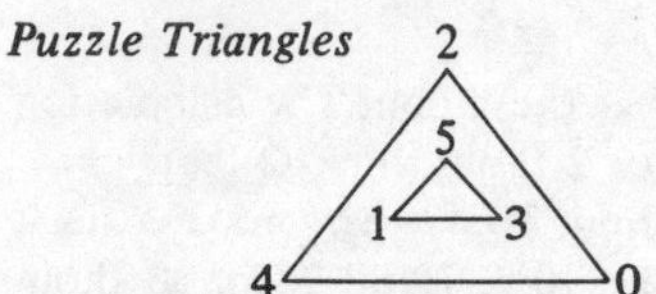

Nice Work If You Can Get It!
The boss hired her because she was smart enough to see the second rate of pay was much, much better. So much better he couldn't pay her the second rate for long. For at the end of the tenth day she would have earned by the first rate $100 in all. But by the second rate she would have earned 2 X 2 X 2 X 2 X 2 X 2 X 2 X 2 X 2 cents which is 512 cents on the tenth day alone; that is 2 times itself 9 times (the first day she only earned 1 cent). Her total earnings would be this 2 times itself 10 times less 1 (you can take this on trust), which comes to $10.23.

By the end of the twenty-seventh day she would have earned $270 by the first rate; by the second rate, she would be a dollar millionaire! She would have earned a total of 2 times itself 27 times less 1 cents, or $1,342,177.27. Very nice work!

12 Days' Gifts
78 gifts.

Dividing-the-Line Code
He counts the number of letters in the message and then notes the next higher number in the series—16, 32, 64, 128, and so on. That will be the key number.

Holiday Message
GOOD HUNTING.

Bottle and Cork
Bottle four cents, cork 1 cent. Were you stuck? Then try guessing: cork

two cents, then bottle five cents (three cents more): total seven cents, no good. And so on.

Juggling and Balancing
You can solve it by trial and error, since the answer is only going to be a *few* mugs, or you can use letters (that is, algebra). Let m stand for a mug, b for a bottle, p for a plate, and j for a jug. Then picture A shows $j = b$. Picture B shows $j = m + p$. So we know $b = m + p$. That is, a bottle weighs the same as a mug and a plate together.

Now for the trick: $3b = 3m + 3p$ simply by tripling up. But picture C shows $2b = 3p$. So $3b = 3m + 2b$. Take two bottles from both sides: $1b = 3m$. That is, a bottle balances three mugs. But a bottle balances a jug. So a jug balances three mugs.

Hidden Animal
LEOPARD.

Pictures by Numbers
A dog.

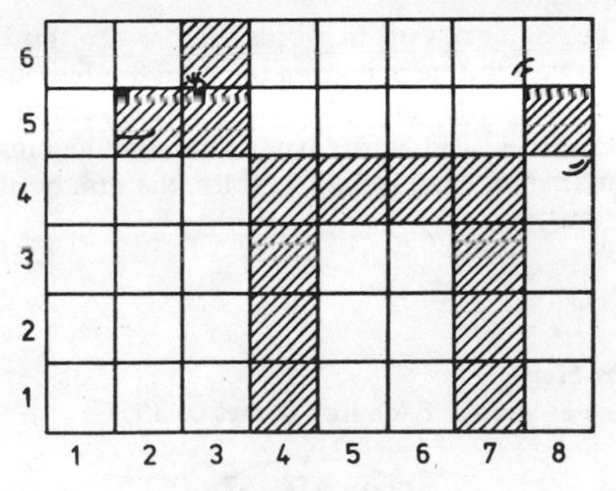

Number Tracks
A: 6, 12, 18—numbers divisible by 6.
B: 2, 4, 8, 10, 14, 16, 20.
C: 3, 9, 15.
D: 1, 5, 7, 11, 13, 17, 19.

Solve It in Your Head
Adding the equations gives: $10x + 10y = 50$, or $x + y = 5$. Taking the lower equation from the top equation gives $4x - 4y = 4$, or $x - y = 1$. You want two numbers, x and y, that add up to 5 with a difference of 1; $x = 3, y = 2$ is the answer.

Movie Times
6:30; 10:30.

Time, Please
One o'clock.

Picture and Frame
Most people think (wrongly) that the picture costs $1 and the frame costs half a dollar more, or $1.50. But then the total cost would be $2.50, not $2 as stated. Algebra, if you know it, makes the problem easy! If not, guess. Put your guesses in a table:

Frame	$0.25	$0.50	$0.75
Picture (costs 50¢ more)	0.75	1.00	1.25
Total	$1.00	$1.50	$2.00

Answer: $0.75 for the frame and $1.25 for the picture.

Idle Ivan and the Devil
We'll solve this puzzle backward in words. Before the third crossing Ivan must have had 4 rubles. But he had given the devil 8 rubles just before that, so he had had 12 rubles after the second crossing. Before the second crossing, then, he had 6 rubles, and before paying the devil he must have had 14 rubles. Before the first crossing he had 7 rubles, the sum he started with.

Happy Landing
Noon.

Cracked-Clock Problem
Split the clockface as shown. Each half comes to 39.

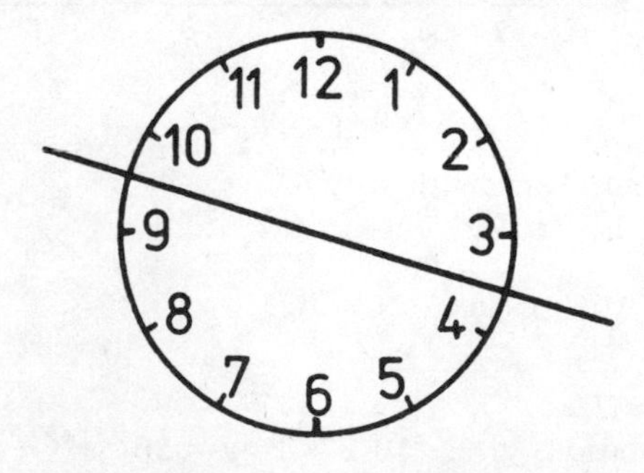

Stamp-Strip Puzzle
The other ways are *a d c b* (did you notice the first stamp is shown printed the wrong way?), *b a d c*, and *a c d b*.

The Smallest Flock

We solve the problem in the same way as we did the hint. The obvious but wrong answer is $(2 \times 3 \times 4 \times 5 \times 6 \times 7 \times 8 \times 9 \times 10) + 1$. We have counted an extra 2 in the 4 (simply multiplying the original 2 by one more 2 would have covered 4); 6 is already covered by 2×3; 8 is covered by another 2 on top of the two 2s we already have; for 9 we only need another 3; and the 10 is covered by the 2×5. So the smallest flock that obeys the rules is $(2 \times 3 \times 2 \times 5 \times 7 \times 2 \times 3) + 1 = 2{,}521$. You notice that the answer is composed of the product of primes (a prime is a number only divisible by itself or 1) plus one. And so the answer must be a prime.

The answer suggests another way of cracking the problem. One less than the answer (2,520) must be cleanly divisible by 2, 3, 4, . . . up to 10. So we know $2 \times a = 2{,}520$, where a is a whole number, and $3 \times b$, another number, $= 2{,}520$. So we can write $2 \times a = 3 \times b = 4 \times c = 5 \times d = 6 \times e = 7 \times f = 8 \times g = 9 \times h = 10 \times i$, where the letters are whole numbers. But $2 \times a$ and $3 \times b$ and $4 \times c$ and $10 \times i$ are "covered" by the others. So the answer is $(5 \times 7 \times 8 \times 9) + 1 = 2{,}521$.

Letter Frame-up

Begin at bottom left corner: *A rolling stone gathers much speed.*

The Farmer's Will

17 horses won't divide cleanly. So they borrowed a horse, making 18 horses, which *will* divide. Ann got 9 horses, Bob 6, and Charlie 2, making 17 in all. They could return the borrowed horse.

The Checkers Match

10 games; each of the five children has to play four others. This suggests 20 games. But this would be counting each pair of players twice. Best way to solve it is to draw a network, as mathematicians call it. Put five dots roughly in a ring on paper for the five players. Then join all the pairs of dots with lines to stand for the games. You'll find there are ten such lines.

The Spelling Bee

8 ways to spell out *rath* and 16 ways to spell out *raths;* you double the number of ways at each row. "And the grave land turtles squeaked out."

Number Oddity

Because $12{,}345{,}679 \times 9 = 111{,}111{,}111$.

Six 1s are 24?

$1 + 1 + 11 + 11 = 24$.

Pairing Puzzle

$1 + 8 = 2 + 7 = 3 + 6 = 4 + 5 = 9$.

Diamonds of Marbles
16 different patterns.

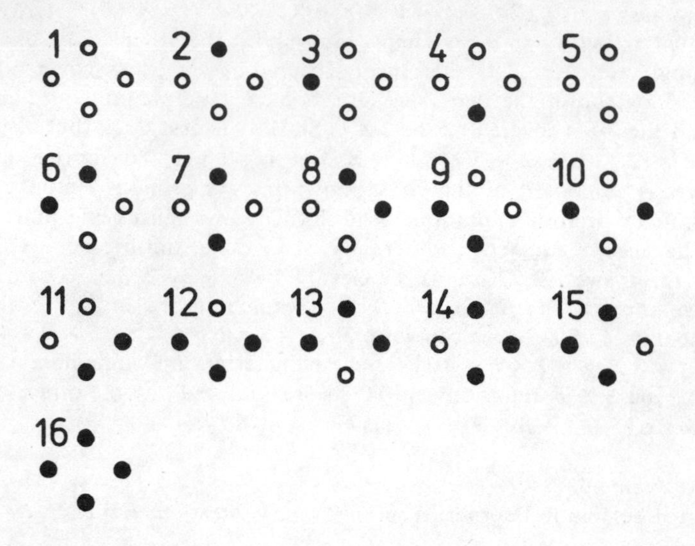

2. Number Patterns

Puzzle Boards
There is no known rule for making up these boards. If you can find one, you are a mathematician of the first order!

Sum of the Whole Numbers
500,500.

Number Crystals

A. 11,115,556 = 3,334 X 3,334
1,111,155,556 = 33,334 X 33,334

B. 11,108,889 = 3,333 X 3,333

C. 443,556 = 666 X 666

Number Carousel

142,857 X 1 = 142,857
X 5 = 714,285
X 4 = 571,428
X 6 = 857,142
X 2 = 285,714
X 3 = 428, 571

The pattern of numbers reading across and down goes in a cycle like this:

$\times 7 = 999{,}999$

$\times 8 = 1{,}142{,}856$—which is 1 in front of the initial number.

The pattern continues:

$142{,}857 \times 9 = 1{,}285{,}713 \quad (285{,}713 + 1 = 285{,}714)$

and so on.

Take-away Number Squares

You should end up with four 0s: 0, 0, 0, 0. In fact any four numbers you pick will always end up in four 0s. The explanation is a little too involved to go into, but is like that of the previous puzzle.

Take Any Three-Digit Number

The way to see how it works is to reverse the process. You end up with your three-digit number; then multiply it in turn by 7, 11, and 13, which is the same as multiplying it by 1,001. So 123 becomes $123 \times 1{,}001 = 123{,}123$, which is what you began with in the trick. This is why it works, whatever three-digits you begin with.

Five 2s

$1 = 2 + 2 - 2 - 2/2$
$2 = 2 + 2 + 2 - 2 - 2$
$3 = 2 + 2 - 2 + 2/2$
$4 = 2 \times 2 \times 2 - 2 - 2$
$5 = 2 + 2 + 2 - 2/2$
$6 = 2 + 2 + 2 + 2 - 2$
$7 = (22 \div 2) - 2 - 2$
$8 = 2 \times 2 \times 2 + 2 - 2$
$9 = 2 \times 2 \times 2 + 2/2$
$10 = 2 + 2 + 2 + 2 + 2$

Four 4s

$1 = 44/44 = 4 - 4 + 4/4 = (4 + 4)/(4 + 4)$
$2 = 4/4 + 4/4$
$3 = (4 + 4 + 4)/4$
$4 = (4 - 4)/4 + 4$
$5 = [(4 \times 4) + 4]/4$
$6 = (4 + 4)/4 + 4$
$7 = 4 + 4 - 4/4$
$8 = 4 + 4 + 4 - 4$
$9 = 4 + 4 + 4/4$
$10 = (44 - 4)/4$

Take-away Number Triangles

You should end up with the trio of numbers 2, 2, and 0. The strange thing is, whatever three numbers you begin with, you will end up with two identical numbers and a zero, such as 1, 1, and 0; 3, 3, and 0; and so on. To simplify things, note that after the first subtraction you always get one number to be the sum of the other two: 11, 5, and 1 became 6, 4, and 10, and we see immediately that 6 + 4 = 10. You can see this with rods, where the difference between the longest and the shortest rod equals the sum of differences between the other two pairs. This means the problem is not really about "any three numbers" but about any two numbers and their sums. Also, further subtractions always replaces the biggest number by the differences between the other two. With these rules it is possible to arrive at an explanation, but it is too involved for such a book as this!

Missing Numbers

a. 8 (numbers go up in 3s).
b. 10 (numbers go up in 2s).
c. 27 (numbers go up in 5s).
d. 3 (there are two patterns: 1, 2, 3, and 3, 4, 5, 6).
e. 36 (they are all squares).
f. 32 (each number is double the previous one).
g. 126 (differences are 2, 4, 8, 16, . . .).
h. 103 (two patterns: 2, 3, 4, 5, . . . and 3, 6, 12, 24, . . . ; the numbers are 2 + 3, 3 + 6, 4 + 12, 5 + 24, . . .).

Sums in the Head

A. Do it this way: 999 is 1,000 less 1. When we multiply this quantity by 3, we get 3,000 less 3, or 2,997.

B. Group the numbers as follows: (645 + 355), (221 + 779), and (304 + 696). The answer to each of the three sums is 1,000. So the grand total is 3,000.

C. You write 112,734, and the total is 999,999. All you do is write the number that makes the figures in each column add up to 9.

D. The answer is the same for both—137,174,205—though it is easier to do the sum on the left because it is set out correctly for adding. But it makes no difference if you use a calculator.

9 in Ten Digits

$$9 = \frac{97{,}524}{10{,}836} = \frac{57{,}429}{06{,}381} = \frac{95{,}742}{10{,}638} = \frac{58{,}239}{06{,}471} = \frac{75{,}249}{08{,}361}$$

Number Patterns

$$4 \times 5 \times 6 \times 7 + 1 = 29 \times 29$$
$$5 \times 6 \times 7 \times 8 + 1 = 41 \times 41$$

To get the right-hand side, you take the second and third number in the multiplication on the left, multiply them together, and take away 1. So for the first line here, $(5 \times 6) - 1 = 30 - 1 = 29$. For the second $(6 \times 7) - 1 = 41$. Yes, the pattern goes on and on.

Another Number Pattern

$$3^3 + 7^3 = 370$$
$$4^3 + 8^3 = 576$$
$$11^3 + 1^3 = 1{,}332$$
$$147 \times (14 + 7) = 14^3 + 7^3 = 3{,}087$$
$$148 \times (14 + 8) = 14^3 + 8^3 = 3{,}256$$

Reverse Sums

$$24 + 3 = 27, \text{ and } 24 \times 3 = 72$$
$$47 + 2 = 49, \text{ and } 47 \times 2 = 94$$

Palindromes in Numbers

$$\begin{array}{r} 139 \\ +\ 931 \\ \hline 1070 \\ +0701 \\ \hline 1771 \end{array}$$

The Next Palindromic Year
1991

Corridors of Numbers
The next three corridors are $3^3 = 27$, $4^3 = 64$, $5^3 = 125$, and $6^3 = 216$.

Multiplying Equals Adding?!
When one number is 3, the other is $\frac{3}{2}$, because $3 + \frac{3}{2} = 3 \times \frac{3}{2}$. There are, actually, an infinite number of answers. Other number pairs that work are: 4 and $\frac{4}{3}$, 5 and $\frac{5}{4}$, 6 and $\frac{6}{5}$, 7 and $\frac{7}{6}$, and so on.

Curious Centuries

$$100 = 1 + 2 + 3 + 4 + 5 + 6 + 7 + (8 \times 9)$$
$$= 123 - 45 - 67 + 89$$
$$= 123 - 4 - 5 - 6 - 7 + 8 - 9$$
$$= \frac{1}{2} + \frac{6}{4} + \frac{5+3}{8} + 97$$

Times-Table Triangle

A. All are squares. **B.** 12 (those two rows down from 2), 21 (three rows down from 3), 72 (six rows down from 6), and 91 (seven rows down from 7).

3. Magic and Party Tricks with Numbers

Dial-a-Number Trick

Look at the numbers in the puzzle:

$$\begin{array}{r} 673 \\ -376 \\ \hline \end{array}$$

When you take away, you "borrow" 10 first in the ones column and then in the tens column. Then you must "pay back" 1 in the tens column and the hundreds column.

6 − 3	7 − 7	3 − 6
6 − 3 − 1	10 + 7 −7 − 1	10 + 3 − 6

Don't *do* the take-away as you normally would. Then you can see the 6s cancel (first and third columns), then the 7s (second column), and the 3s (first and third columns), leaving just two 10s less two 1s, or 18.

"How Old Are You?"

The trick relies on a place-value shuffle by playing about with hundreds, tens, and ones in a disguised way. It also depends on the number 9 being 1 less than 10—the number system we count in. It is usually explained by algebra. However, we will do so using *typical* numbers.

Suppose your friend is 37 years old. Let's see what happens.

Original number: 37 = 3 tens + 7.

Multiply by 10: 370 = 3 hundreds + 7 tens.

Take away 9 X a number (5, say):*

− 9 fives = − 10 fives + 1 five

= − 5 tens + 5.

So we have then: 370 − (9 X 5)

= (3 hundreds + 7 tens) − 5 tens + 5.

The final step in the trick is to add the far right figure (5) to the other two, which become tens and ones instead of hundreds and tens:

3 tens + 7 − 5 + 5,

which is 3 tens + 7, or 37, your friend's age.

It works, and you can test it, with any numbers that fit the trick.

* You note we don't call 9 fives 45.

For Someone Over 10 Years Old
The trick here is that the subject adds 90, which is the same as adding 1 hundred and taking away 1 ten. Another place-value shuffle. He also crosses off the first digit (the hundreds place), which must be 1, and *adds* it. After you yourself add on another 9, 10 will have been added in all. But 1 ten was subtracted before, so we are back where we started.

Fiddling by Numbers
43560 which becomes RESIN.

Using Someone's Age
The year of anybody's birth plus his age must always equal the present year. The year of the great event plus the number of years ago that it happened also must always equal the present year. So the total is twice the present year.

Example: Suppose it is June 1980. Jim is 13. His birthday is in September, when he will be 14.

He was born in:	1966
Big event took place in (say):	1977
His age as of December 31:	14
The great event happened:	+ 3 years ago
	3960

The total you predict is twice the present year, or 2×1980, or 3,960.

Hundred Dollars for Five
You cannot win the bet. Here's why. (If you don't like algebra, skip it and take it on trust.) Suppose you *did* find a way with x half-dollars ($x \times 50$ cents), y quarters ($y \times 25$ cents), and z dimes ($z \times 10$ cents). The total must add up to \$5, or 500 cents. So we can write:

$$50x + 25y + 10z = 500.$$

Dividing through by 5, we get:

$$10x + 5y + 2z = 100. \qquad \text{(Equation 1)}$$

But there must be 10 coins. That is,

$$x + y + z = 10.$$

An algebra trick follows. Double everything in this last equation:

$$2x + 2y + 2z = 20. \qquad \text{(Equation 2)}$$

And subtract Equation 2 from Equation 1:

$$8x + 3y = 80.$$

The idea was to get rid of the z, the number of dimes.

Divide by 8: $x + 3/8y = 10.$

Now you can only have a whole number of each coin, so y must be 8. (It cannot be any other multiple because 10 is the limit.) If $y = 8$, then $x =$

7, and the money subtotal (without *any* dimes, since we haven't yet figured in z) is then $(50 \times 7) + (25 \times 8)$, which is 550, or 50 cents more than the desired grand total.

So there is no combination that fits the terms of the bet.

No Questions Asked

The only way to explain the trick is by algebra. You, the magician, write a number x and put it in the envelope. A friend thinks of a "thought" number, y. You take x from 99 and announce the result, $99 - x$. The friend adds this to his thought number to get $99 - x + y$. This is the same as $100 - 1 - x + y$. He crosses off the first digit and adds it to the number that remains. He ends up with $y - x$, which he takes from his thought number y:

$$\begin{aligned} &y - (y - x) \\ &= y - y + x \\ &= x \end{aligned}$$

All that is left is x, the number in the envelope.

Magic Year Number

This trick uses the same idea as "Using Someone's Age." It is simply: The current year minus somebody's birth year always gives their age. The rest of the calculation is pure hokum to fool the spectator. The shoe size doesn't matter a bit. Multiplying it by 2 then by 50—that is, by 100—puts the shoe into the hundreds place. As you are only likely to meet people below 100 years of age, you are only interested in the last two digits. It is important, however, that the last two digits are 50, as I will show in the next paragraph. When the shoe size was doubled, the result was an even number. It was necessary to add 5 (or *any* other odd number) to this to make an odd number; when this new number is multiplied by 50, the last two digits will be 50.

As I said, only the last two digits of the Magic Year Number matter: the first two digits are a blind. The reason: The first three steps give you 100 times the shoe size, plus 250. So shoe size 6½ (or 6) gives 850, 7 gives 950, 8 gives 1,050, and so on. Forget everything but the last two digits, 50. Add the Magic Year Number (1,230) to it, giving 1,280. The last two digits correspond to—surprise, surprise!—the current year. All you are doing in the last two digit places is adding 50 and then 30 (which comes from the Magic Year Number), which gives the last two digits of the current year.

4. Magic Squares and Sliding-Block Puzzles

Magic Squares

There is an easy way to make up a three-by-three magic square. Some puzzle books give a complicated way of memorizing writing numbers or diagonals. But you may not recall which cell (little square) to start on. So write the numbers to be used in a row:

1 2 3 4 ⑤ 6 7 8 9

Put the middle number, 5, in the middle of the magic square. Now pair off extreme numbers 1, 9; then the next pair 2, 8; and so on. Add each pair to 5 to get the constant magic number, 15. Remember 4, 5, 6, is a diagonal (picture *1*) and the rest follows with very little trial and error.

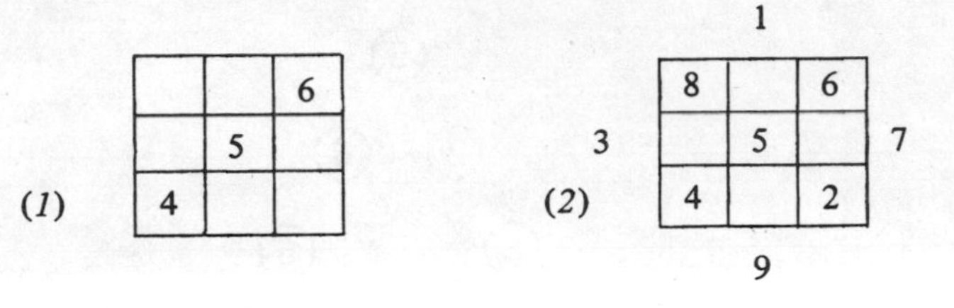

Clearly, the top left cell cannot have 9 because 9 + 6 already equals 15. So try 8 in the top left cell; then 2, its "mate" (because 8 + 2 = 10) must go in the bottom right cell (see picture *2*). The remaining "mates"–1, 9 and 3, 7–are shown outside the square ready to be put into the empty cells, which you have chosen with very little trial and error.

Here is one of the eight 3-by-3 magics:

2	7	6
9	5	1
4	3	8

Cross Sums

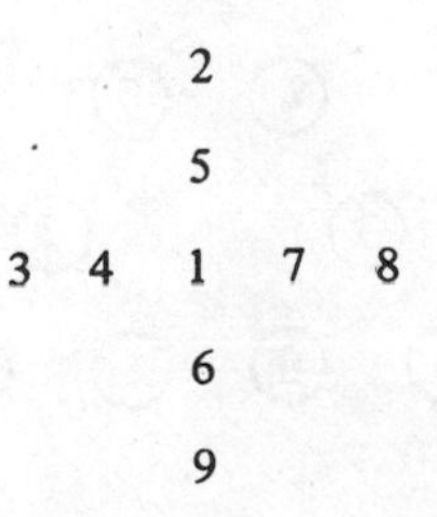

A Number Square

Any of the solutions to "Magic Squares" will do. It is stipulated that the two outside numbers must add up to 10, but since the rows and columns along the outside don't have to obey any rule, it is an easier problem than "Magic Squares."

A Triangle of Numbers

Here is the method behind the first solution diagrammed here. Put 5 at one corner; then 9 and 1 can go in the other two corners. Now take away the corner pairs of numbers from 20. There are three possible number triangles. In the first one you can see that 9 + 5 from 20 leaves 6, and that means the two middle discs on that side can only be filled by numbers adding to 6: 5, 1 or 4, 2. The 5 and the 1 have been used in the corners. So they must be 4 and 2.

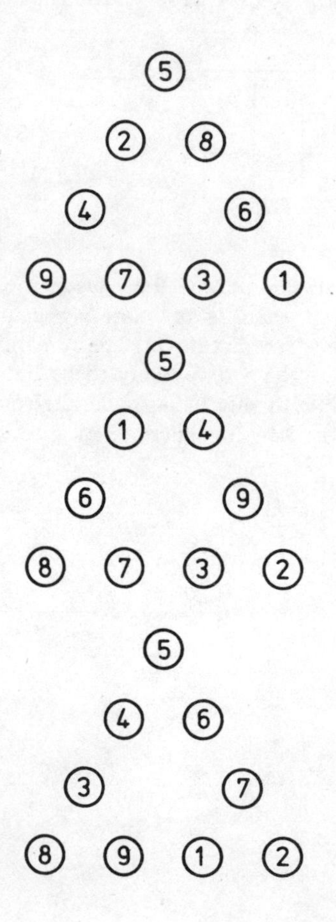

Star of David

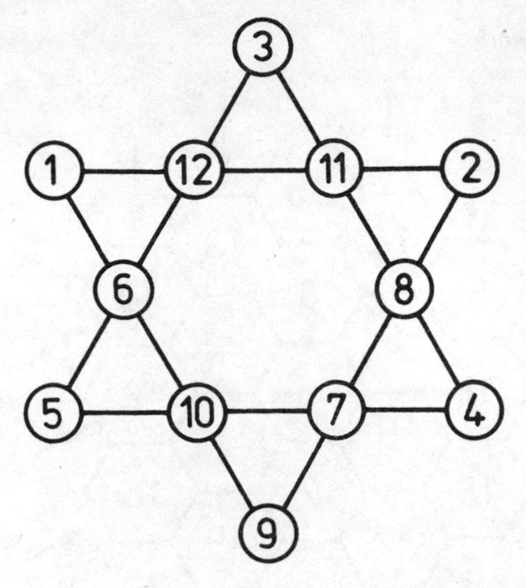

Number Rows

The end circles of each row must add to 8 because 4 has to go in the middle circle.

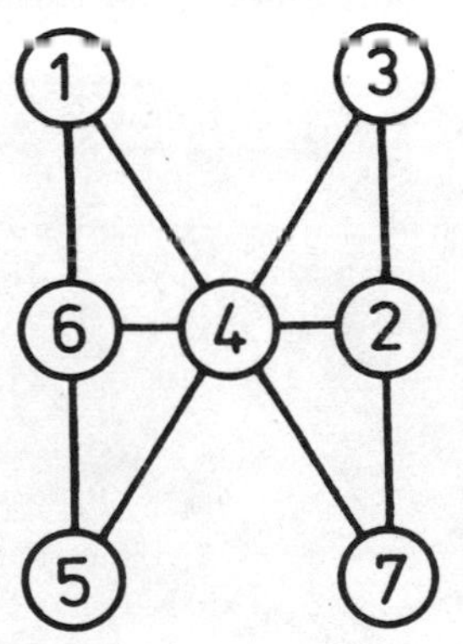

The Eight-Block Puzzle

Move the blocks in this order: 2, 6, 5, 3, 1, 2, 6, 5, 3, 1, 2, 4, 8, 7, 1, 2, 4, 8, 7, 4, 5, 6.

Four-Square Magic

3 + 5 + 12 + 14 is equal to 2 + 8 + 9 + 15. Also the sums of the squares are equal. Date of Dürer's engraving was 1514.

A Magic Honeycomb

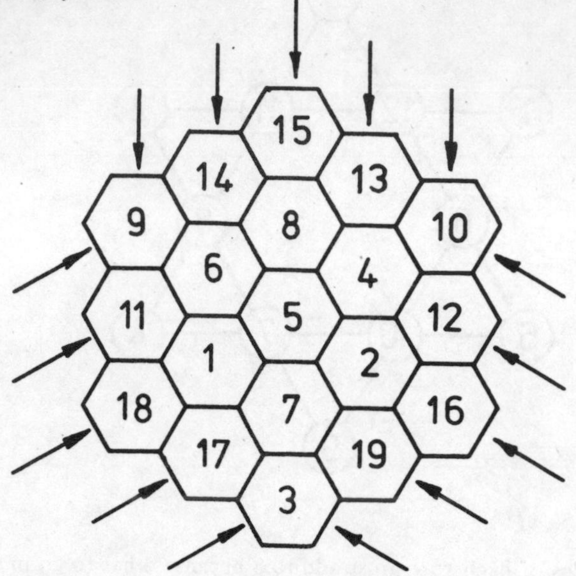

Multi-Magic Square

3	36	2
4	6	9
18	1	12

5. Illusions

Illusive Lengths
AB is same length as *BC*.

Diamond-Square Puzzle
Both are squares, the same size.

Candle Flicker
Both are the same size.

The Three Streetlamps
All three are the same height.

Railroad Track
Both ties are the same length.

Target Square
The square *is* square.

Squaring the Circles
Both circles are the same size.

The Flap Tabletop
All three tabletops are the same length.

Run Rings Around You?
Both circles are the same size.

Circle Counting
Two perfect circles.

Bull's-eye and Ring
Surprisingly, both have the same area.

Circle Sorcery
It is not bent: It is a perfect circle.

Two Tall Hats
The top of band of hat *a* is half the brim's width. This is not true of hat *b*.

The Two T's
a has same height and width, *b* hasn't.

The Herringbone Pattern
The four heavy lines *are* straight. The background pattern fools the eye.

The Picture Frame
The frame *is* square.

The Fraser Spiral
They are not whorls of a spiral but, believe it or not, circles.

The Swollen Ruler
The ruler has not swollen.

Zooming Lenses
The little lens.

The Long Glass
The plate is wider than the glass is tall.

The Black Crosses
They are equal.

The Blacker Squares
They are equal.

Lampshade and Flowerpot
They are equal.

The Top Hats
Hat *a*.

The Fans
They are equal.

The Long and Short of It
The middle line is just half the length of the other lines, although it looks longer.

The Artful Arrows
Arrow shafts are the same length.

Straight As an Arrow
Line *q* is a continuation of the arrow *x*.

Skew Lines?
The horizontal lines are parallel.

Stars and Diamonds
The length of each diamond *is* the same as the distance between tip of the star and diamond tip.

Circles Before Your Eyes
Incredibly, both inner circles are the same size.

Arcs More or Less Curved
All these arcs are equally curved. That is, all are part of the same size circle.

Hickman's Squares
Both figures are squares.

Devilish Diagonals

Both diagonals AB and BC are the same length.

The Extra Cube

Turn the book upside down and a cube magically seems to appear.

6. Dominoes and Dice

Dominoes—with a Difference

Playing "1 difference" you can make a closed chain.

The Dot's Trick

Each value appears in pairs throughout the set of dominoes. So an unpaired 3 at one end of the line must have its "mate" at the other end.

Domino Trick

The trick works for the same reason as "The Dot's Trick": each value has a pair in the set. So the two values on the domino you pocket must appear at the ends, since you left only one of each value and they can only appear in pairs on the inside of the chain.

Magic Domino Squares

In the magic square all rows and columns and both diagonals add up to the magic number 12. In the second magic square the magic number is 15.

Party Trick

The trick works for this reason: With no tiles moved, the thirteenth tile is 0-0, which means that no tiles have been moved. Move one tile to the left end, and the thirteenth tile now shows 0-1, indicating one tile has been moved . . . and so on.

Domino Fractions

$$\frac{4}{1}+\frac{2}{3}+\frac{5}{2}+\frac{4}{2}+\frac{5}{6}=10$$

$$\frac{6}{1}+\frac{1}{3}+\frac{3}{4}+\frac{5}{3}+\frac{5}{4}=10$$

$$\frac{2}{1}+\frac{5}{1}+\frac{4}{6}+\frac{6}{3}+\frac{2}{6}=10$$

Another Magic Square

To solve, write the total values in order:

3 4 5 6 ⑦ 8 9 10 11

and circle the middle number, 7. Now pair the outer numbers 3 and 11 and so on inward. Put 7 in the middle of your magic square and then juggle the pairs in lines that pass through 7.

Answer:

10	3	8
5	7	9
6	11	4

in numbers

or

$\frac{4}{6}$	$\frac{0}{3}$	$\frac{3}{5}$
$\frac{0}{5}$	$\frac{2}{5}$	$\frac{3}{6}$
$\frac{0}{6}$	$\frac{5}{6}$	$\frac{0}{4}$

in dominoes

Domino Window

Dots along each side come to 9. Here are other possibilities:

Reading the Bones

The adding and multiplying you ask of your friend amounts to this: He multiplies one number on the domino bone by 10 and adds in the other number *plus* 20, which you then mentally subtract. The multiplying by 10 is concealed in two stages—first he multiplies by 2, then, after adding in 4, by 5. He now has one number times 10 plus 4×5, which is 20. After you discard the 20, you are left with the first number times 10 (and therefore in the tens place) plus the second number (which is in the ones place).

Hidden Faces of Three Dice

All you need do is glance at the top face and take its number from 21. The top face in the picture was 5, so the sum was 16. The secret is simple: Opposite faces of dice add up to 7. So the three pairs of opposite faces add up to three 7s, or 21. Take away the number on the top face to get the sum for the hidden faces.

Three Dice in a Row

All you have to do is add 7 to the sum of the spots on the top faces, which was $4 + 1 + 6 = 11$. So the subject's total was 18. This is how it works: After the subject sets up the three dice in a row originally, he only handles one of the dice; so when you add up the spots on the top faces, two faces are the same for you and for your subject. You could not know the original top or bottom of the third die, which he has added in individually, but you know that the *total* of opposite sides *must* be 7. After the subject has tossed this third die, he adds in the spots on the top face. This is the face you see and also add in. All you have to do is account for the top and bottom face before that die was tossed—that is, you add in 7.

What Did the Dice Show?

We'll use our sample to explain how the trick works. The number 3,542 could be written as 35 hundreds plus $(7 - 3)$ tens plus $7 - 5$. That is, $35h + (7 - 3)\,t + 7 - 5$, or $35h + 70 - 30 + 7 - 5$, which is $35h - 35 + 77$. Now 35 hundreds less 35 is 35 ninety-nines. So we now have $(35 \times 99) + 77$. The subject had to divide by 11, which gave $(35 \times 9) + 7$. What you did was to take away 7, leaving 35×9; then divide by 9, giving 35. Of course it works for any pair of numbers on the dice. Try it and see.

7. Physics Puzzles

Ruler Rolling
The ruler travels twice as far as the pencils—that is, 4 inches.

Dollar Bill for Free?
The secret is to pull the bill out so quickly the coins don't move with it. And the way to do this is to hold the free end of the bill firmly between the forefinger and thumb of one hand and with the outstretched forefinger of the other hand strike the stretched dollar bill. This brings the bill free of the coins without dislodging them—provided you move quickly and without hesitation.

The Coin-rolling Bet
The rolled coin finishes right side up again if rolled all the way around the stationary coin—just as if it had revolved once completely about its own rim.

Monkey Puzzle
The bananas are pulled up at the same speed as the monkey hauls himself up the rope.

A Weighty Problem
Split the 180 ounces evenly into the two pans, making two lots of 90 ounces. Split one panload again between the two pans to make two lots of 45 ounces. Weigh that against the two weights, 5 ounces in total, and 40 ounces of seed. You now have 40 ounces of seed in one pan, which you tip into one bag; the rest, 140 ounces, goes in the other bag.

Tug of War
100 pounds.

Belts
Yes. *B* turns counterclockwise; *C* and *D* turn clockwise. The wheels can also turn if all four belts are crossed but not if one or three belts are.

Magnetic Puzzle
Move each bar in turn up to the middle of the other bar and at right angles to it. The magnet will attract the other when it is brought up. The non-magnet will not do so.

Leaky Can
Physics shows that the water spurts out fastest from the middle hole. But the math is a little too advanced to go into here.

Measuring Water by Cans
Jack refilled the three-quart can and poured two quarts of the water into the five-quart can till it was full, leaving one quart left in the three-quart can.

More Measuring
Jack measures out one quart as in the previous puzzle. Then he empties the five-quart can and pours this one quart into it. Then he fills the three-quart can again and pours the water into the five-quart can, which is now holding four quarts. He fills the three-quart can again and pours off one quart into the five-quart can, which is now full. The three-quart can now holds two quarts of water.

Yet More Measuring
Jack filled the nine-pint can and then poured off four pints to fill the four-pint can, which he then emptied. This left five pints in the nine-pint can. He then poured four of these pints into the four-pint can, leaving one pint in the nine-pint can. He emptied the four-pint can again and then poured the one pint from the bigger can into it. He filled the nine-pint can again and poured three pints from it to fill the four-pint can. This left six pints in the bigger can.

Bottle in the Lake
He rows one mile in one hour. So his speed was one mile per hour.

Birthday Match
Surprisingly, you only need 60 people at the party to be almost certain to find two people with the same birthday. Of course, this does not mean their birthday is the same as *yours.* With 23 people you have a 50-50 chance of finding two people with birthdays that match.

Tossing Two Coins
These are the possibilities: head head, head tail, tail head, and tail tail. That is, four ways, only one of which gives the two heads. Many great minds thought there were only *three* ways, because they forgot that head tail is not the same as tail head.

Heads or Tails

The odds are still ½ that it will fall heads. The odds of any coin falling heads or tails is *always* 50-50. One way to look at it is this: The coin has no memory: It cannot remember how many times it has fallen one way or the other. Another way is to say: You can toss ten different dimes or one dime ten times. Well, obviously each dime cannot tell how the others are falling—heads or tails—can it? The fact remains, however, that in the long run the number of heads and tails *does* even out. In one experiment 30 pennies were shaken in a box and tossed; this was done 100 times, making 3,000 tosses in all. And 1,492 heads were gotten. That's only 8 tosses short of half (1,500).

VOLUME TWO

MATH PUZZLES & GAMES

BY MICHAEL HOLT

CONTENTS

INTRODUCTION

Here is my second book of mathematical puzzles and games. In it I have put together more brainteasers for your amusement and, perhaps, for your instruction. Most of the puzzles in this book call for practical handiwork rather than for paper and pencil calculations—and there is no harm, of course, in trying to solve them in your head. I should add that none call for practiced skill; all you need is patience and some thought.

For good measure I have included an example of most types of puzzles, from the classical crossing rivers kind to the zany inventions of Lewis Carroll. As with the first book of mathematical puzzles, I am much indebted to two great puzzlists, the American Sam Loyd and his English rival Henry Dudeney.

Whatever the type, however, none call for special knowledge; they simply require powers of deduction, logical detective work, in fact.

The book ends with a goodly assortment of mathematical games. One of the simplest, "Mancalla," dates back to the mists of time and is still played in African villages to this day, as I have myself seen in Kenya. "Sipu" comes from the Sudan and is just as simple. Yet both games have intriguing subtleties you will discover when you play them. There is also a diverse selection of match puzzles, many of which are drawn from Boris A. Kordemsky's delightful ***Moscow Puzzles: Three Hundred Fifty-Nine Mathematical Recreations*** (trans. by Albert Parry, New York: Charles Scribner's Sons, 1972); the most original, however, the one on splitting a triangle's area into three, was given me by a Japanese student while playing with youngsters in a playground in a park in London.

A word on solving hard puzzles. As I said before, don't give up and peek at the answer if you get stuck. That will only spoil the fun. I've usually given generous hints to set you on the right lines. If the hints don't help, put the puzzle aside; later, a new line of attack may occur to you. You can often try to solve an easier puzzle similar to the sticky one. Another way is to guess trial answers just to see if they make sense. With luck you might hit on the right answer. But I agree, lucky hits are not as satisfying as reasoning puzzles out step by step.

If you are really stuck then look up the answer, but only glance at the first few lines. This may give you the clue you need without giving the game away. As you will see, I have written very full answers to the harder problems or those needing several steps to solve, for I used to find it baffling to be greeted with just the answer and no hint as to how to reach it.

However you solve these puzzles and whichever game takes your fancy, I hope you have great fun with them.

—Michael Holt

1. Flat and Solid Shapes

All these puzzles are about either flat shapes drawn on paper or solid shapes. They involve very little knowledge of school geometry and can mostly be solved by common sense or by experiment. Some, for example, are about paper folding. The easiest way to solve these is by taking a sheet of paper and folding and cutting it. Others demand a little imagination: You have to visualize, say, a solid cube or how odd-looking solid shapes fit together. One or two look, at first glance, as if they are going to demand heavy geometry. If so, take second thoughts. There may be a perfectly simple solution. Only one of the puzzles is *almost* a trick. Many of the puzzles involve rearranging shapes or cutting them up.

Real Estate!

K.O. Properties Universal, the sharpest realtors in the West, were putting on the market a triangular plot of land smack on Main Street in the priciest part of the uptown shopping area. K.O.P.U.'s razor-sharp assistant put this ad in the local paper:

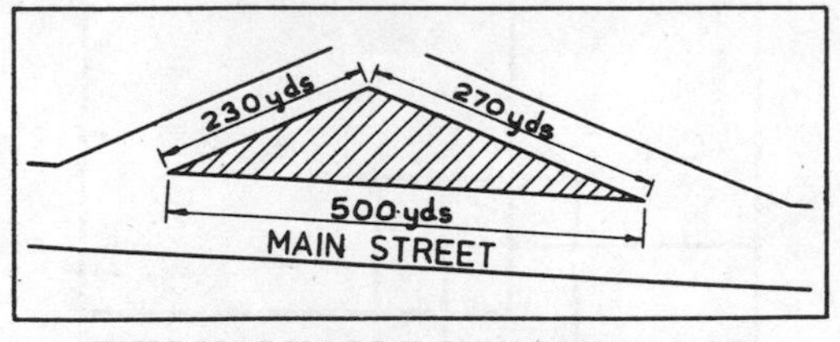

THIS VALUABLE SITE IDEAL FOR STORES OR OFFICES
Sale on April 1

Why do you think there were no buyers?

Three-Piece Pie

How can you cut up a triangular cranberry pie this shape into three equal pieces, each the same size and shape? You can do it easily. First cut off the crust with a straight cut and ignore it.

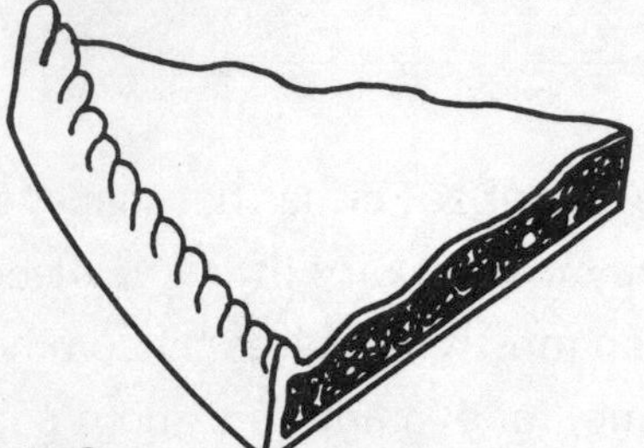

How Many Rectangles?

How many rectangles can you see?

Squaring Up

How many squares can you find here? Remember, some squares are part of other bigger squares.

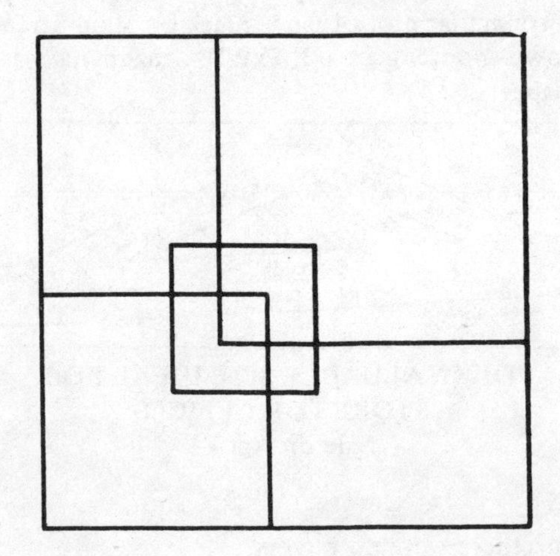

Triangle Tripling

Copy the blank triangle shown here. Divide it into smaller ones by drawing another shaded triangle in the middle; this makes 4 triangles in all. Then repeat by drawing a triangle in the middle of each of the blank triangles, making 13 triangles altogether. Repeat the process. Now how many shaded and blank triangles will you get? And can you see a pattern to the numbers of triangles? If you can, you will be able to say how many triangles there will be in further divisions without actually drawing in the triangles.

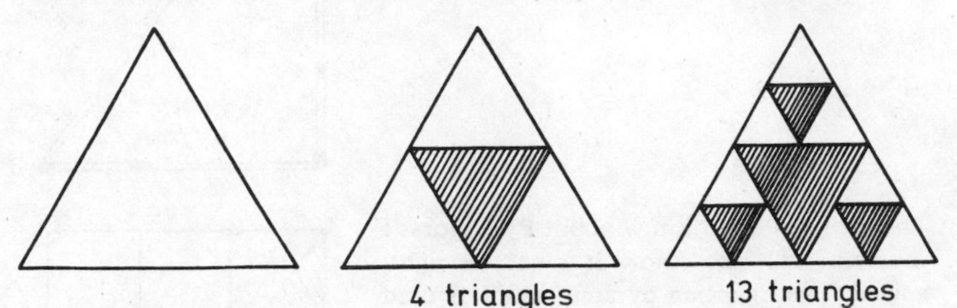

The Four Shrubs

Can you plant four shrubs at equal distances from each other? How do you do it?

HINT: A square pattern won't do because opposite corners are further apart than corners along one side of the square.

Triangle Teaser

It's easy to pick out the five triangles in the triangle on the left. But how many triangles can you see in triangle *a* and in triangle *b*?

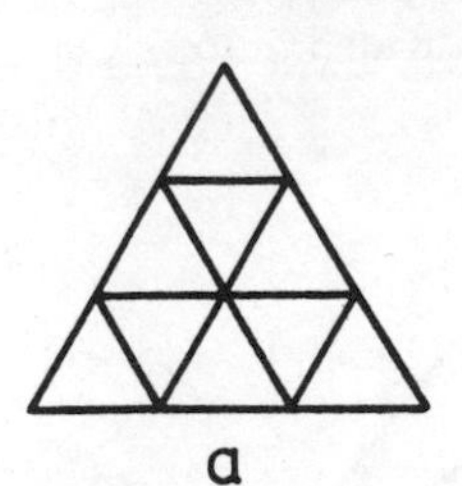

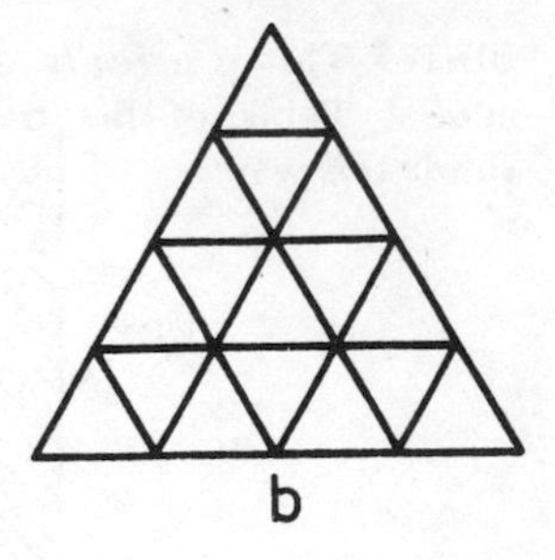

Triangle Trickery

Cut a three-four-five triangle out of paper. Or arrange 12 matches as a three-four-five triangle (3 + 4 + 5 = 12).

Those of you who know about Pythagoras's theorem will also know it must be right-angled. The Egyptian pyramid builders used ropes with three-four-five knots to make right angles. They were called rope stretchers. The area shut in by the triangle is (3 X 4)/2. If you don't know the formula for the area of a triangle, think of it as half the area of a three-by-four rectangle. The puzzle is this:

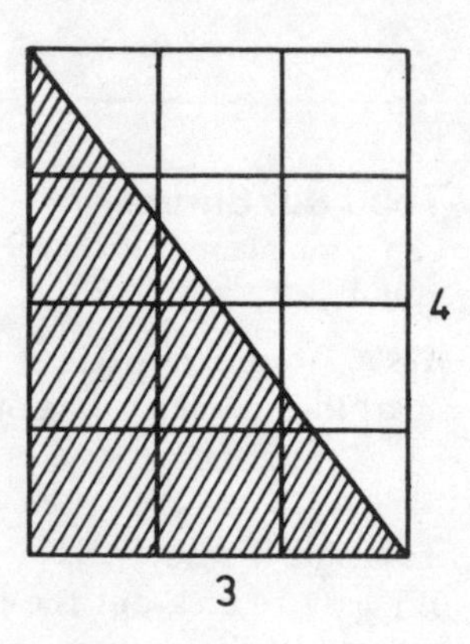

Using the same piece of paper (or the same 12 matches), show 1/3 of 6 = 2.

HINT: This is a *really* difficult puzzle for adults! Think of the triangle divided into thirds this way:

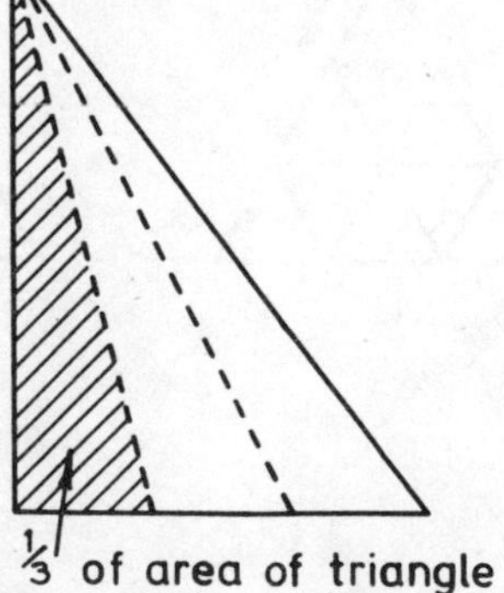

If you are using paper, fold it along the dotted lines.

Fold 'n Cut

Fold a sheet of paper once, then again the opposite way. Cut the corner, as shown. Open the folded sheet out and, as you see, there is one hole, in the middle.

Now guess what happens when you fold three times and cut off the corner. How many holes will there be now?

Four-Square Dance

How many different ways can you join four squares side to side? Here is one way. Don't count the same way in a different position, like the second one shown here, which is just the same as the first. Only count *different* shapes.

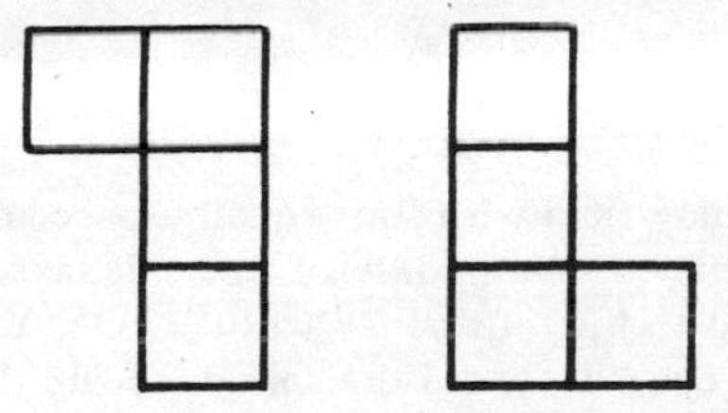

Net for a Cube

Each shape here is made up of six squares joined side to side. Draw one, cut it out, and it will fold to form a cube. Mathematicians call a plan like this a net. How many different nets for a cube can you draw? Only count *different* ones. For instance, the second net is the same as the first one turned round.

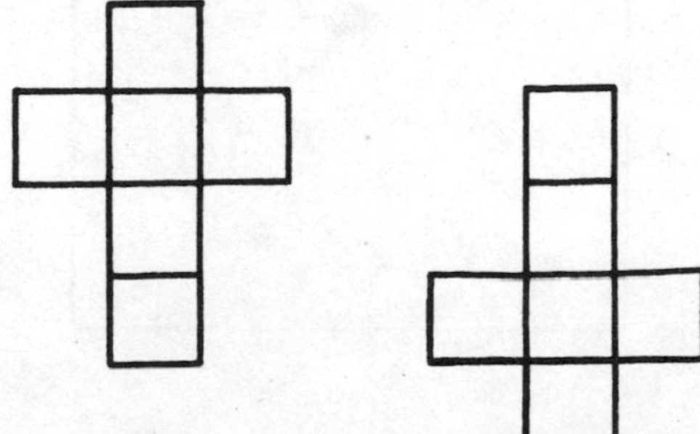

Stamp Stumper

Phil A. Telist had a sheet of 24 stamps, as shown. He wants to tear out of the sheet just 3 stamps but they must be all joined up. Can you find six *different* ways Phil can do so? The shaded parts show two ways.

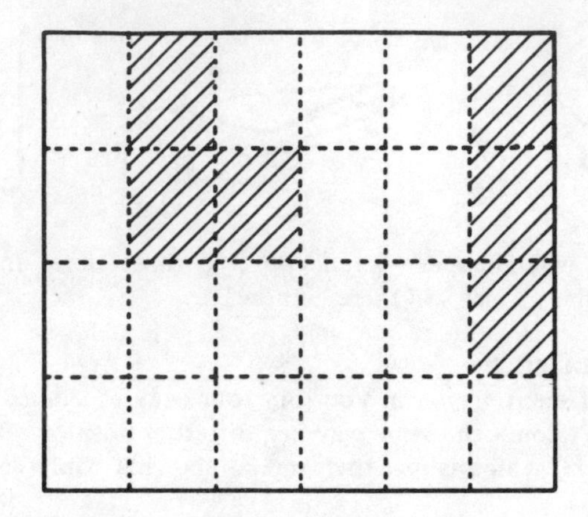

The Four Oaks

A farmer had a square field with four equally spaced oaks in it standing in a row from the center to the middle of one side, as shown. In his will he left the square field to his four sons "to be divided up into four identical parts, each with its oak." How did the sons divide up the land?

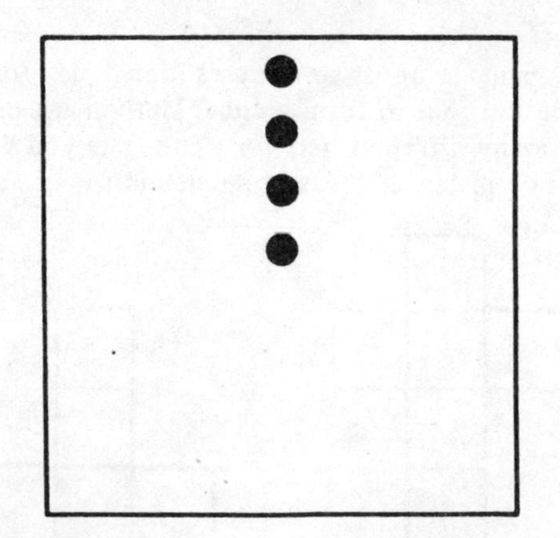

Box the Dots

Copy this hexagon with its nine dots. Can you draw nine lines of equal length to box off each dot in its own oblong? All oblongs must be the same size, and there must be no gaps between them.

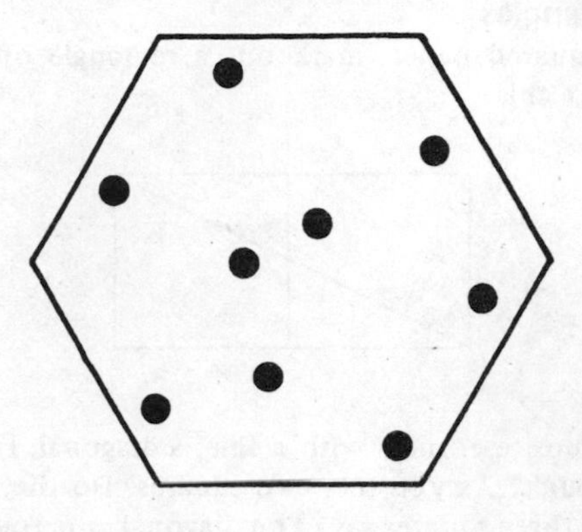

Cake Cutting

Try to cut the cake shown into the greatest number of pieces with only five straight cuts of the bread knife.

HINT: It's more than the 13 pieces shown here.

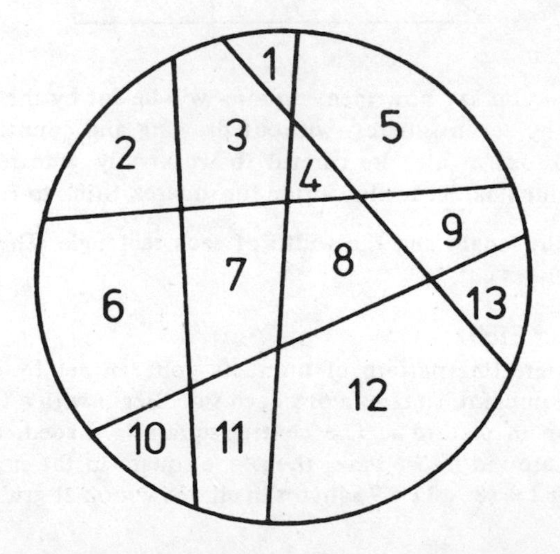

Four-Town Turnpike

Four towns are placed at the corners of a ten-mile square. A turnpike network is needed to link all four of the towns. What is the shortest network you can plan?

Obstinate Rectangles

On a sheet of squared paper, mark out a rectangle one square by two squares in size, like this:

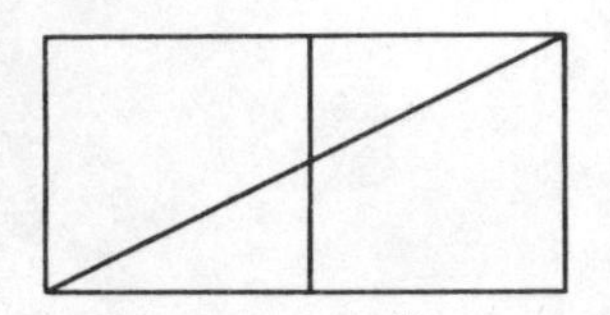

Join a pair of opposite corners with a line, a diagonal. How many squares does it slice through? As you see, two squares. Do the same for a bigger rectangle, two by three squares say. The diagonal cuts four squares.

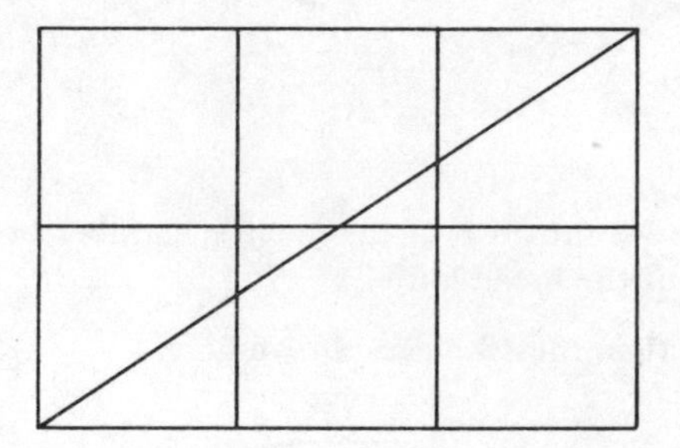

PUZZLE: Can you say how many squares will be cut by the diagonal of a rectangle six by seven squares—without drawing and counting? In short, can you work out a rule? Be careful to work only with rectangles, not squares. It's much harder to find a rule for squares. Stick to rectangles!

HINT: Add the length and the width of each rectangle. Then look at the number of squares cut.

One Over the Eight

Here is an interesting pattern of numbers you can get by drawing grids with an odd number of squares along each side. Begin with a three-by-three grid, as shown in picture *a*. The central square is shaded, and there are eight squares around it. We have, then, one square in the middle plus the other eight, or $1 + (8 \times 1) = 9$ squares in all. Now look at grid *b:* It has one central square, shaded, and several step-shaped jigsaw pieces, each made up of three squares. By copying the grid and shading, can you find how many jigsaw pieces make up the complete grid? Then the number of squares in the complete grid should be the number in each "jig" times 8, plus 1: 1 + (8 X 3) = 25. Next, in grid *c* see if you can copy and finish off the jigsaw pieces; one has been drawn for you. Then complete the number pattern: 1 + 8 jigs = 49. You've got to find what number of squares there are in a jig. Could you write the number pattern for a nine-by-nine grid—without even drawing it?

a

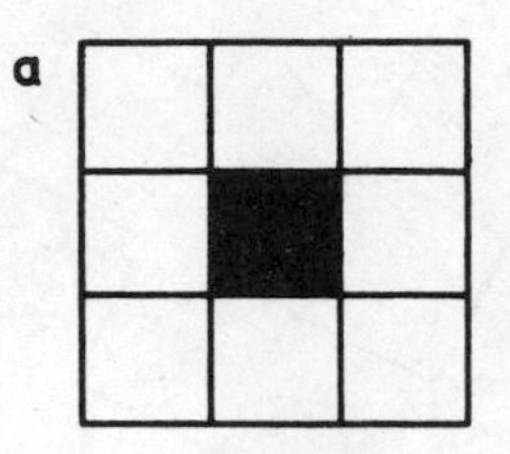

b

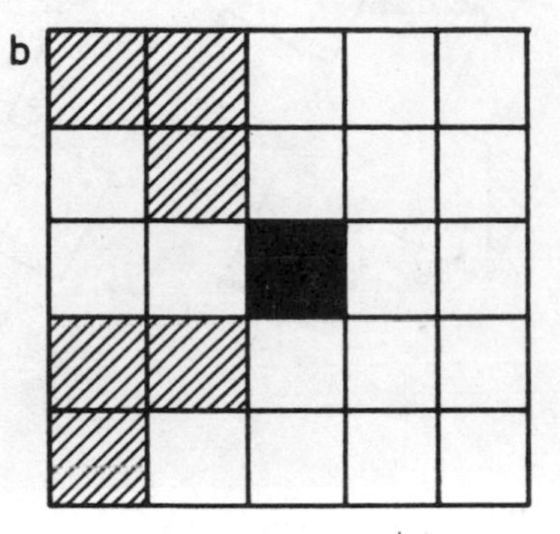

c

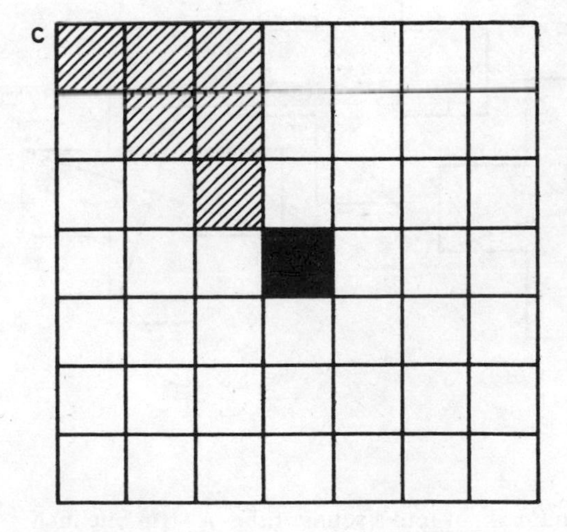

Greek Cross into Square

Out of some postcards cut several Greek crosses, like these shown here. Each, as you can see, is made up of five squares. What you have to do is cut up a Greek cross and arrange the pieces to form a perfect square. The cuts are indicated on drawings *a*, *b*, and *c*. In the last two puzzles, *d* and *e*, you need two Greek crosses to make up a square. See if you can do it. There is no answer.

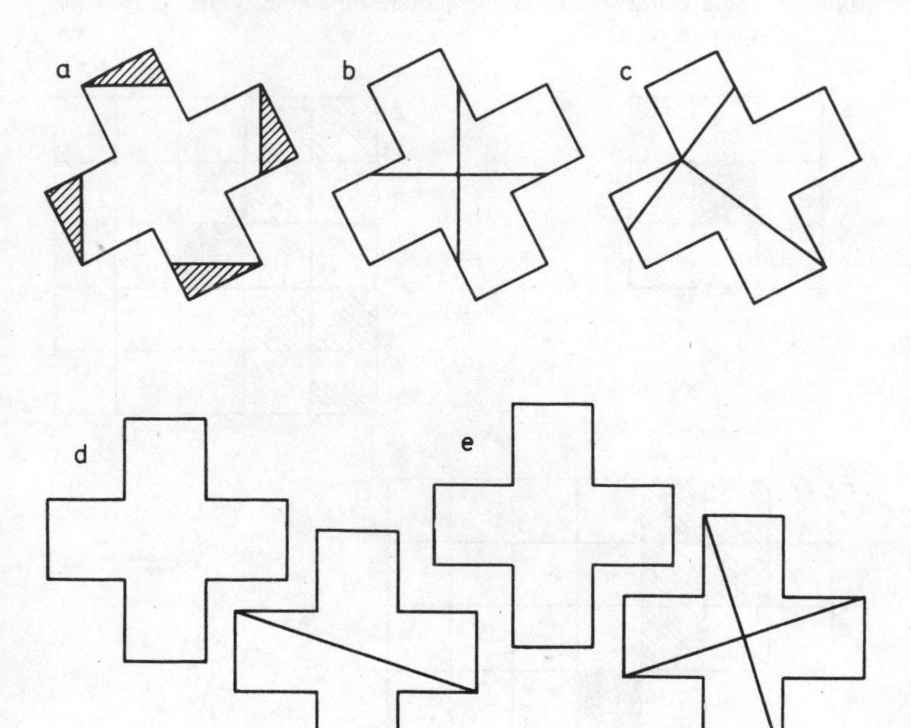

Inside-out Collar

Take a strip of stiff paper and make it into a square tube. A strip one inch wide and four inches long—with a tab for sticking—will do nicely. Crease the edges and draw or score the diagonals of each face before sticking the ends of the strip together; scissors make a good scoring instrument.

The trick is to turn the tube inside out without tearing it. If you can't do it, turn to the answer section.

Cocktails for Seven

The picture shows how three cocktail sticks can be connected with cherries to make an equilateral triangle. Can you form seven equilateral triangles with nine cocktail sticks? You can use matchsticks and balls of plasticine instead.

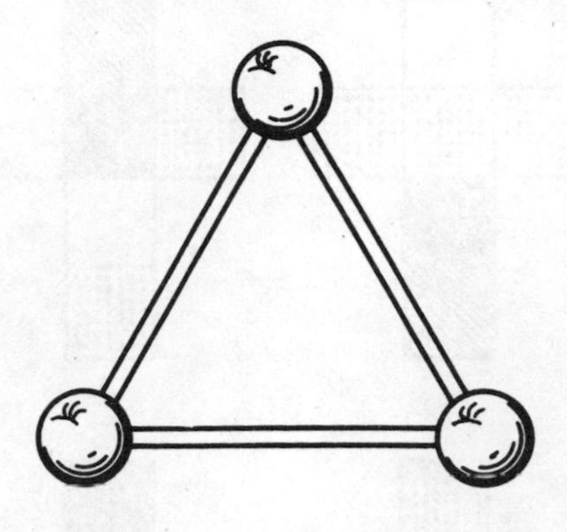

The Carpenter's Colored Cubes

A carpenter was making a child's game in which pictures are pasted on the six faces of wooden cubes. Suddenly he found he needed twice the surface area that he had on one big cube. How did he double the area without adding another cube?

Painted Blocks

The outside of this set of blocks is painted. How many square faces are painted?

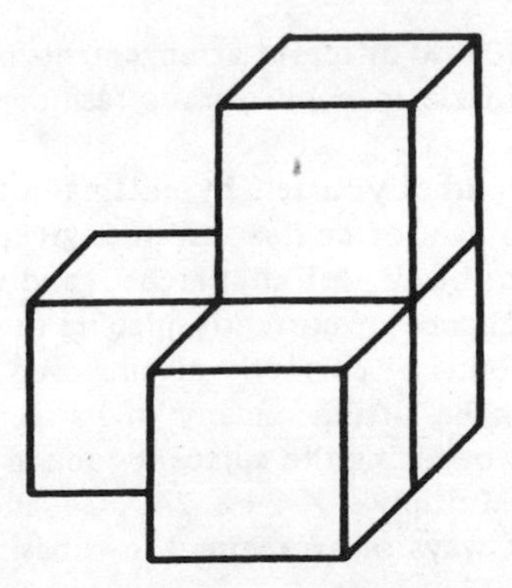

Instant Insanity

This is a puzzle of putting four identically colored cubes together in a long block so no adjacent squares are the same color. You can make the cubes yourself from the four nets shown in the picture.

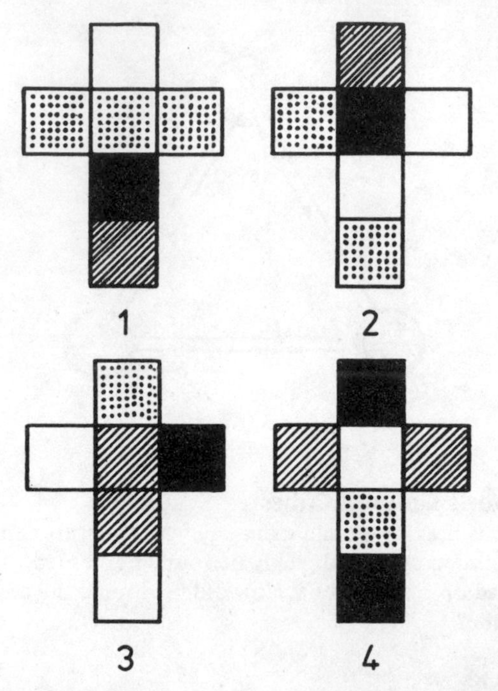

In this puzzle you have four cubes. Each cube's faces are painted with four different colors. Put the four cubes in a long rod so that no colors are repeated along each of the rod's four long sides.

Since there are over 40,000 different arrangements of the cubes in the rod, trying to solve the puzzle in a hit-or-miss fashion is likely to drive you insane!

You can make the cubes yourself by cutting out the four cross-shaped nets shown here. You can, of course, use red, green, blue, and white, for instance, instead of our black, dotted, hatched, and white.

There is a 1-in-3 chance of correctly placing the first cube, which has three like faces. The odds of correctly placing each of the other cubes is 1 in 24: Each cube can be sitting on any of its six faces; and for each of these positions it can be facing the adjacent cube in four different ways—a total of 24 positions. Multiply 3 X 24 X 24 X 24, and the answer is 41,472 —the total number of ways of arranging the cubes. See answer section for solution.

The Steinhaus Cube

This is a well-known puzzle invented by a mathematician, H. Steinhaus (say it *Stine-house*). The problem is to fit the six odd-shaped pieces together to make the big three-by-three-by-three cube shown at top left of the picture. As you can see, there are three pieces of 4 little cubes and three pieces of 5 little cubes, making 27 little cubes in all–just the right number to make the big cube.

To solve the puzzles, the best thing is to make up the pieces by gluing little wooden cubes together.

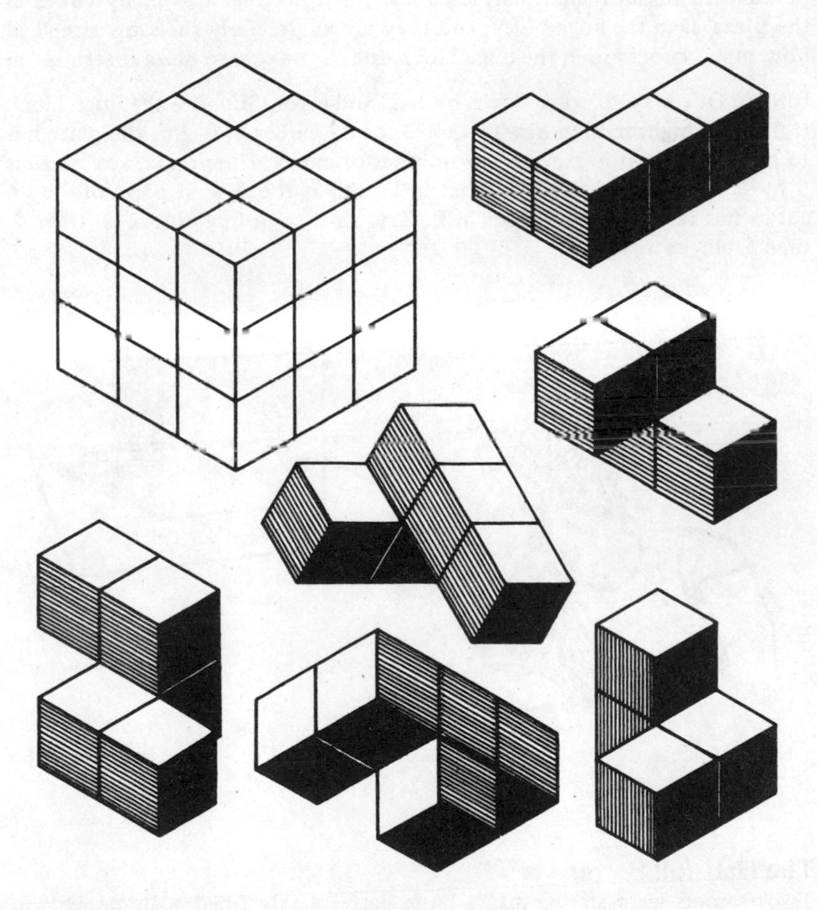

How Large Is the Cube?

Plato, the Greek philosopher, thought the cube was one of the most perfect shapes. So it's quite possible he wondered about this problem: What size cube has a surface area equal (in number) to its volume? You had better work in inches; of course, Plato didn't!

Plato's Cubes

A problem that Plato really did dream up is this one: The sketch shows a huge block of marble in the shape of a cube. The block was made out of a certain number of smaller cubes and stood in the middle of a square plaza paved with these smaller marble cubes. There were just as many cubes in the plaza as in the huge block, and they are all precisely the same size. Tell how many cubes are in the huge block and in the square plaza it stands on.

HINT: One way to solve this is by trial and error. Suppose the huge block is 3 cubes high; it then has $3 \times 3 \times 3$, or 27, cubes in it. But the plaza has to be surfaced with exactly this number of cubes. The nearest size plaza is 5 by 5 cubes, which has 25 cubes in it; this is too few. A plaza of 6 by 6 cubes has far too many cubes in it. Try, in turn, a huge block 2, then 4, then 5 blocks high.

The Half-full Barrel

Two farmers were staring into a large barrel partly filled with ale. One of them said: "It's over half full!" But the other declared: "It's more than half empty." How could they tell without using a ruler, string, bottles, or other measuring devices if it was more or less than exactly half full?

Cake-Tin Puzzle

The round cake fits snugly into the square tin shown here. The cake's radius is 5 inches. So how large must the tin be?

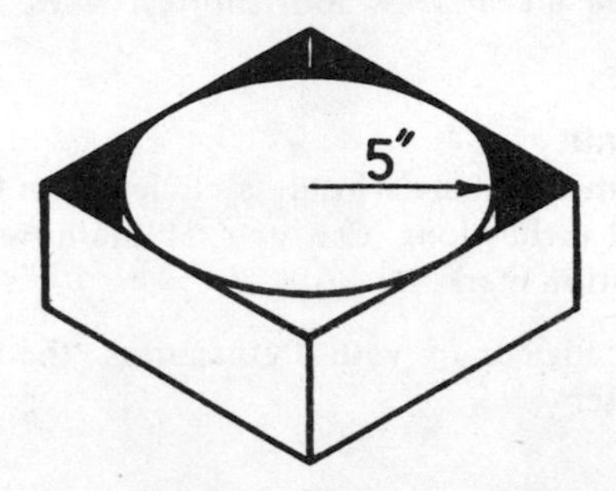

Animal Cubes

Look at the picture of the dinosaur and the gorilla made out of little cubes. How many cubes make up each animal? That was easy enough, wasn't it? But can you say what the volume of each animal is? The volume of one little cube is a cubic centimeter.

That wasn't too hard, either, was it? All right then, can you say what the surface area of each animal is? The surface area of the face of one little cube is 1 square centimeter.

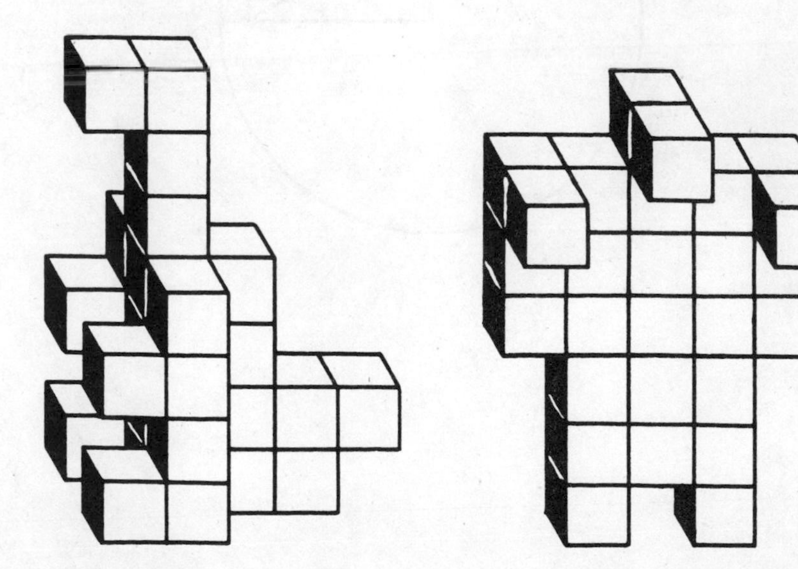

Spider and Fly

A spider is sitting on one corner of a large box, and a fly sits on the opposite corner. The spider has to be quick if he is to catch the fly. What is his shortest way? There are at least four shortest ways. How many shortest lines can you find?

The Sly Slant Line

The artist has drawn a rectangle inside a circle. I can tell you that the circle's diameter is 10 inches long. Can you tell me how long the slant line, marked with a question mark, is?

HINT: Don't get tangled up with Pythagoras's theorem. If you don't know it, all the better!

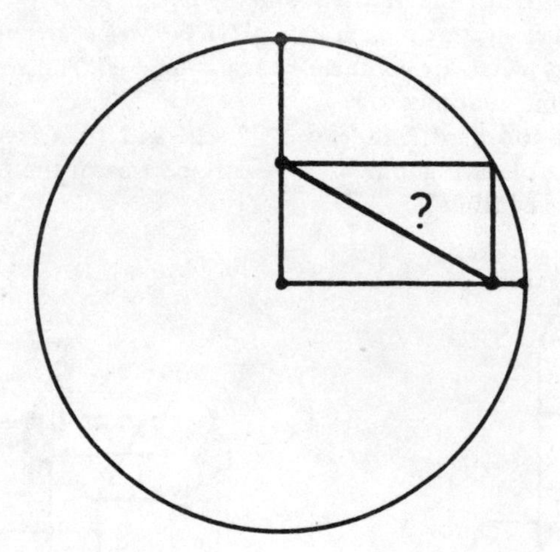

2. Routes, Knots, and Topology

In fact all these puzzles are about the math of topology, the geometry of stretchy surfaces. For a fuller description of what topology is about, see the puzzle "The Bridges of Königsberg" on page 25. The puzzles include problems about routes, mazes, knots, and the celebrated Möbius band.

In-to-out Fly Paths

A fly settles inside each of the shapes shown and tries to cross each side once only, always ending up outside the shape. On which shapes can the fly trace an in-to-out path? The picture shows he can on the triangle. Is there, perhaps, a rule?

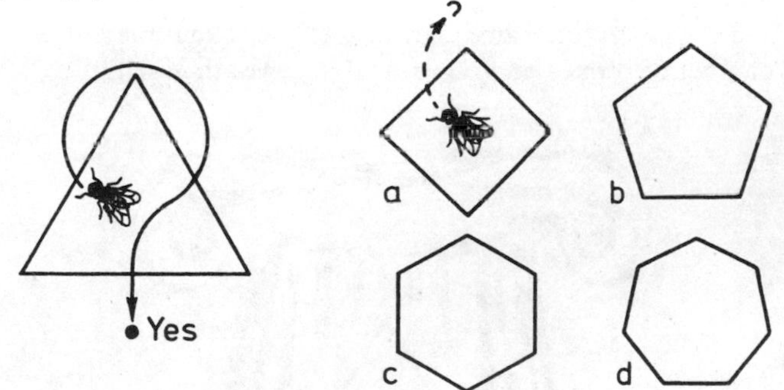

In-to-in Fly Paths

This time the fly begins *and* ends inside each shape. Can he cross each side once only? The picture shows he cannot do so on the triangle: He cannot cross the third side *and* end up inside. Is there a rule here?

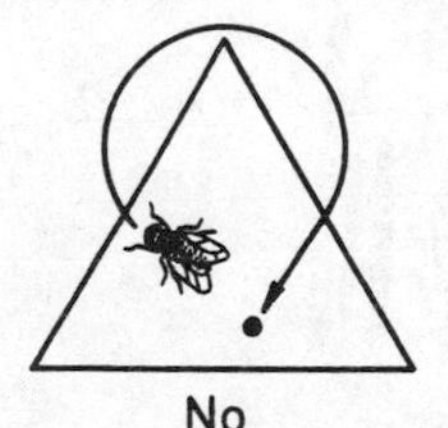

ABC Maze

Begin at the arrow and let your finger take a walk through this maze. Can you pass along each path once only and come out at *A?* at *B?* and at *C?*

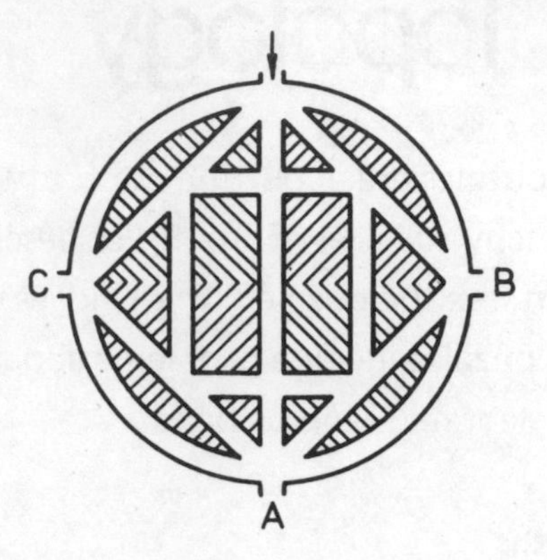

Eternal Triangle?

Can you draw this sign in one unbroken line without crossing any lines or taking your pencil off the paper? The sign is often seen on Greek monuments. Now go over the same sign in one unbroken line but making the fewest number of turns. Can you draw it in fewer than ten turns?

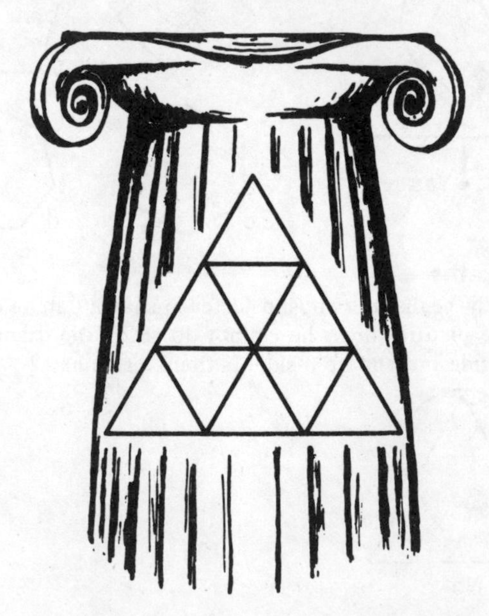

The Four Posts

Draw three straight lines to go through the four posts shown here without retracing or lifting your pencil off the paper. And you must return finally to your starting point.

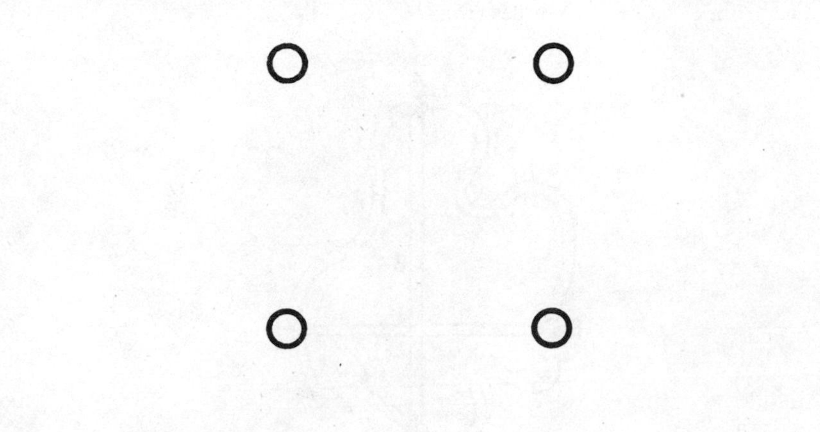

The Nine Trees

Find four straight lines that touch all nine trees. In this puzzle you don't have to return to your starting point; indeed you cannot! Do the "Four Posts" puzzle and you should be able to do this one.

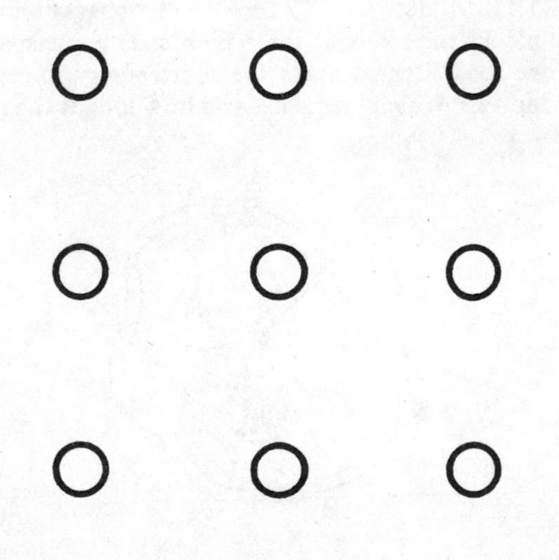

Salesman's Round Trip

A traveling salesman starts from his home at Anville (A). He has to visit all three towns shown on the sketch map—Beeburg (B), Ceton (C), and Dee City (D). But he wants to save as much gas as he can. What is his shortest route? The map shows the distances between each town. So A is eight miles from C, and B is six miles from D.

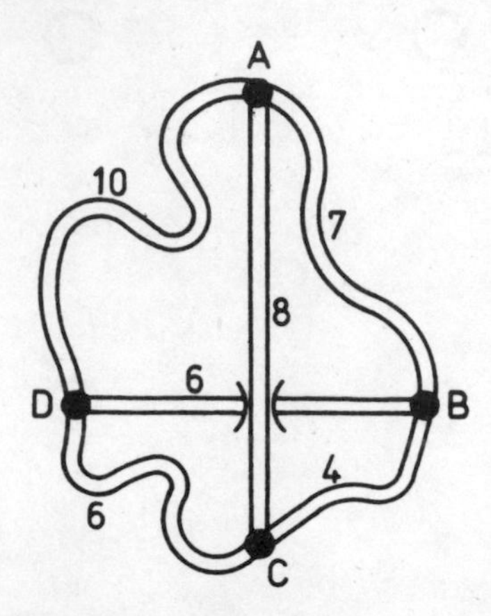

Swiss Race

The sketch map here shows the roads on a race through the Swiss Alps from Anlaken (A) to Edelweiss (E) through the checkpoints B, C, and D. An avalanche blocks the roads at three points, as you can see. You've got to clear just one roadblock to make the shortest way to get through from Anlaken to Edelweiss. Which one is it? And how long is the route then?

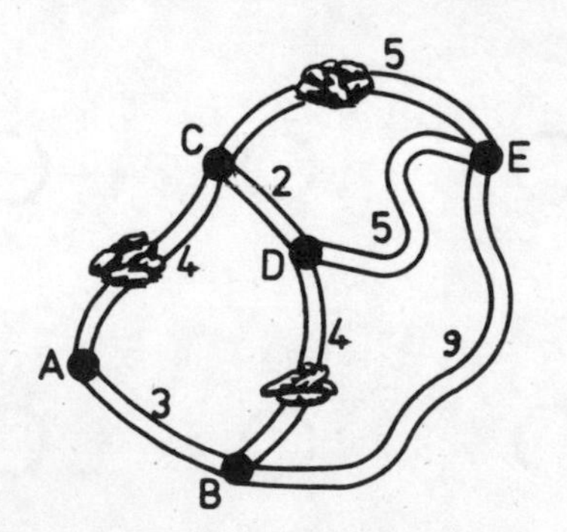

Get Through the Mozmaze

The maze shown here is called a mozmaze because it is full of awful, biting dogs, called mozzles. Top Cat is at the top left-hand corner, and he has to get through the mozmaze to the lower right corner, where it says END. But on his way he has to pass the biting mozzles chained at the various corners of the mozmaze. The triangles mark the position of the dogs that give three bites as Top Cat passes each of them; the squares of the dogs that give two bites; and the circles of the dogs that give only one bite.

What is Top Cat's best way through the mozmaze so that he gets bitten the fewest times? What's the fewest number of bites he can get by with? Can you do better than 40 bites?

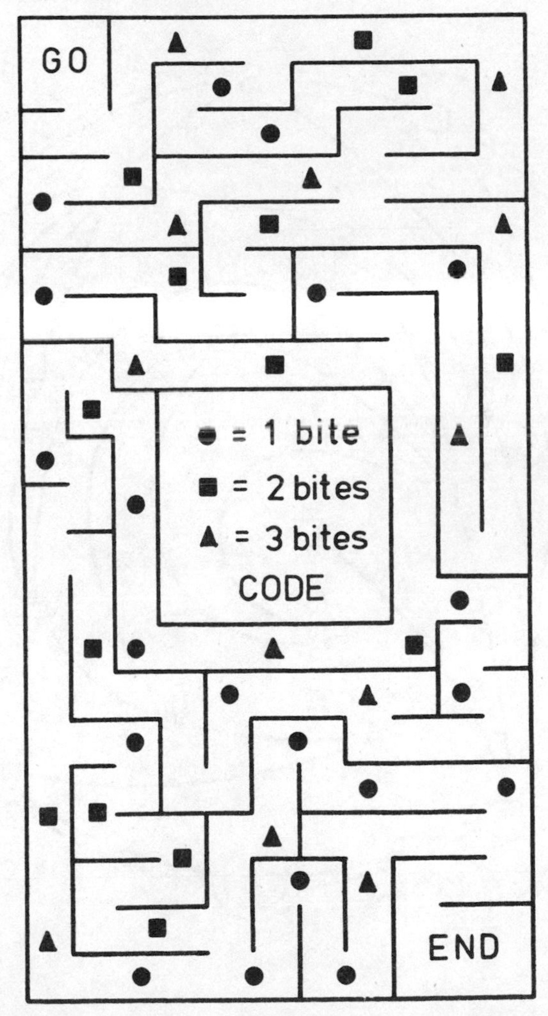

Space-Station Map

Here is a map of the newly built space stations and the shuttle service linking them in A.D. 2000. Start at the station marked *T*, in the south, and see if you can spell out a complete English sentence by making a round-trip tour of all the stations. Visit each station only once, and return to the starting point.

This puzzle is based on a celebrated one by America's greatest puzzlist, Sam Loyd. When it first appeared in a magazine, more than fifty thousand readers reported, "There is no possible way." Yet it is a really simple puzzle.

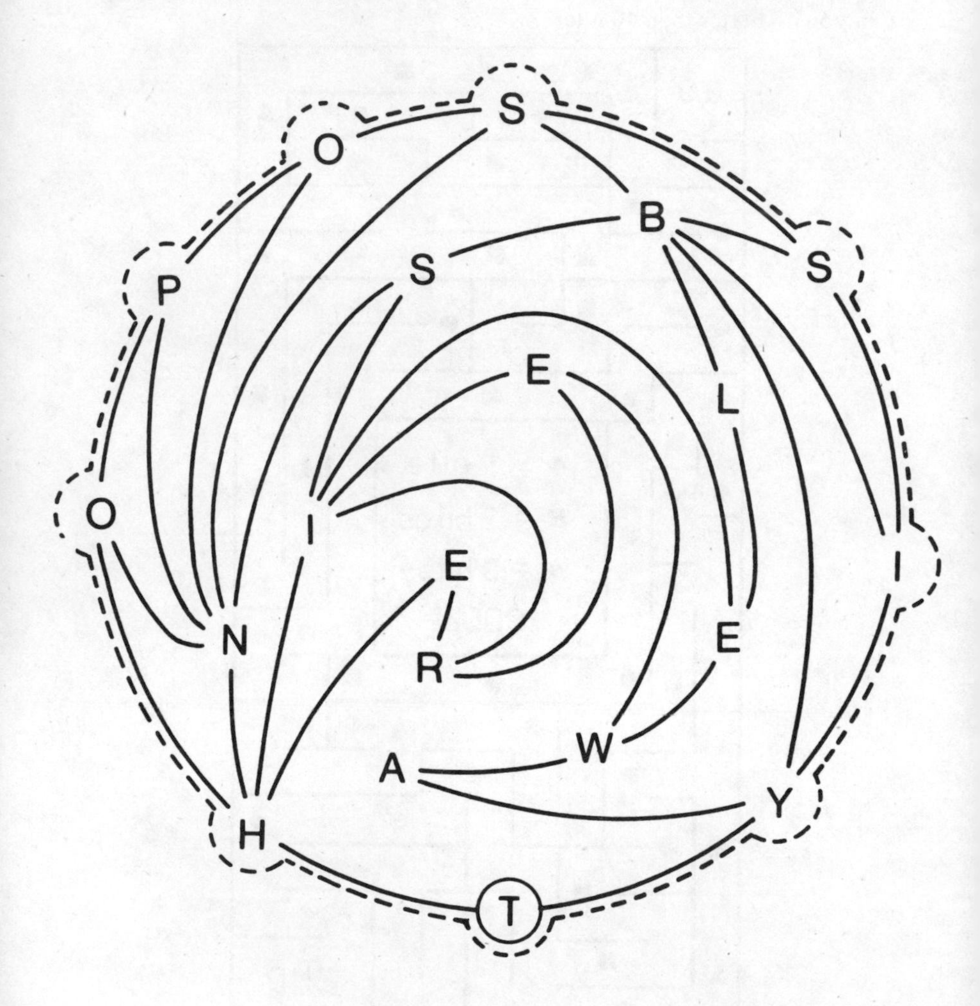

Round-Trip Flight

Trans-Am Airways offers flight links between these five cities: Albany, Baltimore, Chicago, Detroit, and El Paso. There are eight flights, as follows: Baltimore to Chicago, Detroit to Chicago, Albany to Baltimore, Chicago to El Paso, Chicago to Detroit, Baltimore to Albany, Albany to El Paso, and Chicago to Albany. What is the shortest way to make a trip from Albany to Detroit and back again?

HINT: Draw a sketch map of the flights, beginning: $A \leftrightarrows B \longrightarrow C$. This will show you how to avoid making too many flights *or* getting stuck in a "trap!"

Faces, Corners, and Edges

Here is a surprising rule about shapes you should be able to puzzle out for yourself. Find a box—a matchbox, a book, or a candy box, say. Now run your finger along the *edges* and count them (12) and add 2 to the number you found (making 14). Now count the number of faces (6) and add to that number the number of corners (8), making 14 in all. It seems that there is a rule here. Count faces and corners and edges of the shapes shown in our picture; the dotted lines indicate hidden edges that you cannot see from the head-on view. Can you find the rule? The great Swiss mathematician Leonhard Euler (say it *oiler*) was the first to spot it. The names of the shapes are *tetrahedron* (4 faces), *octahedron* (8 faces), *dodecahedron* (12 faces), and *icosahedron* (20 faces).

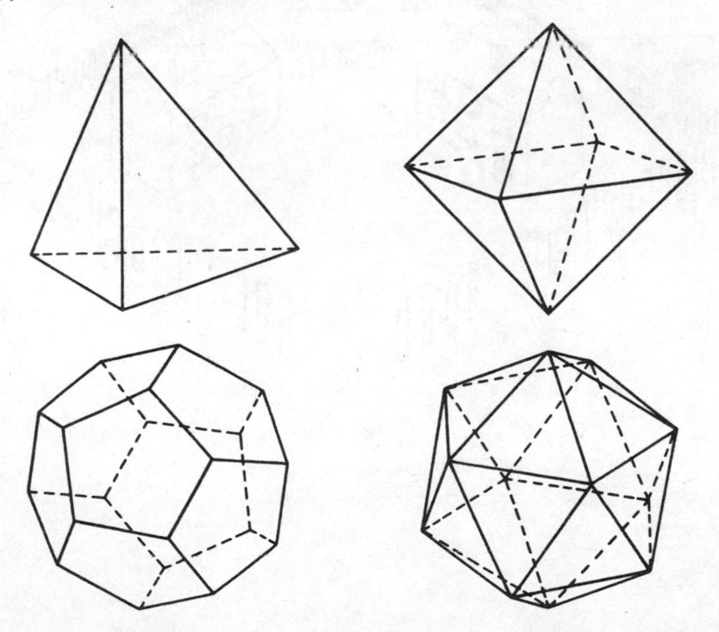

Five City Freeways

A planner wants to link up five cities by freeways. Each city must be linked to every other one. What's the least number of roads he must have? Roads can cross by means of overpasses, of course.

The planner then decides that overpasses are very costly. What is the fewest number of overpasses he needs?

The Bickering Neighbors

There were three neighbors who shared the fenced park shown in the picture. Very soon they fell to bickering with one another. The owner of the center house complained that his neighbor's dog dug up his garden and promptly built a fenced pathway to the opening at the bottom of the picture. Then the neighbor on the right built a path from his house to the opening on the left, and the man on the left built a path to the opening on the right. None of the paths crossed.

Can you draw the paths?

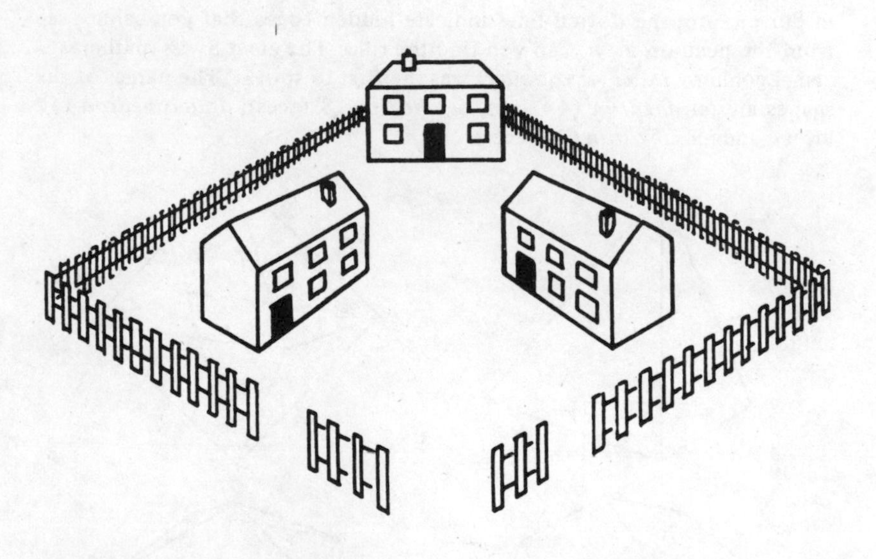

The Bridges of Königsberg

This is one of the most famous problems in all math. It saw the start of a whole new branch of math called *topology*, the geometry of stretchy surfaces. The problem arose in the 1700s in the north German town of Königsberg, built on the River Pregel, which, as the picture shows, splits the town into four parts.

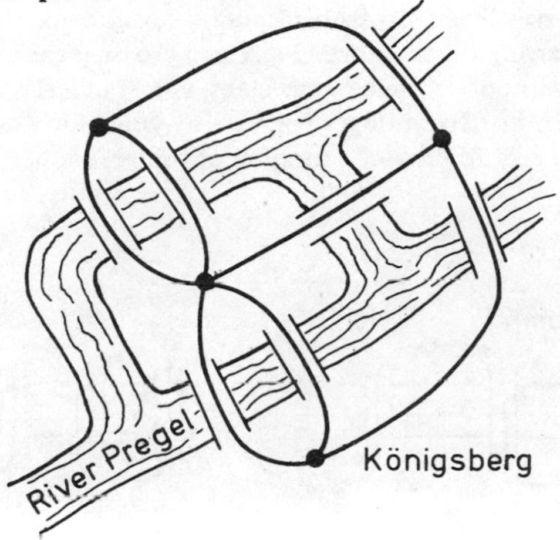

In summer the townsfolk liked to take an evening stroll across the seven bridges. To their surprise they discovered a strange thing. They found they could not cross all the bridges once and once only in a single stroll without retracing their steps. Copy the map of Königsberg if this is not your book, and see if you agree with the Königsbergers.

The problem reached the ears of the great Swiss mathematician Leonhard Euler. He drew a basic network, as mathematicians would say, of the routes linking the four parts of the town. This cut out all the unnecessary details. Now follow the strolls on the network. Do you think the Königsbergers could manage such a stroll or not?

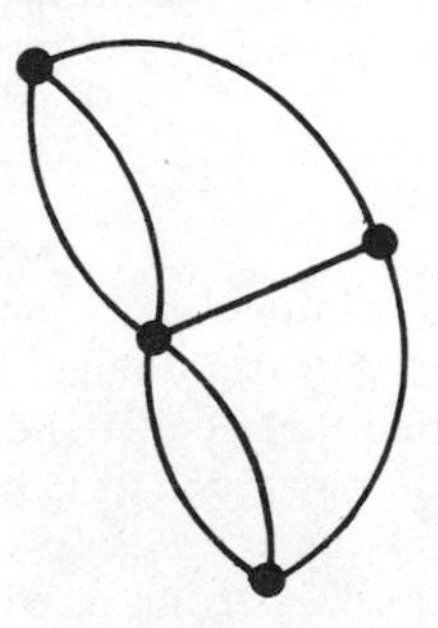

Euler's Bridges

Euler actually solved the last problem in a slightly different way from the one we gave, which is the way most books give. What he did was to simplify the problem. He started off with the very simple problems we give below. He then went on from their solutions to arrive at the solution we gave to "The Bridges of Königsberg." The little problems go like this:

A straight river has a north bank and a south bank with three bridges crossing it. Starting on the north bank and crossing each bridge once only in one stroll without retracing your steps, you touch the north bank twice (see picture *a*). For five bridges (picture *b*) you touch north three times. Can you find a rule for any odd number of bridges?

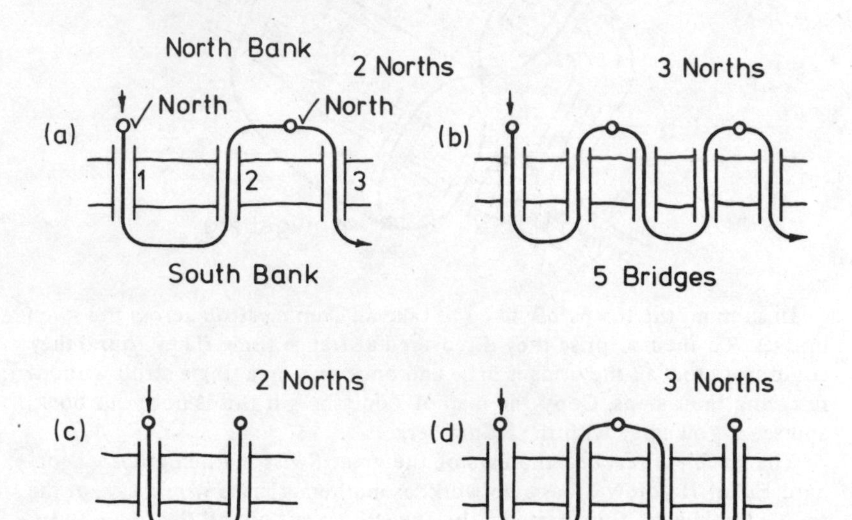

Now look at picture *c*. You touch the north bank twice for two bridges; and as shown by picture *d*, you touch north three times for four bridges. Can you find a rule for any even number of bridges?

Möbius Band

One of the most famous oddities in topology is the one-edged, single-surfaced band invented by August Möbius. He was a nineteenth-century German professor of math. Take a collar and before joining it give it one half-twist. Now cut it all the way along its middle. How many parts do you think it will fall into? You can try this on your friends as a party trick. Then try cutting it one third in from an edge, all the way round. How many parts do you think it will fall into now?

Double Möbius Band

Take two strips of paper and place them together, as shown. Give them both a half-twist and then join their ends, as shown in the picture. We now have what seems to be pair of nested Möbius bands. You can show there are two bands by putting your finger between the bands and running it all the way around them till you come back to where you started from. So a bug crawling between the bands could circle them for ever and ever. It would always walk along one strip with the other strip sliding along its back. Nowhere would he find the "floor" meeting the "ceiling." In fact, both floor and ceiling are one and the same surface. What seems to be two bands is actually . . . . Find out and then turn to the answer section to see if you were right. As an added twist, having unnested the band(s), see if you can put it (them) back together again.

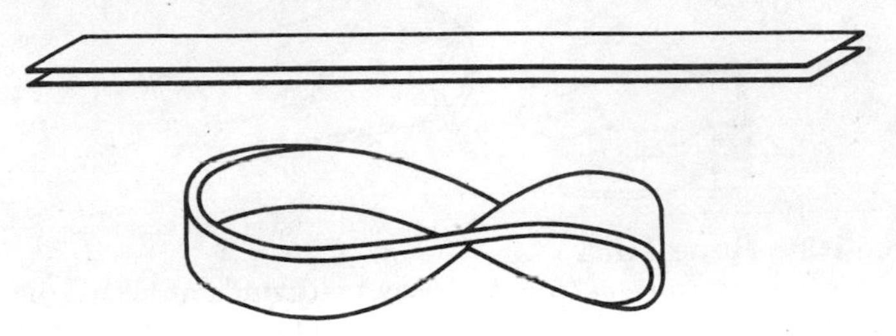

Viennese Knot

In the 1880s in Vienna a wildly popular magician's trick was to put a knot in a paper strip simply by cutting it with scissors. This is how it was done:

Take a strip of paper, about an inch wide and a couple of feet long. Just before joining the ends, give one end a twist of *one and a half* turns. (If you have read about the Möbius band, you'll know this is like making one with an extra twist in it.) Then tape the ends together to form a band. That done, cut along the middle of the closed band until you come back to where you started. At the last snip you will be left with one long band, which you will find has a knot in it. Pull it and you should see a knot in the shape of a perfect pentagon.

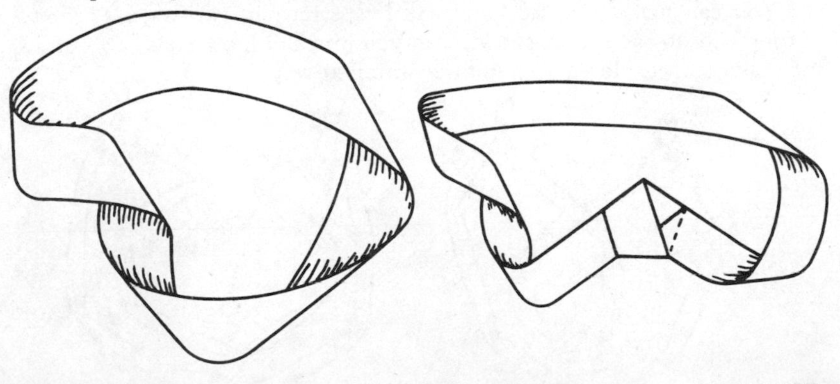

Release the Prisoners

Here is another problem in topology. Connect your wrists with a longish piece of rope. Make sure the loops around your wrists are not too tight. Have a friend do the same, but before completing the tying up, loop his rope around yours, as shown in the picture.

Can you separate yourself from your friend without untying the knots or cutting the rope? It can be done!

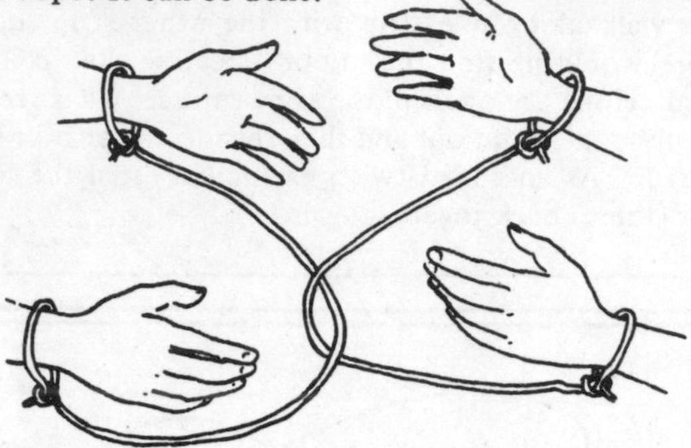

Three-Ring Rope Trick

This is a famous problem from topology that with a little trial and error I am sure you can solve for yourself. First make three loops of rope or string and link them in a chain like a Christmas decoration. Cut the middle loop and all three pieces of rope will come unlinked. Cut either end loop and the other two stay linked. The puzzle is this: Can you link three loops of rope so that all three will come unlinked if any one is cut? It can be done.

Wedding Knots

Russian girls use straws to foretell whether they will be married during the year. A girl will take six straws and fold each of them in half, keeping the folds hidden in her fist. Then she asks another girl to tie the 12 straw ends together in pairs; if a complete circle of straws is formed, she will be married within the year.

You can make a closed loop with four straws in two ways, as shown. String will do instead of straws. Can you join the loose ends of six straws to make a single closed loop in three different ways?

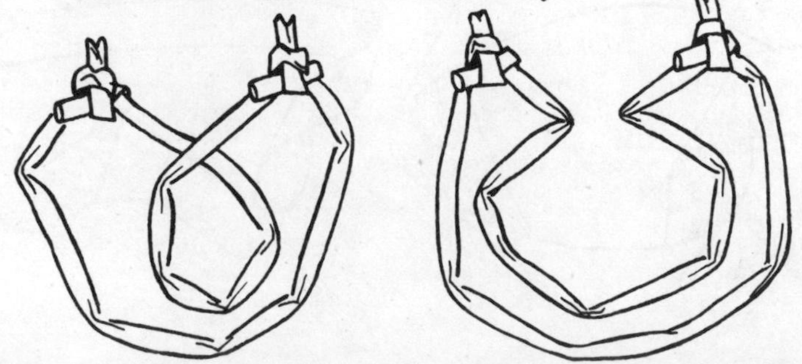

Amaze Your Friends

Ask a friend to draw a maze with a pencil on a large sheet of paper. He can make it as twisty as he likes, but none of the lines may cross and the ends must join to make a closed loop. Now newspapers are placed around the edges as shown here so that only the middle part of the maze shows. The

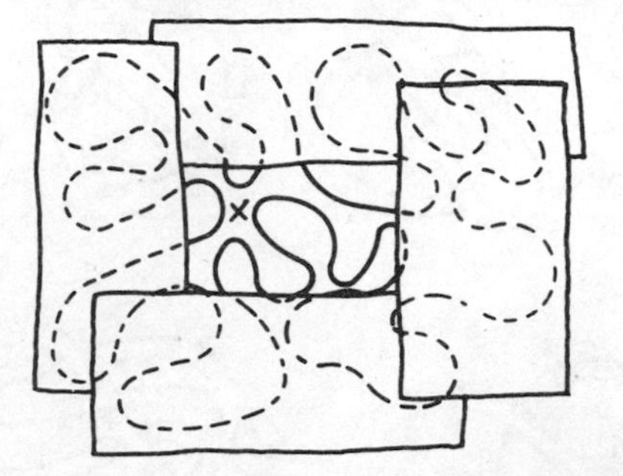

friend now places his finger anywhere in this still exposed area. Is his finger inside or outside the maze? The maze is so complicated it must be impossible to say which points are inside the closed loop and which points are outside. All the same you state correctly whether his finger is inside or outside the maze.

Another way to present the trick is with string or rope. Take a good length and tie the ends to form a long loop. Then ask the friend to make a closed-loop maze with it. Put newspapers down to hide the outside of the maze. The friend puts his finger on some spot in the maze. Take one newspaper away and pull an outside part of the string across the floor. Will the string catch on the friend's finger or not? Again you predict correctly each time the trick is performed. How is it done?

The secret is this: Take two points in the maze and join them with an imaginary line. If the points are both inside the loop, then the line will cross an *even* number of strings. If both points are outside, the same rule holds. But if one point is inside and the other outside, then the line connecting them will cross an *odd* number of points. The easiest way to remember the rule is to think of the simplest maze possible, a circle. If both points are inside the circle (or both outside it), then the line connecting them will cross either no strings or two strings; both 0 and 2 are even numbers. If one point is inside the other outside, then the line will cross the circle once; 1 is an odd number.

To do the stunt, as the newspapers are being placed, let your eye move through the maze from the outside until you reach a spot near the center that is easy to remember. You know that spot is outside the maze. When your friend places his finger, you have only to draw mentally a line from your "outside" spot to his finger and note whether you cross an even number of strings (then his finger is outside) or an odd (his finger is inside). A little practice will show that the trick is easier to do than to describe.

Tied in Knots?

Pull the ends of each rope shown here and find out which will tie itself in a knot. Knot *h* is very interesting; it is often used by magicians. It is known as the Chefalo knot. It is made from the reef knot shown in *g*.

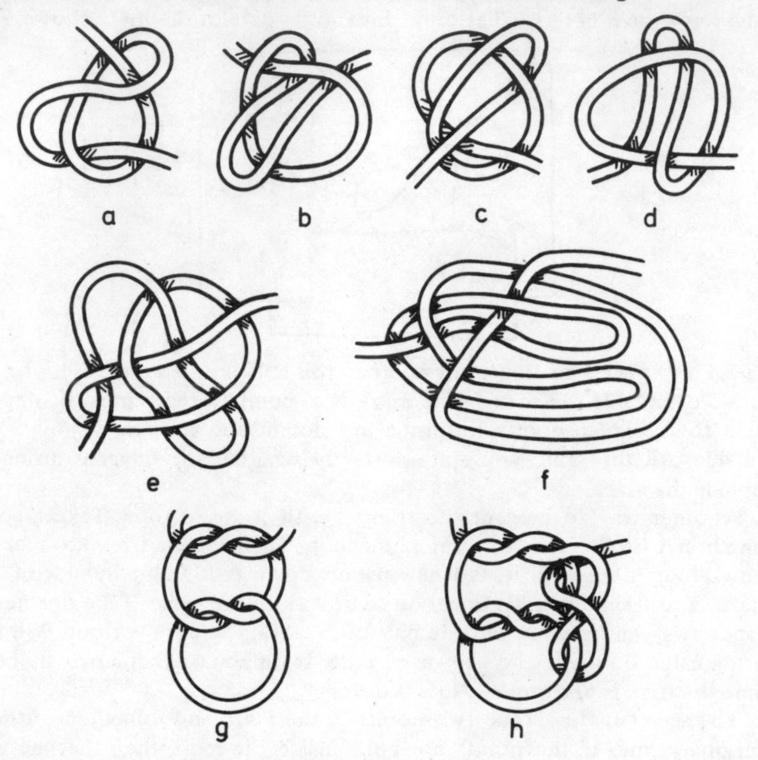

The Bridges of Paris

In 1618 the plan of Paris and its bridges over the River Seine looked like the sketch map here. The famous Nôtre Dame Cathedral is shown by the † on the island. Could the Parisians then take a stroll over the bridges and cross each one only once without retracing their steps? Draw a network as was done for "The Bridges of Königsberg."

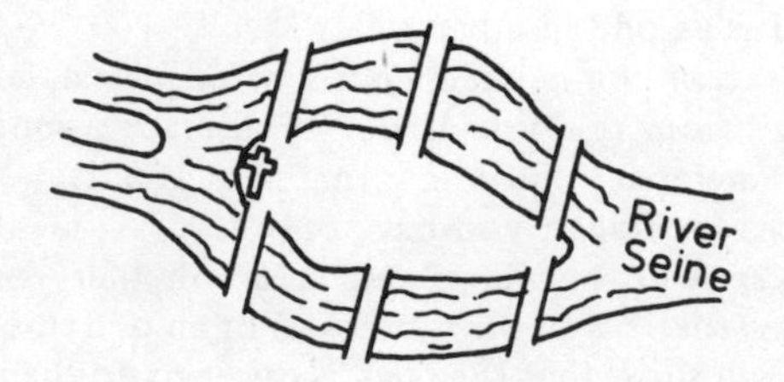

Tour of the Castle

The idea here is that you have to visit each room in the castle only once on a tour of it, starting at the *in* arrow and leaving by the *out* arrow. With the *exit* placed as in the first of the little 4-roomed castles shown here you can do it; in the second you cannot.

Try your hand at (*1*) the 9-roomed castles, and (*2*) the 16-roomed castles.

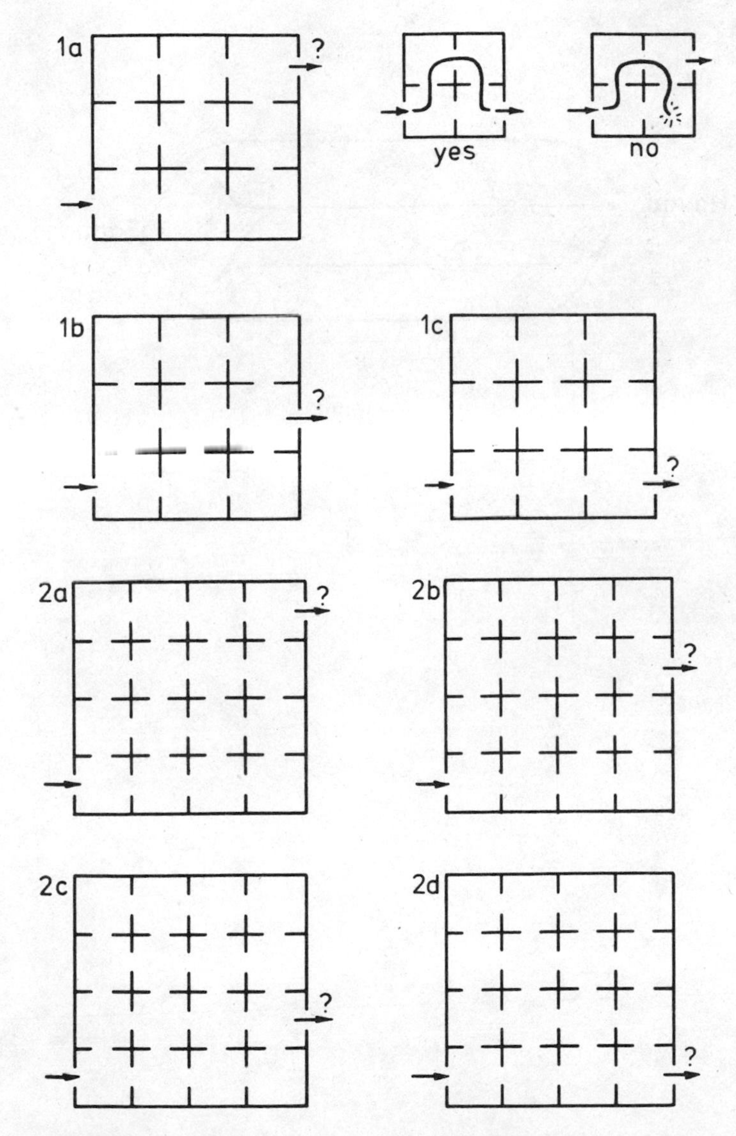

The Cuban Gunrunners Problem

The Cuban gunrunners plan to transport a trainload of guns and bombs from Havana to Santiago. There are several rail routes they could take, as you can see on the map of the rail system shown. How can they be stopped from getting through? The easiest way is to blow up a few bridges. What is the fewest number of bridges you must blow up? And which ones are they?

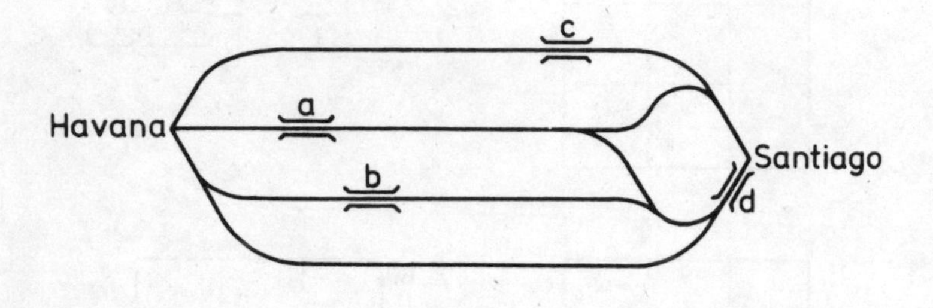

3. Vanishing-Line and Vanishing-Square Puzzles

To Martin Gardner, America's leading popularizer of math and purveyor of puzzles, I owe ideas for this next lot of puzzles, all of which, and more, are to be found in his excellent *Mathematics, Magic and Mystery* (New York: Dover, 1956).

These puzzles all depend on a strange quirk of geometry. All but the first involve cutting and rearranging parts of a figure. When that is done, a part of the figure or a line apparently vanishes. Where has it gone? is the question. Before I describe some of these puzzles and explain them, look at the following puzzle, about counting, not about cutting up figures; it gives the clue to the puzzles of the vanished lines.

There are no answers except to the next puzzle.

Mr. Mad and the Mandarins

Mr. Mad was having three children to tea. Four places were laid, each with three mandarin oranges on a plate. But one of the children didn't turn up. So how should the others divide up the spare plateful of mandarins? Mr. Mad suggested this way, as shown:

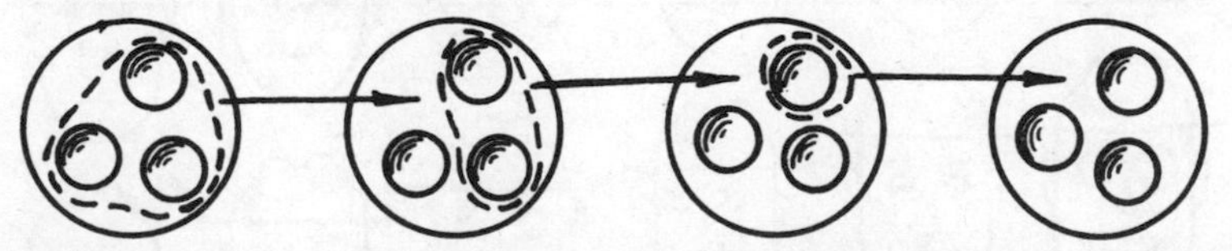

All three mandarins on the first plate went to the second plate, from which two mandarins were put on the next plate, from which one mandarin was placed on the last plate, Mr. Mad's. "There!" exclaimed Mr. Mad. "Fair shares for all. But I bet you can't tell me which plateful has vanished?" None of the children could give an answer. Can you suggest one?

The Vanishing-Line Trick

Mightily simplified though this puzzle is, it forms the heart of many brilliant puzzles created by Sam Loyd, the great puzzlist. Draw on a card three equal lines, as shown here. Make certain that both the first and the third line touch the diagonal of the card (the broken line), each with one of its ends. Cut the card along the diagonal. Slide the top half to the right until the lines coincide again, as in the second picture. There are now only two lines where before there were three. What has happened to the third line? Which line vanished and where did it go? Slide the top part back and the third line returns.

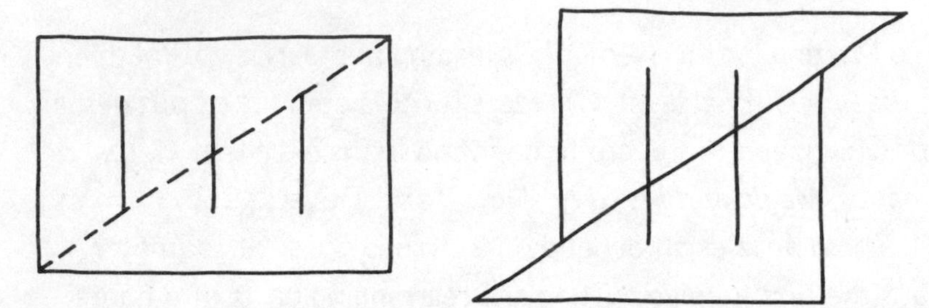

It is like the vanishing group of mandarins in "Mr. Mad and the Mandarins" puzzle. What happens is that the middle line is broken into two parts —one going to lengthen the first line, the other lengthening the third line. With more lines the distribution of the lines is less obvious and the disappearance of the center line becomes even more puzzling.

The Vanishing-Face Trick

We can doll up "The Vanishing-Line Trick" by drawing pictures instead of lines. Our top picture shows six cartoon faces divided by a broken line into two strips.

Copy and cut out the strips in the top picture and stick each strip on a card. Shift the upper strip to the right, and—as the bottom picture shows—all the hats remain, but one face vanishes. You cannot say which face has vanished. Four of them have been split into two parts and the parts redistributed so that each new face has gained a small bit.

The Vanishing-Square Trick

Conjurers perform miraculous-seeming tricks where a rectangular or square figure is cut up and rearranged and in the process a whole square is lost to view. The simplest and oldest example explains how it is done. The following explanation is based on Martin Gardner's excellent book *Mathematics, Magic and Mystery*:

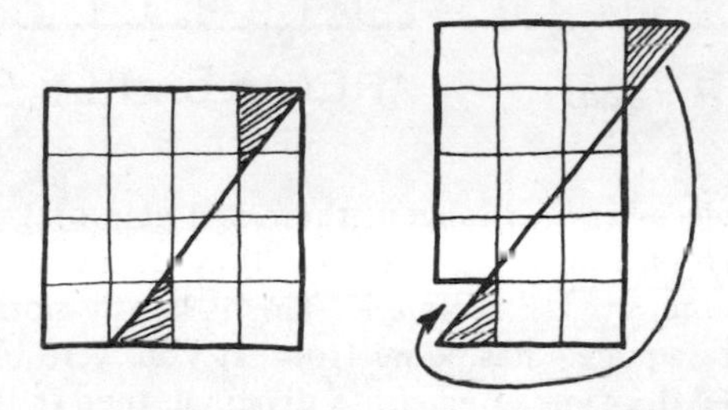

Start with a 4-by-4 square; its area is 16. This square is cut along the slant line. This line is *not* a diagonal, since it passes through only one of the corners. This is the secret of the trick. Now shift the lower part of the board to the left, as shown in the right-hand picture. Snip off the shaded triangle sticking out at the top right corner and fit it into the space at the lower left corner, as shown by the arrow. This produces a 3-by-5 rectangle; its area is 15. Yet we started with a big square of area 16. Where has the missing little square gone? As we said, the secret lies in the way the slant line was drawn. Because that line is not a diagonal, the snipped-off triangle is taller than 1: It is $1\frac{1}{3}$ in height. So the rectangle's height is actually $5\frac{1}{3}$, not 5. Its actual area is then $3 \times 5\frac{1}{3} = 16$. So, you see (or rather you didn't "see"), we haven't lost a square. It just looks like it.

The trick is not very baffling with such a small board. But a larger number of squares will conceal the secret. You can see that this puzzle is like "The Vanishing-Line Trick" when you look at the squares cut by the slant line. As you move up the line, you find that the parts of the cut squares above the line get smaller and smaller while those below get larger and larger—just like the vertical lines in the earlier puzzle.

Sleight of Square

In "The Vanishing-Square Trick" all the trickery is confined to the squares either side of the slant line. The rest of the square plays no part in the trick at all; it is there merely for disguise. Now instead of cutting the square board into two pieces, suppose we chop it into four. The trick would become even more mysterious. One way to do this is shown in the picture of the 8-by-8 board.

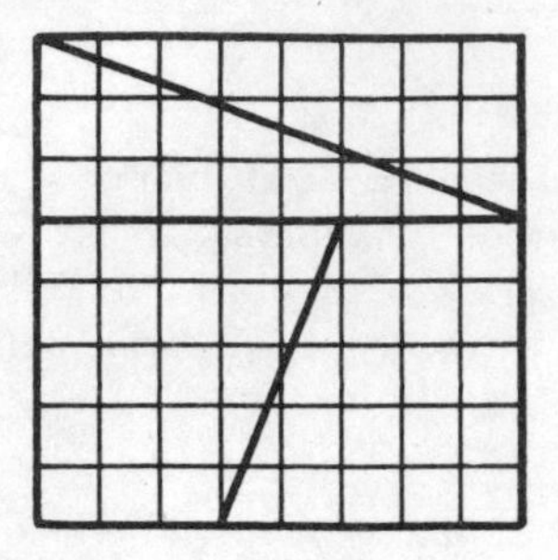

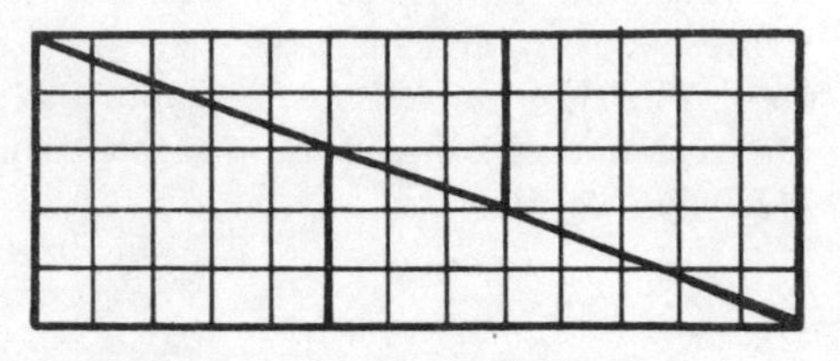

AREA = 8 × 8 = 64

When the four pieces are rearranged, there is a gain of 1 square—from 64 to 65 squares. You'll find there is a long, thin, diamond-shaped gap along the diagonal of the 5-by-13 rectangle. This is hardly noticeable. But it is where the "extra square" has come from. If you were to begin with the 5-by-13 rectangle, drawing an accurate diagonal, then in the 8-by-8 square the upper rectangle would be a shade higher than it should be and the lower rectangle a bit wider. This bad fit is more noticeable than the slight gap along the diagonal. So the first method is better.

Sam Loyd, Jr., discovered how to put the four pieces together to get an area of only 63—that is, to lose a square. This picture shows how it is done.

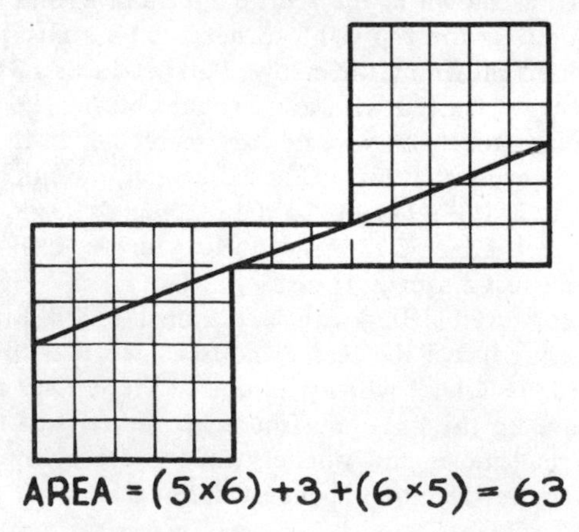

The Secret Fibonacci Lengths

You can make a square come and go at will with other size boards–provided you know the secret lengths of the perpendicular sides (excluding the slant lines) of all pieces–both the inner cutouts and the boards made out of them. In "Sleight of Square" these lengths were 3, 5, 8, and 13. These numbers are part of a famous number series, the Fibonacci (say it *fib-o-NAH-chee*) numbers. It goes 1, 1, 2, 3, 5, 8, 13, 21, 34, and so on. Each number from 2 onward is the sum of the two previous numbers: 3 = 1 + 2, 5 = 3 + 2, and so on. Fibonacci, an Italian, was the first great European mathematician; he lived in the 1200s. I doubt if he ever foresaw this curious use of his number series for geometrical trickery!

So we started with an 8-by-8 square with an area of 64 and ended up with a 5-by-13 rectangle with an area of 65. And you notice 8 lines between 5 and 13 in the Fibonacci series.

The trick works with higher numbers in the series; the higher the better because the "extra square" is more easily lost in a longer diagonal. For example, we can choose a 13-by-13 square, with an area of 169, and divide its sides into lengths of 5 and 8, as shown.

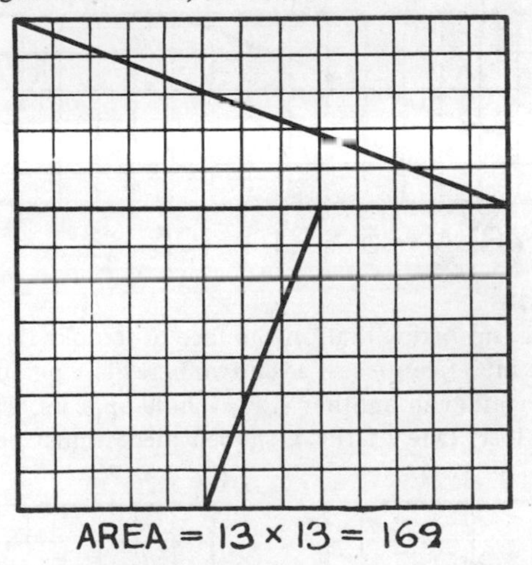

Cutting along the lines, we can rearrange the pieces into an 8-by-21 rectangle, with area 168. A little square has been *lost*, not gained, this time. The Fibonacci numbers used are 5, 8, 13, and 21. There is a loss of a square because the pieces along the diagonal overlap instead of having a gap between them. An odd fact emerges. A board using the lengths 3, 8, 21, and so on–that is, every other Fibonacci number–gives a gain of a square. A board using the lengths 5, 13, 34, and so on results in a loss of a little square.

If you cut up a 2-by-2 board, making a 3-by-1 rectangle, the overlap (resulting in a loss of a quarter of the board) is too obvious. And all the mystery is lost.

Langman's Rectangle

A rectangle can also be cut up and the pieces fitted together to make a larger rectangle. Dr. Harry Langman of New York City has devised a way of cutting up a rectangle. His method, shown below, makes use of the Fibonacci numbers 2, 3, 5, 8, 13, and 21.

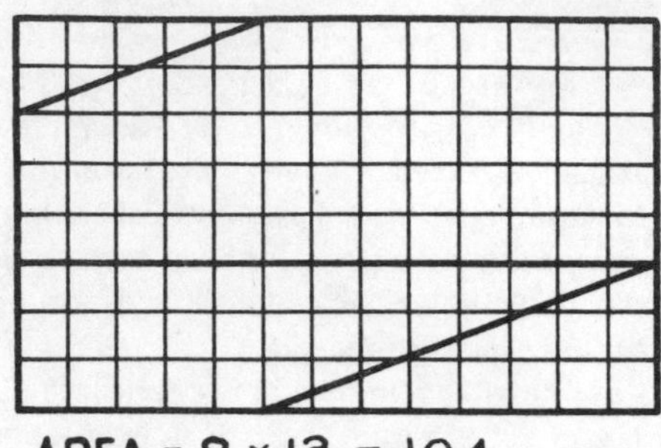

AREA = 8 × 13 = 104

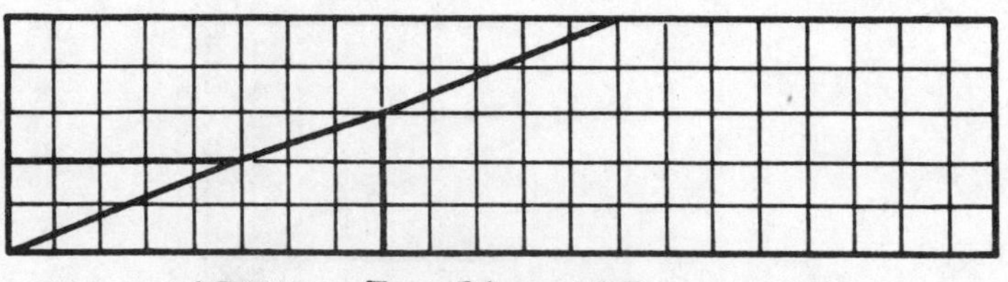

AREA = 5 × 21 = 105

Curry's Paradox

A paradox is an absurd trick that on the face of it looks flawless. An 11-by-11 square is cut into five pieces, as shown here. The paradox is: When the pieces are put together in another way, a hole appears. Two squares have seemingly been lost. One of the **L**-shaped pieces must be shifted to produce the effect.

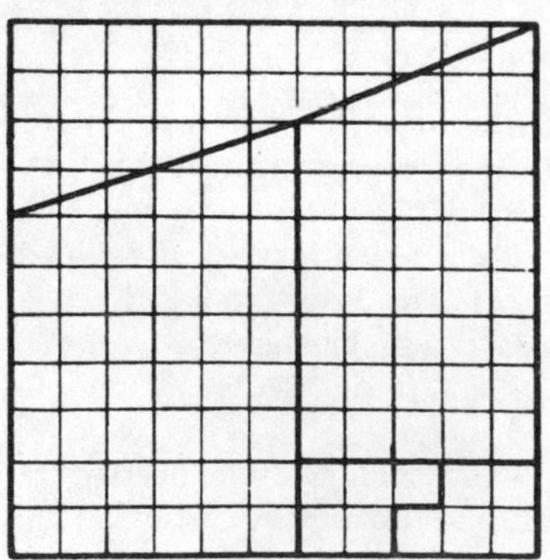

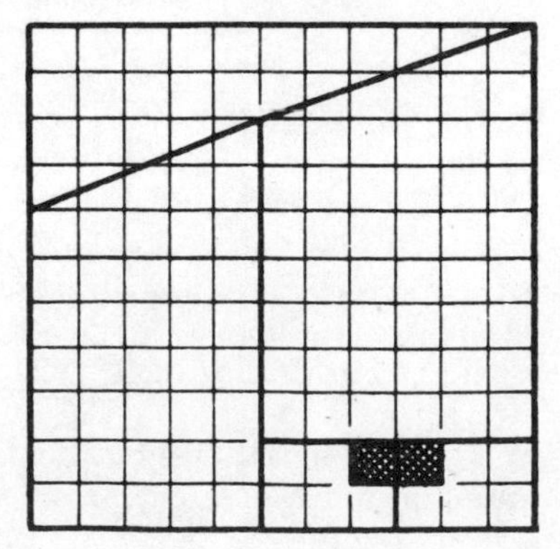

This paradox was invented by a New York City amateur magician Paul Curry in 1953. He also devised a version using a 13-by-13 square where a still larger hole appears and three squares are lost. As you see, Curry's paradox uses Fibonacci numbers.

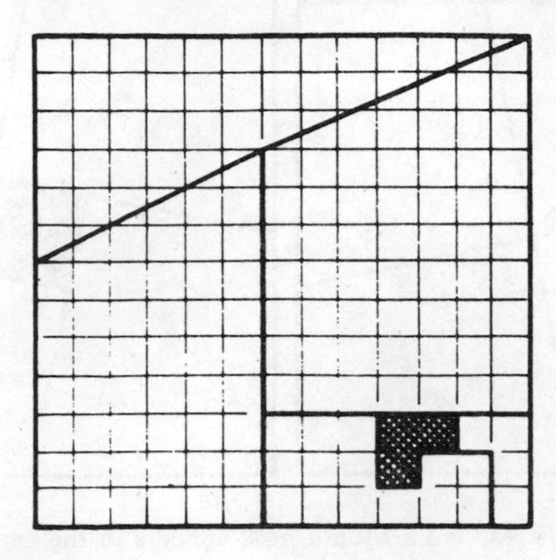

Gardner's Triangle

It's possible to make part of a triangle disappear. Martin Gardner has applied Curry's paradox to a triangle. His method is shown in the picture of the triangles with two equal sides. By rearranging the six pieces, two squares are lost.

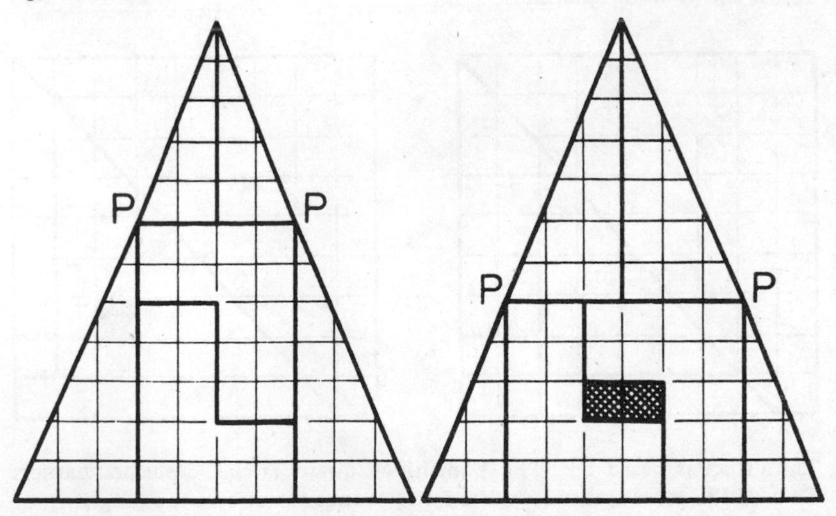

The deception is increased by having the points *P* fall exactly on the crossings of the grid, since the sides will slightly cave in or out.

Hole in the Square

Another quite different way of losing area is to cut a square into four exactly equal pieces, as shown, by two crosscuts.

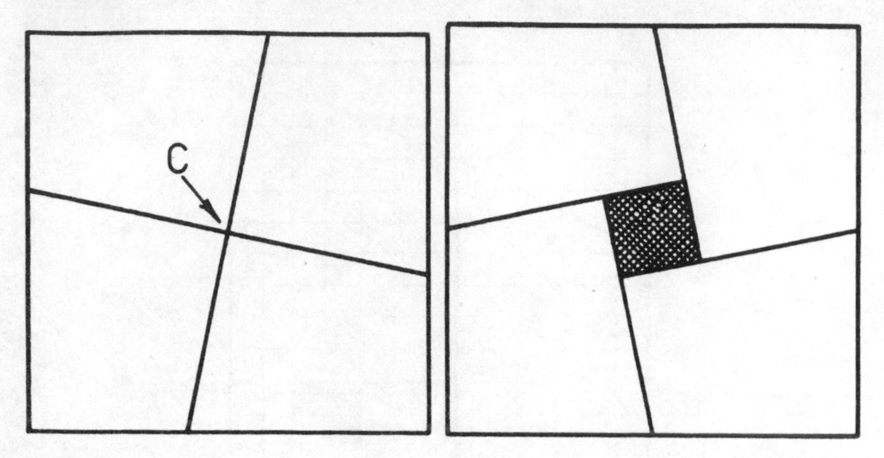

Rearrange the pieces, and a square hole appears in the center. The size of the hole varies with the angle of the cuts. The area of the hole is spread around the sides of the square. This trick suffers from the fact that it is fairly obvious that the sides of the square with the hole are a bit longer than the sides of the first square.

A more mysterious way of cutting a square into four pieces to form a hole is shown in this picture.

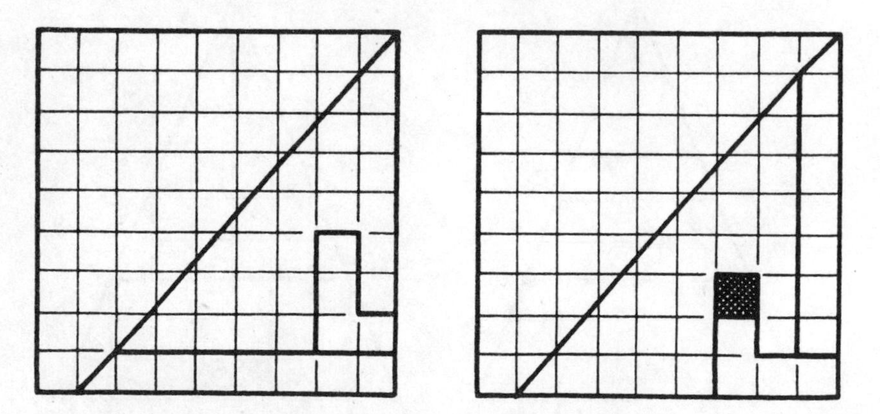

The effect is based on "The Vanishing Square Trick," described earlier. Two of the pieces must be shifted to produce the effect–the long strip of the lower edge and the L-shaped piece. If you remove the largest piece (top left), you are left with another Gardner triangle.

4. Match Puzzles

The next batch of puzzles all make use of matches. Toothpicks or orange sticks all the same length are equally good.

Squares from 24 Matches

Take 24 matches. How many squares the same size can you get with them? With 6 matches to a side you get one square. You can't come out even with squares with 5 and 4 matches to a side. With 3 matches to a side, you get two squares, as shown.

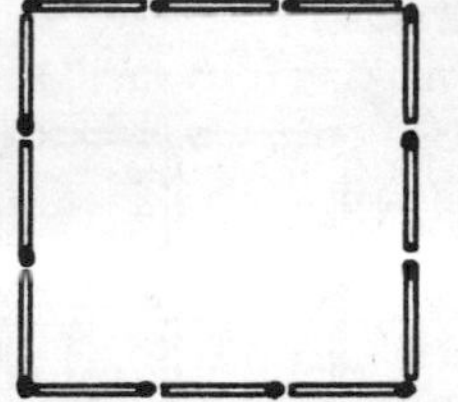
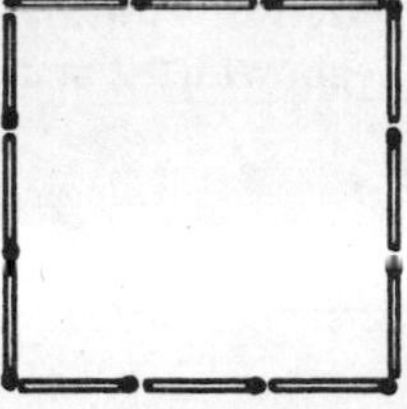

With 2 matches to a side, you get three squares:

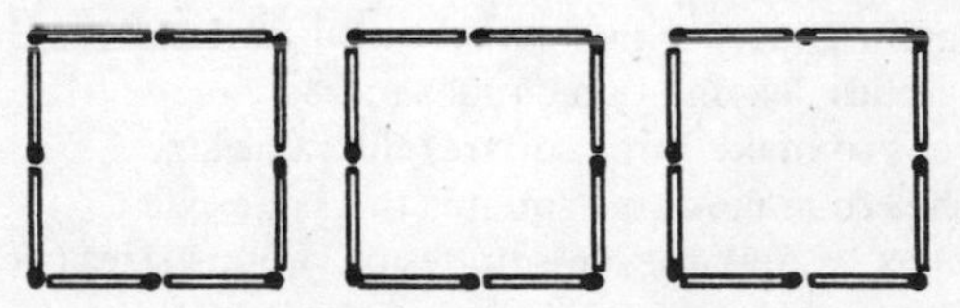

Suppose we allow squares of *different* sizes. (*a*) With 3 matches to a side, how many extra, smaller squares can you get now? (*Clue:* Squares can overlap.) (*b*) With 2 matches to a side show how you can get a total of seven squares.

With 1 match on a side you can make six identical squares, as shown.

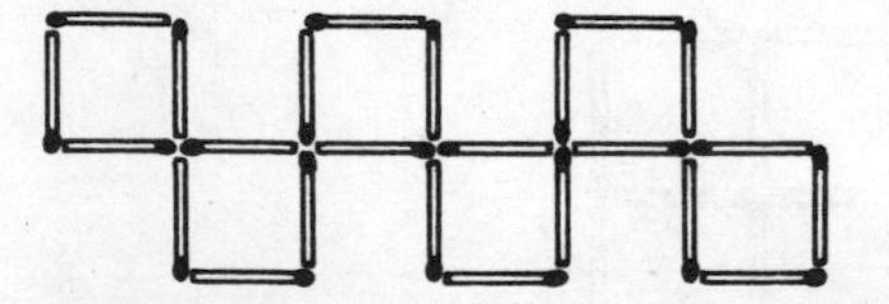

(*c*) With 1 match on a side how do you make seven identical squares? Eight identical squares? And nine identical squares? There'll be some extra, bigger squares too. With the nine squares there are five extra squares.

PART-MATCH SQUARES

The next three puzzles need 24 matches. You make half-match squares and other part-match squares by crossing one match over another.

Half-Match Squares

Use half a match as the side of a square. Can you get 16 small squares? How many larger squares can you see?

Third-Match Squares

Can you get 27 small squares, one third of a match on each side? How many larger squares can you see?

Fifth-Match Squares

Can you get 50 small squares in 2 match-stick size squares? How many larger squares of all sizes can you see?

Move-or-Remove Puzzles I

Begin with 12 matches, making four small squares as shown.

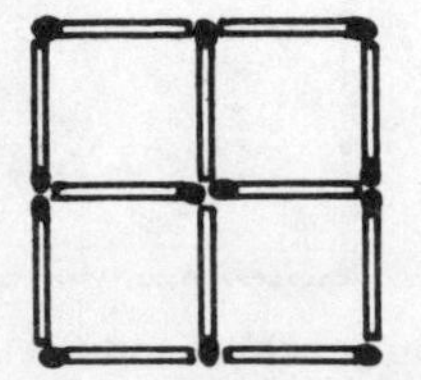

(*a*) Remove 2 matches, leaving two squares of different sizes
(*b*) Remove 4 matches, leaving two equal squares
(*c*) Move 3 matches to make three squares the same size
(*d*) Move 4 matches to make three squares the same size
(*e*) Move 2 matches to make seven squares of various sizes (you'll have to cross one match over another)
(*f*) Move 4 matches to make 10 squares, not all the same size (you'll have to cross one match over another more than once)

Move-or-Remove Puzzles II

Begin with 24 matches, making nine small squares as shown.

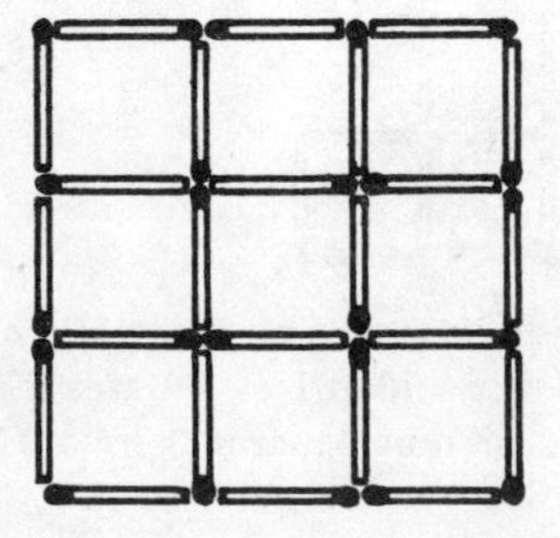

(*a*) Move 12 matches to make two squares the same size
(*b*) Remove 4 matches, leaving four small squares and one large square
(*c*) Remove 6 matches, leaving three squares
(*d*) Remove 8 matches, leaving four squares, each 1 match to a side (two answers)
(*e*) Remove 8 matches, leaving two squares (two answers)
(*f*) Remove 8 matches, leaving three squares
(*g*) Remove 6 matches, leaving two squares and two **L**-shaped figures
(*h*) Remove 4, 6, then 8 matches to make five squares, each 1 match to a side

Windows

Make six squares—not all the same size—with nine matches. The answer looks like two windows.

Greek Temple

The temple shown is made out of 11 matches.

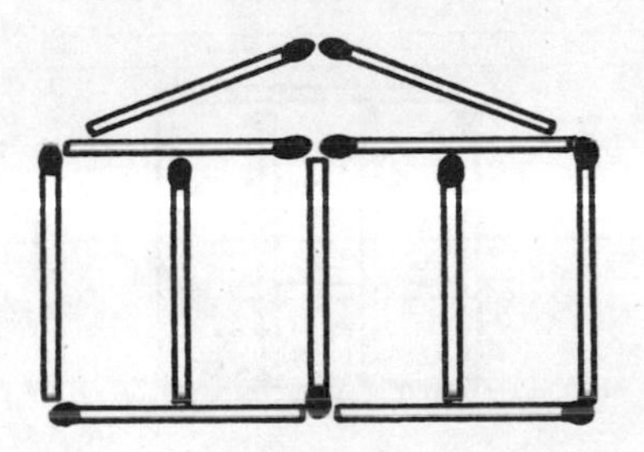

(*A*) Move 2 matches and get 11 squares
(*B*) Move 4 matches and get 15 squares

An Arrow

This arrow is made of 16 matches.

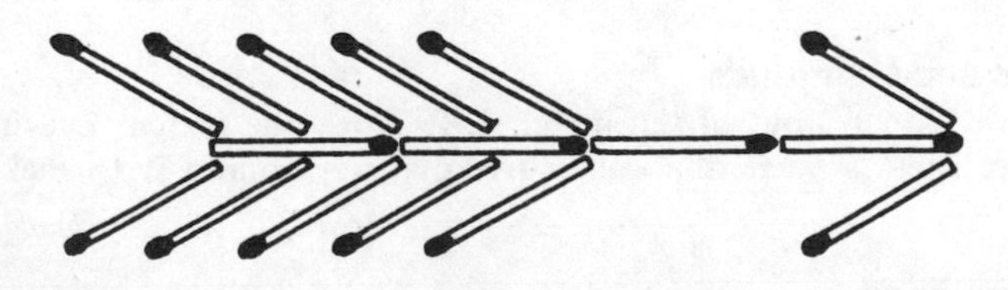

(*A*) Move 10 matches in this arrow to form eight equal triangles
(*B*) Move 7 matches to make five equal four-sided figures

Vanishing Trick

There are 16 squares here with one match on a side. But how many squares in all?

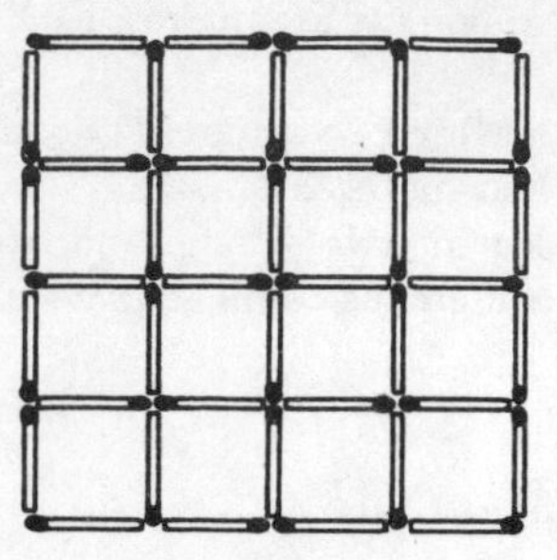

Take away nine matches and make every square—of any size—vanish.

Take Two

The eight matches here form, as you see, 14 squares.

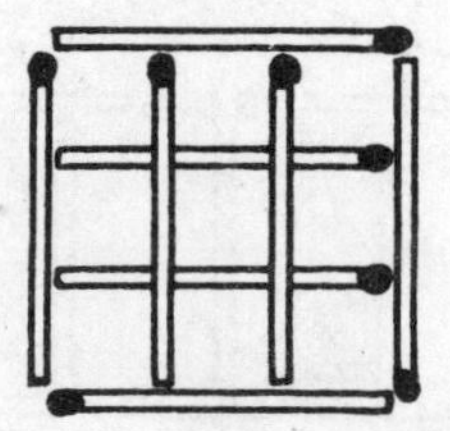

Take two matches and leave only 3 squares.

Six Triangles

Three matches make an equal-sided, or equilateral, triangle. Use 12 matches to make six equilateral triangles, all the same size. That done, move 4 of the matches to make three equilateral triangles *not* all the same size.

Squares and Diamonds

Form three squares out of ten matches. Remove one match. Leaving one of the squares, arrange the other five matches around it to make two diamonds.

Stars and Squares

Put down eight matches to make two squares, eight triangles, and an eight-pointed star. The matches may overlap.

A Grille

In the grille shown here move 14 matches to make three squares.

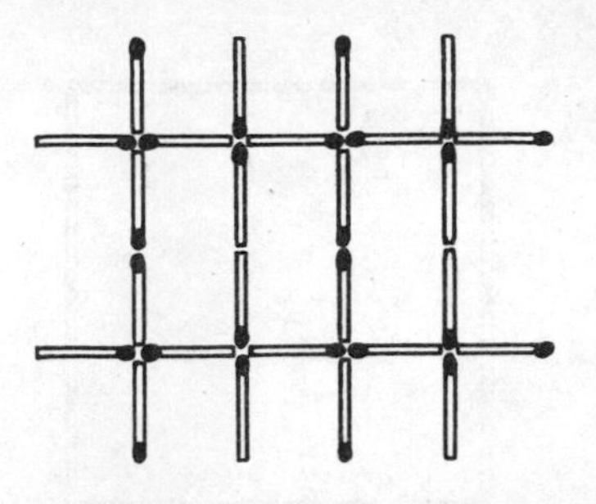

The Five Corrals

Here is a field, four matches square. In it there is a barn one match square. The farmer wishes to fence off the field into five equal **L**-shaped corrals. How does he do it? (Use ten more matches for the fencing.)

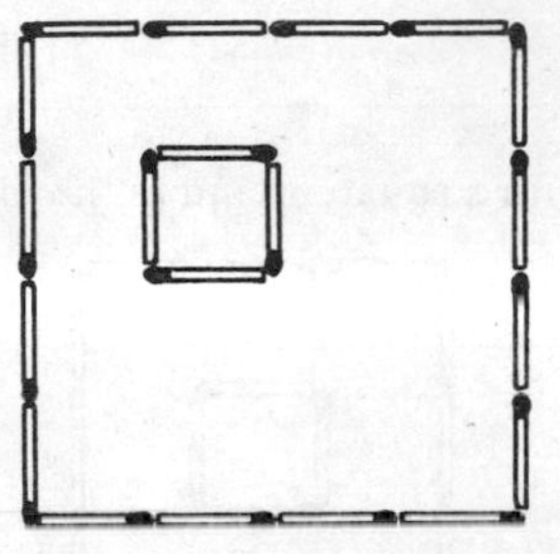

Patio and Well

In the middle of this patio, five matches square, is a square well.

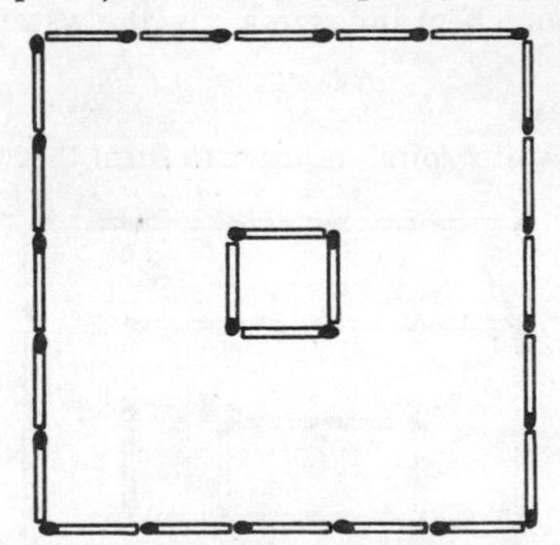

(*a*) Use 18 more matches to split the patio into six **L**-shaped tiles all the same size and shape

(*b*) Use 20 more matches to split the patio into eight equal **L**-shaped tiles

Four Equal Plots

Here is a square building site 4 matches on a side. We will call its area 16 square match units (4 X 4 = 16).

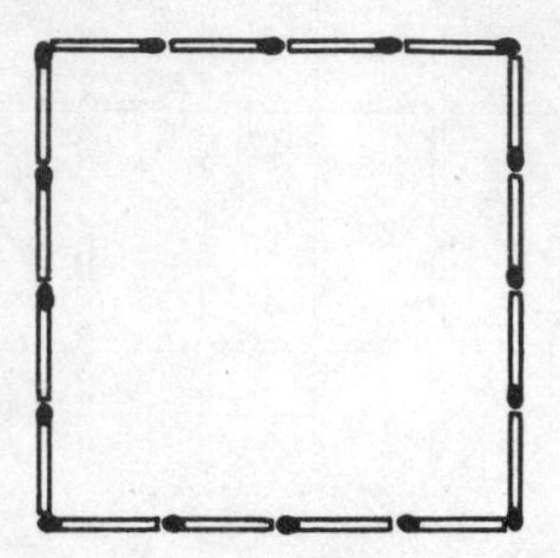

Add 11 matches to fence off the site into four plots, each with an area of 4 square match units. But you must do it so that each plot borders on the other three. One of the plots is a square, two are L-shaped, and one is a rectangle.

Get Across the Pool

Here is a garden pool with a square island in the middle.

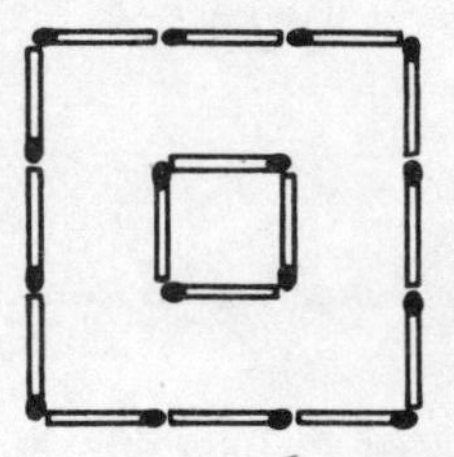

Add two "planks" (matches) and step across the water onto the island.

Spiral into Squares

Move four matches in this spiral in order to form three squares.

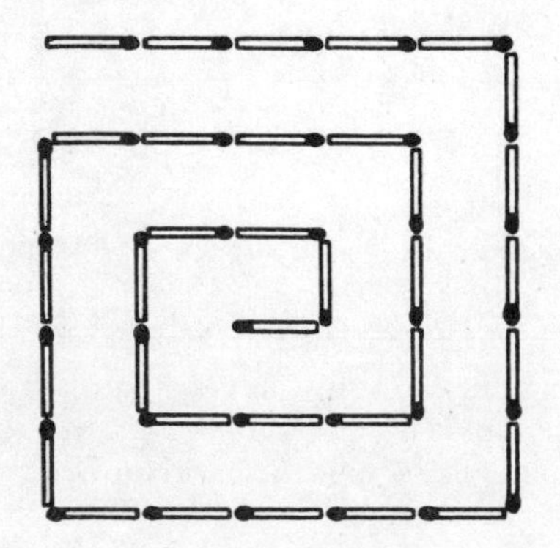

More Triangle Trickery

Make a three-four-five triangle out of 12 matches. The matches shut in an area of 6 square match units. (This is easy to see because the triangle is exactly half of a three-by-four rectangle, whose area would be 12 square match units.)

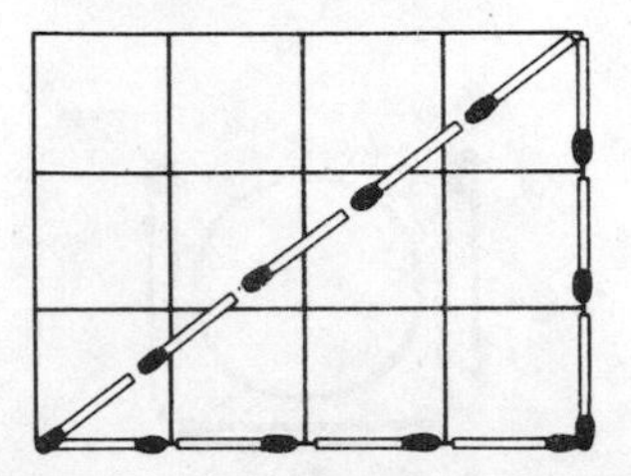

(*a*) Move 3 matches to form a shape with area 4 square match units
(*b*) Move 4 matches to form a shape with area 3 square match units

CLUE: In both *a* and *b* move the matches from the shorter sides of the triangle.

Triangle Trio

Can you make just three equal-sided triangles out of seven matches?

Triangle Quartet

With these six matches can you make four equal-sided triangles?

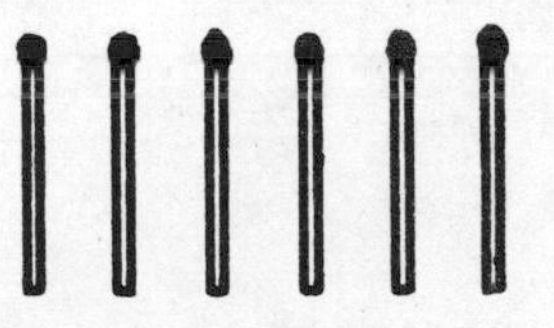

3 Times the Area

Look at the rectangle on the left. It has 3 times the area of the rectangle on the right, as the dotted lines show.

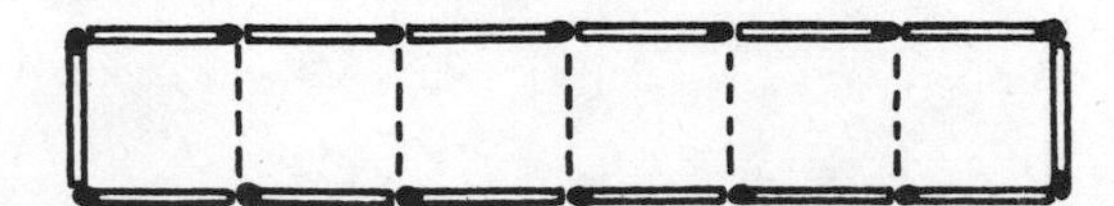

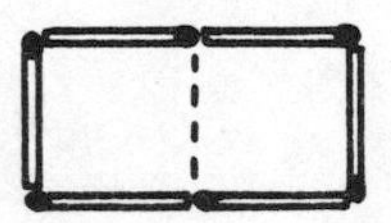

Add one match to the smaller rectangle so it has 7 matches. Make it into a box-girder shape made up of three equal-sided triangles. Now add four matches to the rectangle on the left and make it into a shape made up of 19 equal-sided triangles—so it has an area 3 times as great as the box-girder shape.

Cherry in the Glass

Arrange a penny and four matches as shown. This is your cherry in a glass. Take the cherry out of the glass simply by moving two matches. You must not touch the cherry (penny), of course.

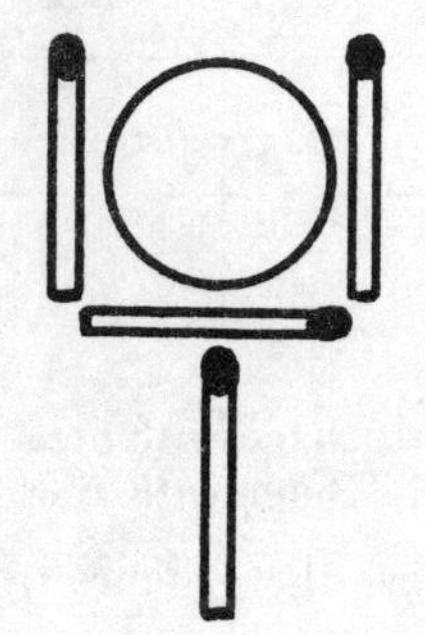

5. Coin and Shunting Problems

The next section includes puzzles about shuffling coins and the classic puzzles of ferrying people across rivers in boats. Also there is a wide selection of railway shunting problems. The best way to solve these is by actually drawing a plan of railway tracks, making coins or bits of paper stand for the engines and their cars, and moving them about on the tracks. It is a good idea to jot down the moves you make so you don't forget them, particularly if you are successful and solve the problem. There is nothing more vexing than to solve such a puzzle and then not be able to remember your moves!

Coin Sorting in Pairs

Arrange three pennies and two dimes in a row, penny-dime-penny-dime-penny. Move the coins in pairs so that the three pennies are together and next to them the two dimes, as shown in the second picture.

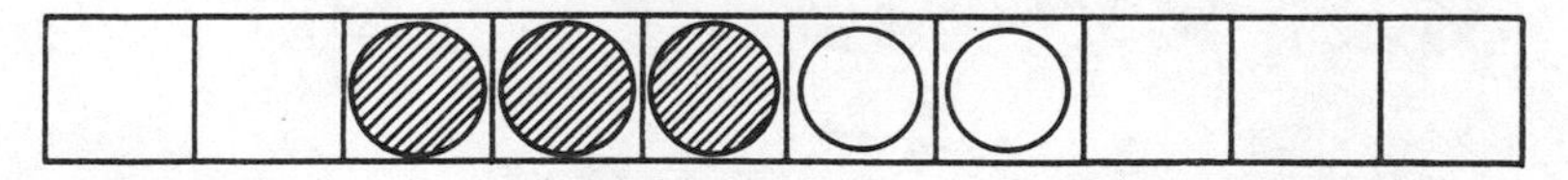

A move is like this: You place the tips of your first and second fingers on any two coins—the coins don't have to be next to each other or of the same denomination—then you slide the pair to another part of the row, but you must keep the same spacing between the coins. It helps to use squares to keep the spacing. You must not make any pair of coins merely change places. When you finish, there must be no spaces between any of the coins. You can move the coins as many spaces as you like left or right. But ten spaces should be enough. Can you do it in three moves?

Rats in a Tunnel

Two brown rats and two white rats met head on in a tunnel. How did they pass one another and change ends of the tunnel? They could only move by moving forward into a space or by hopping over another rat (of their own or the other color) into a space. Or they could move back. What is the fewest number of moves needed to change the rats over? Here are the kind of moves you can make:

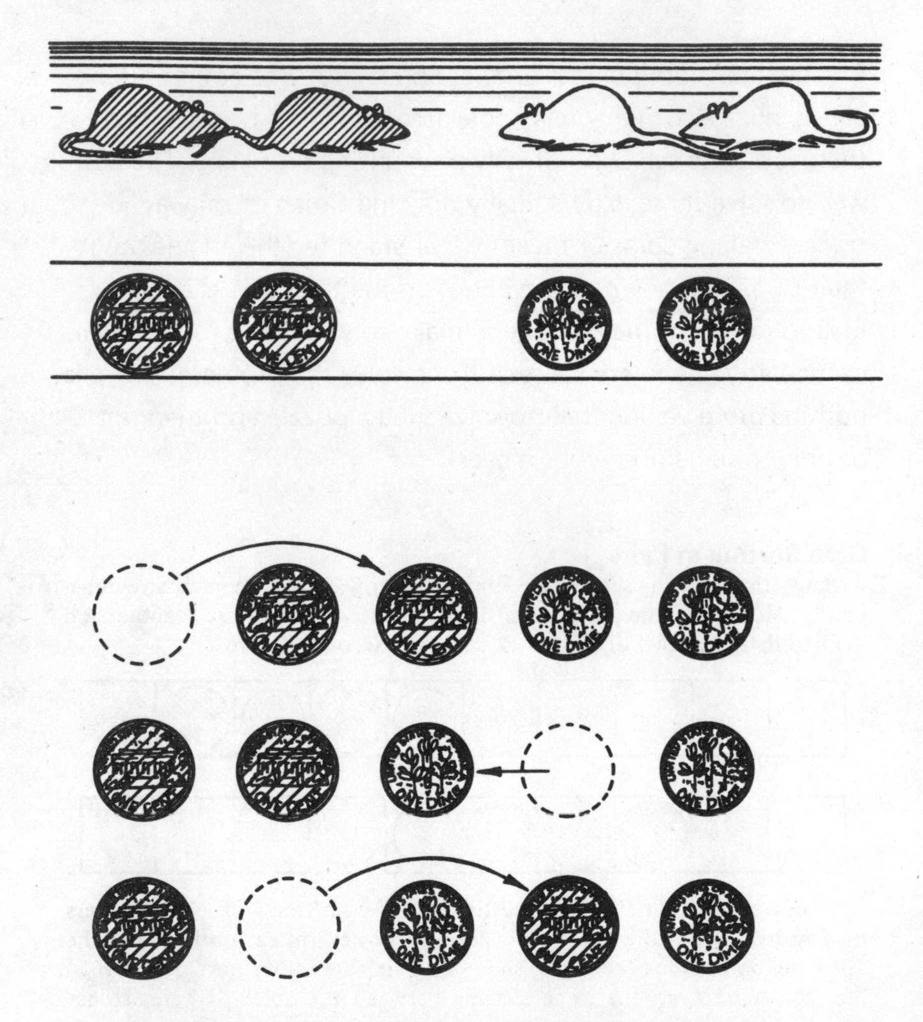

To work it out, use two pennies (for the brown rats) and two dimes (for the white rats). Put them in a line with a gap between, as shown in our sketch.

Three-Coin Trick

Begin with three coins showing a head placed between two tails. Each move in this puzzle consists of turning over two coins *next* to each other.

(*a*) Can you get all the coins showing heads in just two moves?
(*b*) Can you make them show all tails in any number of moves?

Triangle of Coins

Start with a triangle of ten coins pointing upward, as shown. Can you move three coins only and make the triangle point downward?

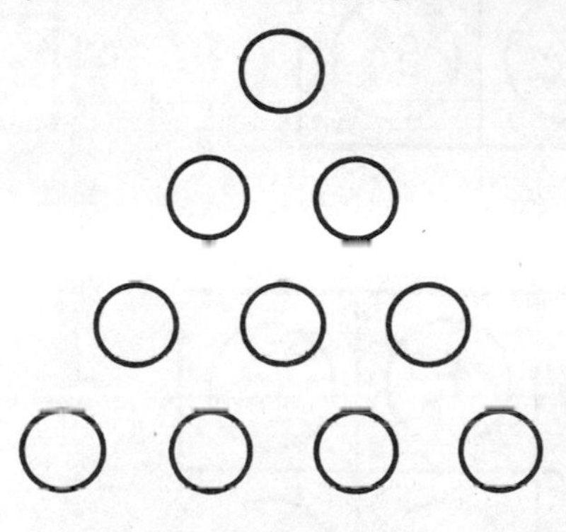

Five-Coin Trick

Take five coins, all the same kind–say all dimes. Can you place them so that each coin touches the other four?

Five-Coin Puzzle

Can you shift the coins shown on this board so that the penny and the half-dollar on the left swap places?

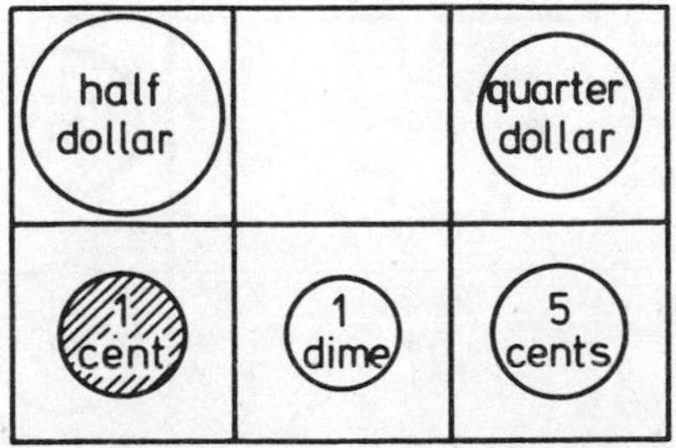

Coin Changeovers

Place three pennies and three nickels as shown here. Can you make the pennies and nickels change places? You may move only one coin at a time. Move it directly to an empty place, or jump it over another coin to an empty space. You can move or jump up and down or across but not diagonally.

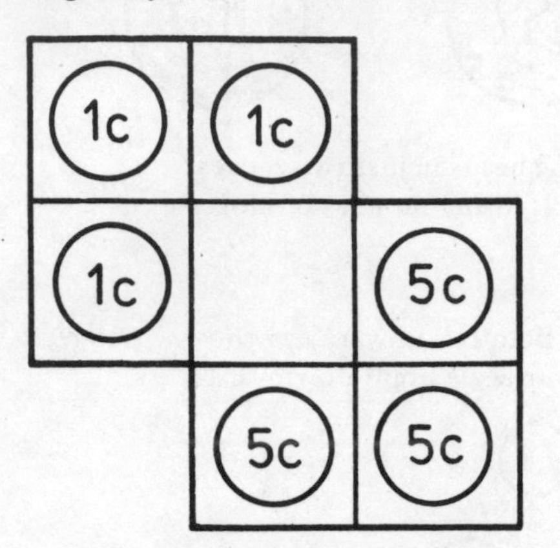

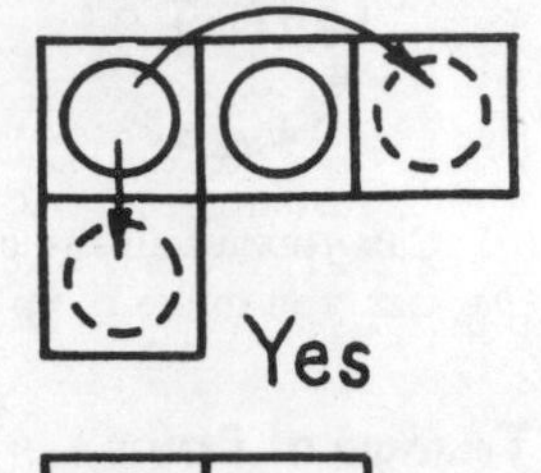

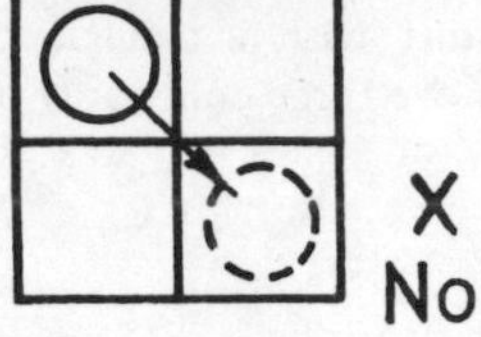

Now try this puzzle:

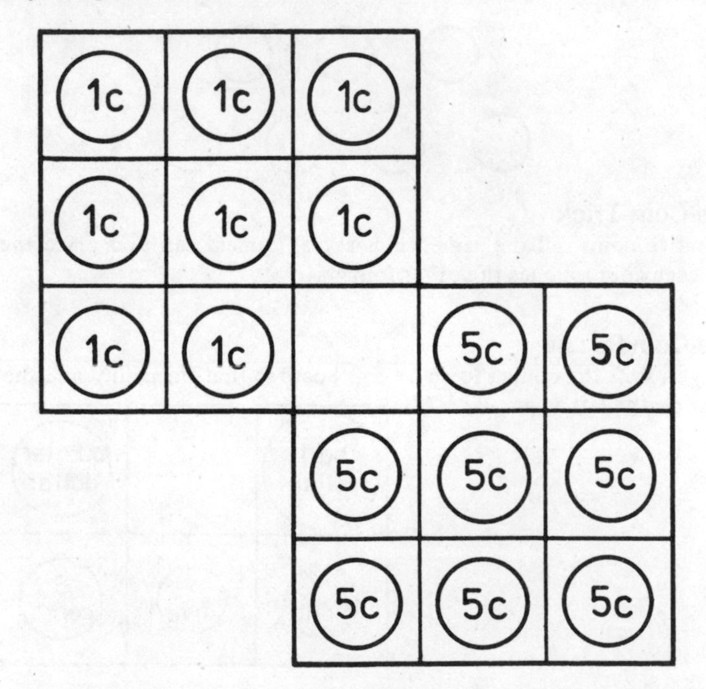

Mission Impossible?

Two secret agents, 005 and 007, are each trying to get this top scientist out of Slobodia. The only way out is across the Red River Danube. Agent 005's man is Dr. Fünf and 007's man is Dr. Sieben. None of them can swim. A rowing boat awaits them, hidden on the Slobodian side. It carries only two people at a time. Neither scientist dare be alone with the other agent unless his own agent is also with them. Nor can the two scientists be left alone together, in case they swap top secrets. It's a case of two's not allowed, three's company!

For instance, Dr. Fünf cannot row across the river alone with the other agent, 007, or be alone with him on either river bank; but he can be on either bank when *both* agents are with him. How did the agents row the scientists across the river?

HINT: Five crossings from bank to bank should complete the mission.

Railroad Switch

The driver of a shunting engine has a problem: to switch over the black and white cars on the triangle-shaped siding shown here. That is, he must shunt the white car from the branch *AC* to the branch *BC* and the black car from *BC* to *AC*. The siding beyond is only big enough to take the engine or one car. That's all. The engine can go from *A* to *B*, back up past *C*, and then forward along *AC*. But when it does so, it will end up facing the other way along the tracks *AB*. The driver isn't bothered about which way his engine faces. Can you switch the cars in six moves? Each coupling and uncoupling counts as one move. Remember, the driver can couple up both cars to the engine and then uncouple just one of them.

To solve the shunting problem, draw a large map of the railroad and use coins on it.

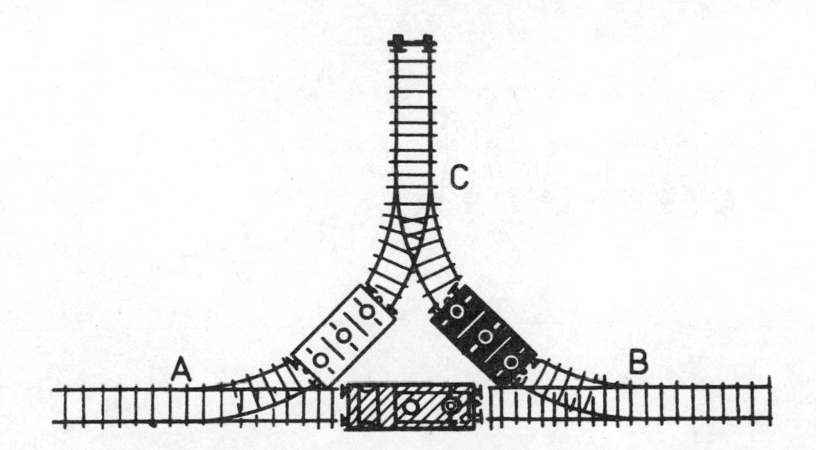

Restacking Coins

There used to be a toy called the Tower of Hanoi. It was in the form of 64 wooden rings of graded sizes stacked on one of three pegs–largest at the bottom, smallest at the top. The rings had to be restacked in the same order on a different peg by moving them one at a time. A story goes that this problem was sent to Buddhist monks. Working at a move a second, they would have needed some 585 billion years to finish it!

Here is a new–and shorter!–version of this old puzzle. Place three saucers or table mats in a line. In the first saucer on the left stack a quarter, a penny, and a dime; the quarter must be at the bottom, the penny on top, as shown. Restack the coins in exactly the same way in the far right saucer. You must follow these rules: Move only one coin at a time, from one saucer to another. *Always* put a smaller coin on a larger coin. *Never* put a larger coin on top of a smaller one. Use all three saucers when moving the coins. You can move to and fro.

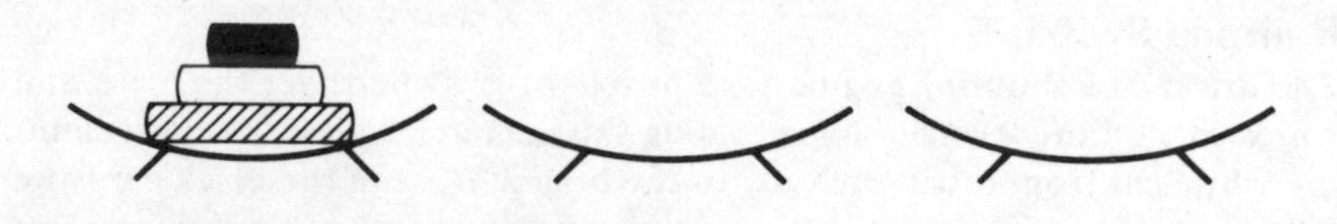

River Crossing

A platoon of soldiers must cross a river. The bridge is down, the river wide. Suddenly the platoon's officer spots two boys playing in a tiny rowboat. The boat only holds two boys or one soldier–*not* a boy and a soldier, for instance. All the same, the platoon succeeds in crossing the river in the boat. How? Work it out with matches and a matchbox on the table across a make-believe river.

Collision Course?

Two trains have met head on on a single track in the desert. A black engine (*B*) and car on the left; a white engine (*W*) and car on the right. There is a short switch just large enough for one engine or one car at a time. Using the switch, the engines and cars can be shunted so they can pass each other. How many times will the drivers have to back or reverse their engines? Count each reversal as a move. A car cannot be linked to the *front* of an engine.

6. Reasoning and Logical Problems

In this section I've included some novel thinking exercises with blocks. And there is also a selection from several types of IQ tests that are visual and mathematical in nature. The section continues with a sprinkling of some of the better known (and lesser known) logical puzzles that call for strict reasoning. I have concluded the section with some unusual logical puzzles not often seen in puzzle books.

Thinking Blocks

The following are problems about placing six rectangular blocks so that they touch only so many other blocks. They were originally included in a book by Edward de Bono, *Five-Day Course in Thinking* (New York: Basic Books, 1967). He used the problems as a cunning thinking exercise. You may find you simply cast your six blocks on the table in random fashion and hope for the best. Of course, you've still got to check the pattern of blocks you get this way. Or you can adopt a less higgledy-piggledy approach and carefully build up a pattern, block by block. One way is as good as the other. Any method will serve just so long as it gives you the correct answer.

There is a simple lesson to be learned from this puzzle. We often cannot solve a problem because we get a thinking block. We get blocked in our thinking, or rather, in *one* way of thinking. So the lesson is this: If one way of thinking proves unhelpful, try another. Often the more ridiculous the new way of thinking seems, the better it may be.

One other tip: Don't discard ideas that didn't work. To know that a certain pattern of blocks doesn't give the right answer is in itself useful. The trick is to *remember* all these "blind alleys" so that you don't try them repeatedly and thus lose patience. Matchboxes make good homely blocks.

A. Place six blocks so that each touches only two other blocks. They must touch flush along their sides, you cannot have the point of one block "digging into" another. To help you solve this puzzle, you can copy each pattern you form and jot down the number of touching blocks on each block, as shown here. This pattern won't do because two of the blocks touch *three* others.

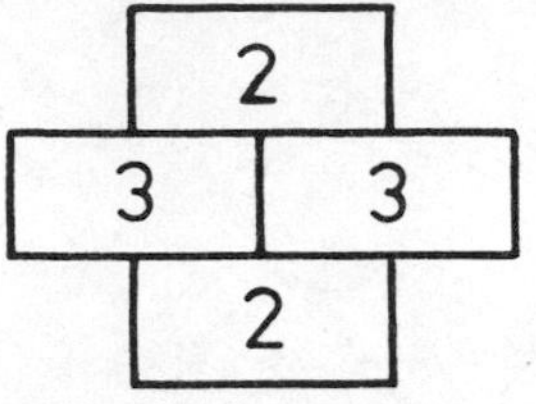

B. Place the six blocks so that each touches only three other blocks.
C. Place the blocks so that each touches four others.
D. Place them so that each touches five others.

Martian Orders!

On Mars young Martians have to line up at school in order, according to two rules. First, girls come before boys. Second, where two girls come next to each other, the taller girl goes first; and the same goes for two boys together in a line. Zane is a Martian boy who is the same height as Thalia (a girl), but he is taller than his friend Xeron (another boy). (*a*) How do the three line up, from left to right? (*b*) They are joined by Thalia's friend Sheree (another girl), who is taller than she is. Now how do they line up?

What Shape Next?

Here are two picture puzzles of the kind you see in intelligence tests. Follow the pattern of shapes in each from left to right. Then work out which of the lettered shapes best fits onto the end of the line.

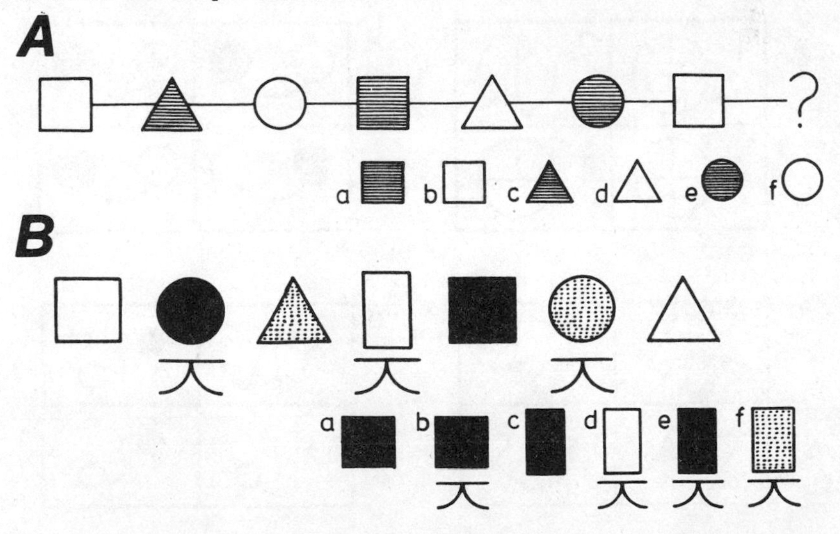

IQ Puzzle

Another IQ-style puzzle. Look at the four numbered shapes and say which one best fits the space in the bottom right-hand corner of the picture.

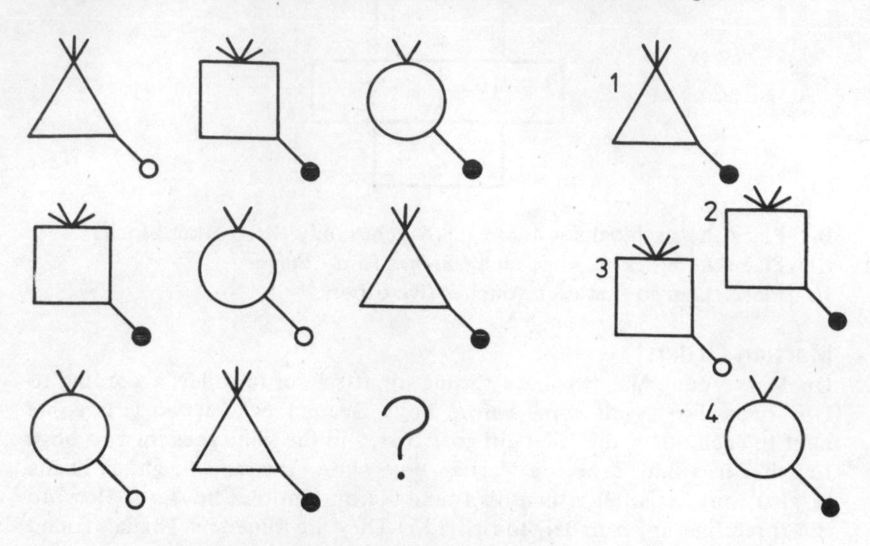

Odd Shape Out

In each of the sets of shapes shown here one of them (1, 2, 3, or 4) is the odd shape out: It is different in some way from the other three shapes. Can you pick it out in each set?

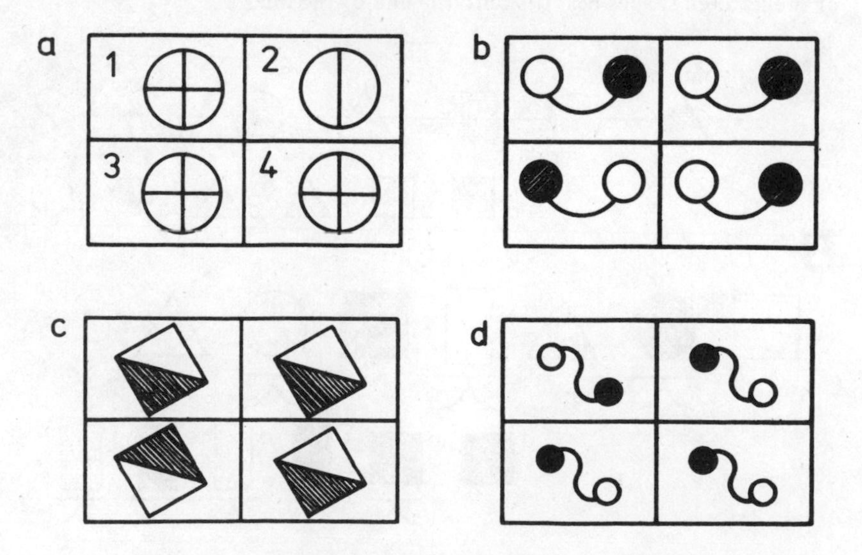

The Same Shape

Which of the shapes shown here is the same as the boxed one on the left?

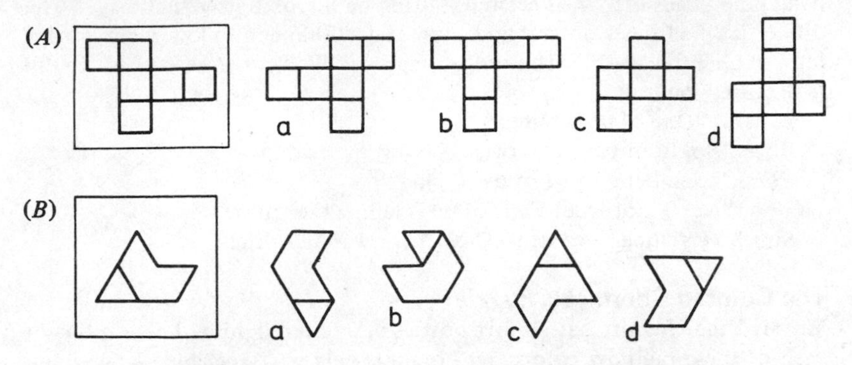

Next Shape, Please

Can you say which is the next shape in the pattern?

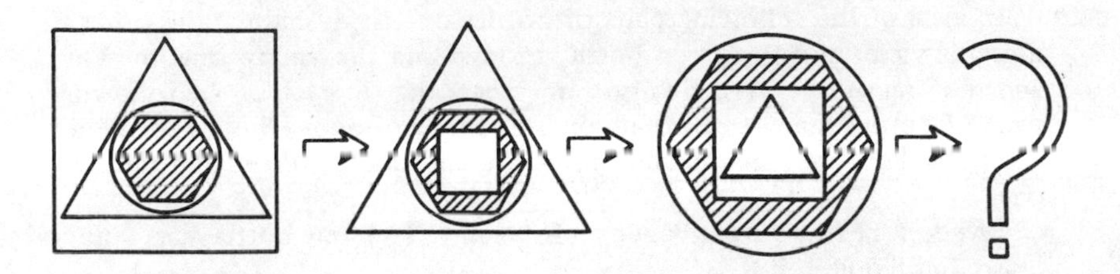

The Apt House

Yet another of those IQ-like tests, or rather "aptitude" tests. Look at the numbered houses. Only one can be made by folding the plan. Which house is it?

If you can see this easily in your mind's eye, then the testers say you should be good at being an engineer. Or maybe you know your *apt* (apartment) houses!

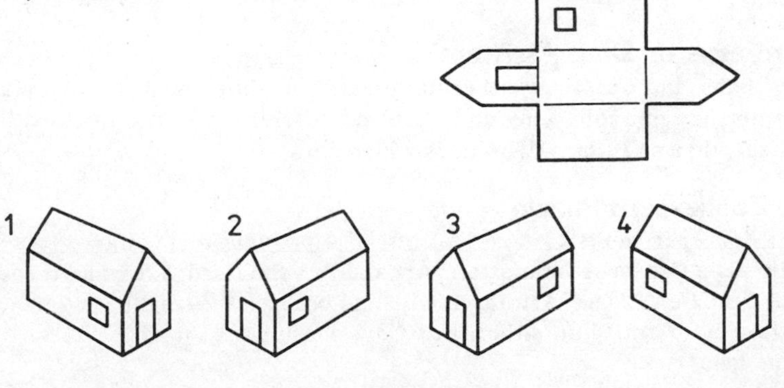

Who Is Telling the Truth?

The judge listened quizzically to the four well-known crooks. "You're lying your heads off," he declared. "Still you'll look better that way!" The officer laughed dead on cue and then said: "I happen to know *one* of this lot *is* telling the truth." The judge snapped: "Well, what've you got to say in defense, you lot?"

Al said: "One of us is lying!"

Bob: "No, I tell you, two of us is lying."

Con: "Look here, three of us is lying."

Don: "Nope, not true! Four of us is telling the truth."

So who *is* telling the truth? The officer was quite right.

The Colored Chemicals Puzzle

Mr. Mad the chemist has six big bottles of colored liquids. There is one of each of these rainbow colors: red, orange, yellow, green, blue, and violet. Mr. Mad knows that some of the bottles contain poison. But he can't remember which! However, he *can* remember the facts from which you should be able to work out which colored bottles contain poison.

In each of the following pairs of bottles one is poisonous, the other is not: the violet and the green bottle; the red and the yellow one; the blue and the orange one. And he also remembers that in each of the following pairs of bottles there is one that contains a nonpoisonous liquid: the violet and the yellow one; the red and the orange one; and the green and the blue one.

"And, I nearly forgot," adds Mr. Mad. "The red bottle has a nonpoisonous liquid in it."

Which bottles have poison in them?

Mr. Black, Mr. Gray, and Mr. White

Three men met on the street–Mr. Black, Mr. Gray, and Mr. White. "Do you know," asked Mr. Black, "that between us we are wearing black, gray, and white? Yet not one of us is wearing the color of his name!" "Why, that's right," said the man in white. Can you say who was wearing which color?

Hairdresser or Shop Assistant?

Amy, Babs, and Carol are either hairdressers or shop assistants. Amy and Babs do the same job. Amy and Carol do different jobs. If Carol is a shop assistant, then so is Babs. Who does which job?

The Zookeeper's Puzzle

The Zookeeper wants to take two out of a possible three chimps to a TV studio. The two male chimps are Art and Bic; the third, a female, is called Cora. He daren't leave Art and Bic behind because they fight. And he cannot take both with him either. But Cora doesn't get on with Bic. So who can he take?

Who's Guilty?

Alf, Bert and Cash are the suspects in a robbery case. Their trial shows up the following facts: Either Cash is innocent or Bert is guilty. If Bert is guilty, then Cash is innocent. Alf and Cash never work together and Alf never does a job on his own. Also, if Bert is guilty, so is Alf. Who is guilty?

Who's in the Play?

Alice won't take part in the Buskin Players annual (amateur) play if Betty is in it! But Charles will only play if Alice *is* in it. The poor producer insists that *one* of the girls is in the play. Two people are needed. Who is in the play?

Tea, Coffee, or Malted Milk?

The professor had enjoyed his usual after-lunch beverage so much he thought he'd have another. But he could not for the life of him remember what he had drunk. So he called the waiter over. And this is what he said to him: "Now, if this was coffee, I want tea, and if this was tea, bring me a malted milk. But if this was malted milk, bring me a coffee."

The waiter, who was logically minded, then brought him coffee. Can you say what drink—tea, coffee, or malted milk—the waiter had originally served the professor?

Soda or Milkshake?

Three friends—Alan, Bet, and Cis—often go to the same soda fountain. Each either orders a soda or milkshake. The soda jerk notices: (*a*) when Alan chooses a soda, Bet has a milkshake; (*b*) either Alan or Cis has a soda, but never both; and (*c*) Bet and Cis never both have a milkshake. There are only two possible orders they can make. What are they?

HINT: Since this is a hard one, we'll tell you that only Bet has a choice of drinks.

Newton's Kittens

Isaac Newton, as you probably know, was one of the cleverest men the world has ever known. He was the great scientist and mathematician who solved the riddle of gravity, of why things fall to the ground. Well, Newton had a cat and she used to come and go into his house near Cambridge, England, through a large hole bored in the bottom of his kitchen door. One day the cat had three kittens. And so Newton had three small holes bored in the door for them.

Why do you think this was funny?

March Hare's Party

The March Hare was giving a party. His young guests had to get to their rightful tables—1, 2, 3, or 4—by one of the four paths shown in the picture. As you see, he wouldn't let any boys go along one path, which would later fork into two paths. Al wanted to have tea on an island with Barbra, but he refused to have tea with Silvie or Don. Sylvie said she wouldn't have tea near water. On top of this, Gary just *had* to roller-skate over one of the bridges. To make matters worse, Don and Gary wouldn't have tea with each other. By the way, only the boys could row, and the single boat was only big enough for one child and could only travel to table 4. Where did each guest have tea?

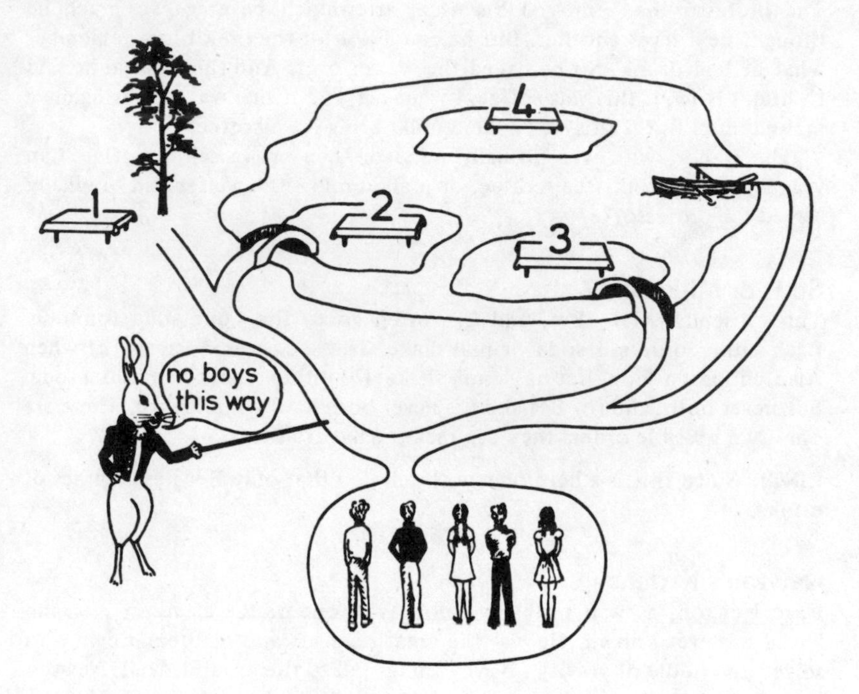

Marriage Mix-up

The absent-minded professor had just been to a party. His wife naturally wanted to know who was there. "Usual crowd," he replied. "And some new faces. Ted, Pete, and Charlie. And their wives—Barbra, Sue, and Nicola. Can't remember who's married to whom. Anyway, each couple has one child: They're called Ruth, Wendy, and Dick. Told me all about them. Barbra said her child was playing Annie in *Annie Get Your Gun,* the school play. Pete told me his child was playing Ophelia. I do remember Ted pointing out that his daughter was not Wendy. And Charlie's wife is not Sue. I suppose we can work out the marriage partners from that."

See if you can work out who is married to whom and who their children are.

Who Does Which Job?

There are three men—Orville, Virgil, and Homer. Each has two jobs. The jobs are: private eye, racing driver, singer, jockey, bartender, and cardsharp. Try to find each man's two jobs from these facts:

(*1*) The bartender took the racing driver's girl friend to a party
(*2*) Both the racing driver and the singer like playing cards with Homer
(*3*) The jockey often had a drink with the bartender
(*4*) Virgil owes the singer a buck
(*5*) Orville beat both Virgil and the jockey at cards

Birds and Insects

Here's an easy logical poser—or is it? Think about these statements:

No birds are insects.
All swallows are birds.

Which of the next sentences follows *logically* from the above two statements?

(*A*) No swallows are insects
(*B*) Some birds are not swallows
(*C*) All birds are swallows
(*D*) No insects are birds

Wonderland Golf

The American mathematician Paul Rosenbloom specially devised this zany golf game for youngsters. He set it as a piece of mathematical research, actually. On the Wonderland Golf Course the holes are numbered 1, 2, 3, and so on up to 18. The links are laid out in a spiral, as shown, to make the shots easier! You have two special clubs. One of them holes out in one for you! This is the Single-Shot Iron, or S iron for short. The other club even lets you skip holes! It hits your ball from any hole to the one double its number; so it hits your ball from, say, hole 1 to hole 2, hole 3 to hole 6, and hole 9 to hole 18. Call it the D (for double) iron.

PUZZLE: What is the smallest number of shots, using either iron, to get from hole 1 to hole 18? That is, what is par for the course? Strangely, it is the same as for holes 11, 13, 14, and 17! Don't suppose you can spot a pattern, can you?

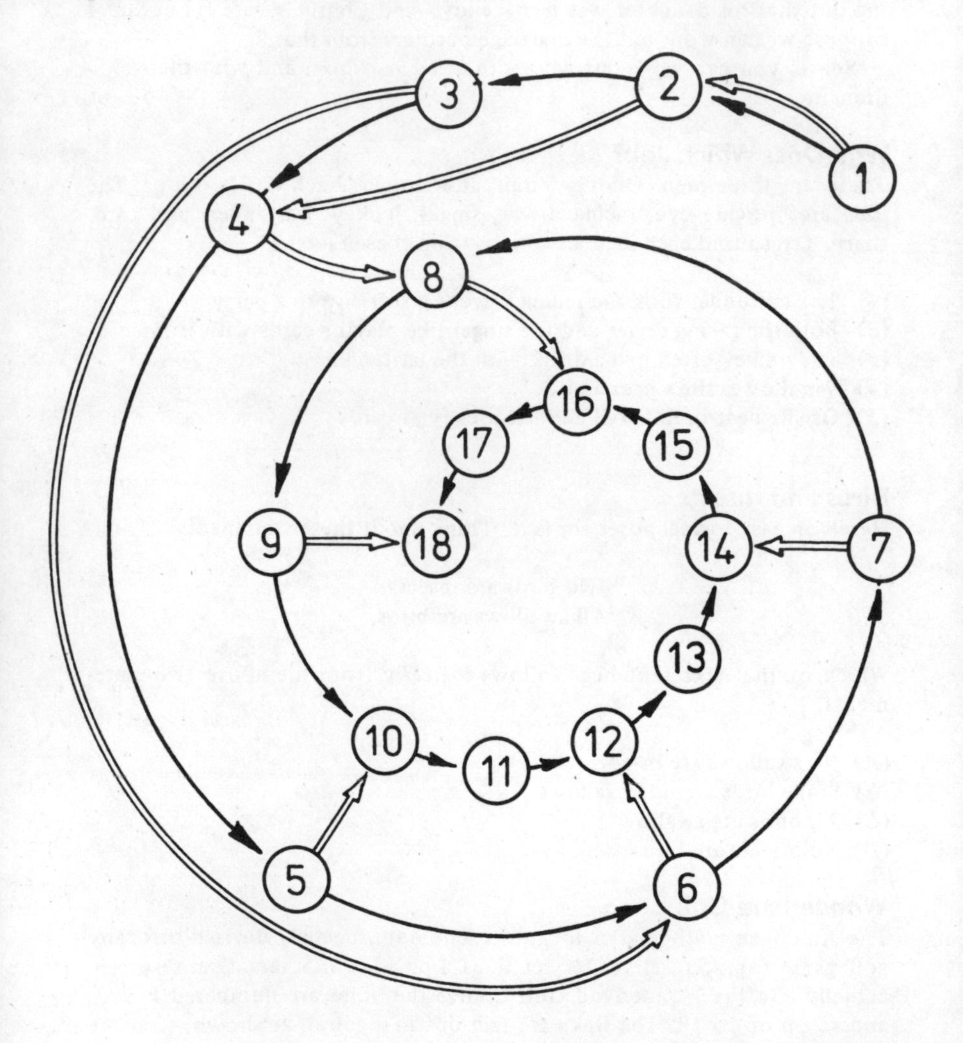

Mad Hatter's Tea Party

The Mad Hatter had planned a special children's tea party. He had laid out the tables in the garden in the way our picture shows. He had split his guests into three sets–*G:* all girls; *B:* all boys; and *M:* boys and girls, mixed. You can see them in their sets, on the left of the picture, waiting to have tea. He told them: "Everybody in each set has to get to his table by taking the correct path through the garden. You can see which way to go by the words set in the paths."

Can you work out which of the tables–1, 2, 3, or 4–each set should get to? One of the tables remains empty. Which one?

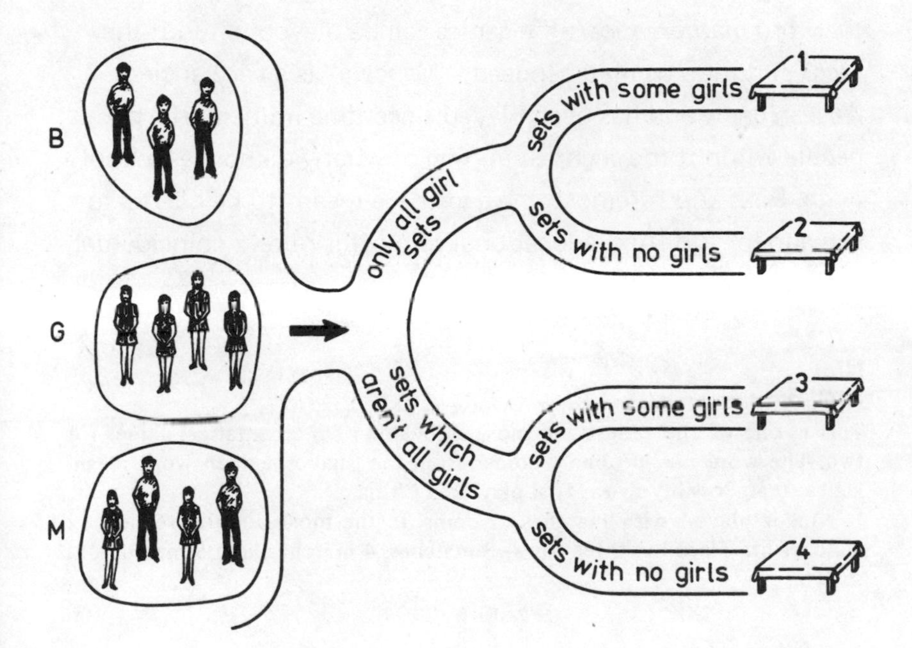

7. Mathematical Games

All but two of these games are mathematical; I have included two word games, "Coincidences" and "The Crossword Game," because they are so good and so popular. Do not be put off by the word ***mathematical***: the games can be played without the foggiest notion of math. Indeed, "Mancala" is a very ancient African game and has been played since time immemorial by people without the slightest inkling of what we know as school math. First and foremost, the games are meant to be played to win and for fun. Any educational spin-off is purely coincidental, as they say.

Nim

A Game for Two

This is one of the oldest and most enjoyable of mathematical games for two. The word *nim* probably comes from the Shakespearean word meaning to steal. Possibly it was first played in China.

Nim is played with matches or coins. In the most popular version 12 matches are placed in three rows—3 matches, 4 matches, and 5 matches, as shown.

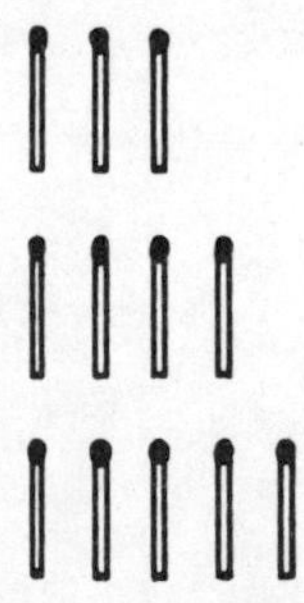

The rules are simple. The players take turns in removing one or more matches, but they must all come from the same row. The one who takes the last match wins. (You can also play the other way: The one to take the last match loses.)

Playing a few games will soon show you how you can always win: (*a*) Your move must leave two rows with more than 1 match in a row and the same number in each; (*b*) your move leaves 1 match in one row, 2 matches in the second row, and 3 in the third; or (*c*) if you play first, on your first move you take 2 matches from the top row and after that play according to the first two winning strategies just given.

You can play Nim with any number of matches or pennies in each row, and with any number of rows. As it happens, there is a way of working out how to take the right number of matches to get into a winning position. You simply use "computer counting," or binary. This method was first given in 1901. A description of it is given in the answers section.

Tac Tix
A Game for Two

Tac Tix is an exciting version of "Nim," invented by the Danish puzzlist Piet Hein. Hein is the inventor of "Hex," page 86. In Tac Tix pennies or counters are placed in a square, as shown in the picture. Players in turn remove one to four pennies from the board; they may be taken from any row or column. But they must always be adjacent pennies with no gaps between them. For example, say the first player took the two middle pennies in the top row; the other player could not take the other two pennies in that row in one move.

Tac Tix has to be played with the player taking the *last* penny losing. This is because a simple tactic makes playing the usual way uninteresting—perhaps the reason for the game's name—for it allows the second player to always win. All he has to do is play symmetrically—that is, he takes the "mirror" penny or pennies to the one(s) the first player removed. The game can also be played on a three-by-three board, and there, when playing the usual way, the first player can win by taking the center penny, a corner one, all of a central row, or all of a central column.

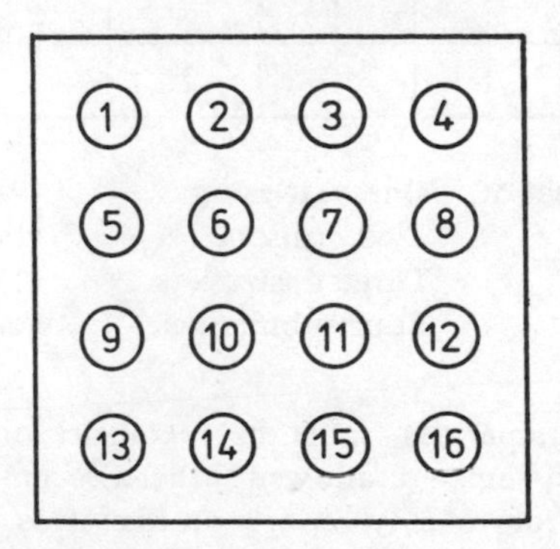

Battleships

A Game for Two

One of the most popular of all paper-and-pencil games, Battleships can also be a serious exercise in math! Each player has a fleet of ships, which he marks on a grid; he fires salvos at named enemy squares, and the enemy tells him if he has hit a ship or not and, if so, what kind of ship is hit. From this he tries to work out where the enemy ships lie. To sink an enemy ship, he must hit every square of that ship. First to sink the enemy's fleet wins.

Each player needs two ten-by-ten grids marked *A, B, C, . . . , J* along the top and *1, 2, 3, . . . , 10* along the left side, as shown in the picture. On one sheet he marks the positions of his fleet; the other sheet is for marking his own shots at the enemy fleet. (The second sheet represents a different area from the first; otherwise it would be possible for a player's ship and his enemy's to occupy the same spot.) The picture shows the position and size of each kind of ship.

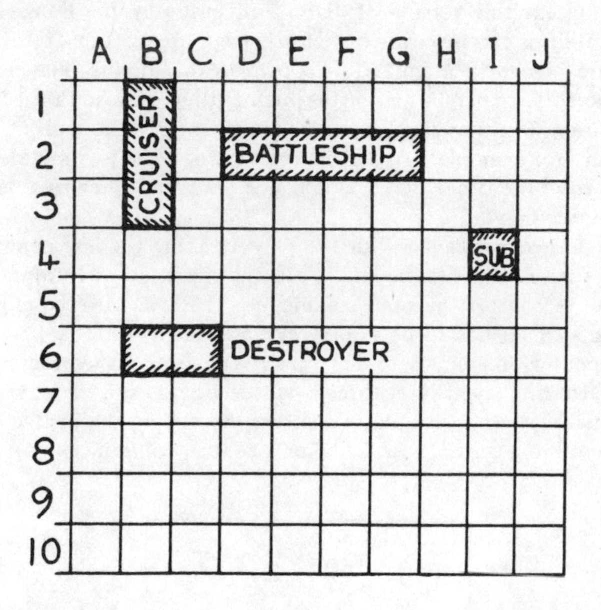

Each player has a fleet of:	One battleship	(four squares each)
	Two cruisers	(three squares each)
	Three destroyers	(two squares each)
	Four submarines	(one square each)

All ships except submarines, must be rectangles one square wide. No L-shaped or crooked ships are allowed; otherwise a player could not work out how ships lie from enemy reports on his salvos without tremendous difficulty. Two ships may not touch, even at corners. And a ship can have at most one side of a square on the border of the "sea." So a submarine cannot be placed in a corner.

When the two fleets have been marked in position on the grids, one of the players fires a salvo of three shots: He tells the enemy player where he wants the three shots to land; they don't have to land on adjacent squares. His enemy must then tell him how many shells fell in the sea and how many hit which types of ships, but he does not have to say which shot did what. For example, he might say, "Two in the sea and one on a destroyer." No matter what order these results were gotten. The second player now fires a salvo, and the first player tell him what happened. Each player keeps a record of his hits and misses on his chart of "enemy waters" to work out where the enemy fleet is moored. Play continues until one of the players sinks the enemy's entire fleet and announces the fact.

Boxes

A Game for Two

This is a game of drawing boxes on a grid of dots. It is very much like "Snake" (page 77) and can be played on the same sort of grid. Players take turns drawing a line across or down to link adjacent dots not yet linked. A player wins a box when he draws the fourth and last side of a square; he then writes his initial into the box to show he made the box. And he can then take another turn. If he's lucky, he may be able to make several boxes without his opponent having a turn. BUT after making a box he must draw one more line *immediately*. One line may make two boxes at once, but the player takes only one further turn for that line. A player does not *have* to make a box even though there may be a square with three sides drawn.

POINT ABOUT STRATEGY: Near the end of the game you usually get open "corridors" of lines, like two uprights of a "ladder." Once one player has closed off one end of the corridor (or indeed put in a rung anywhere on the ladder), the other player can make all the boxes in the corridor during his turn. The winner is the one who has made more boxes. It is best to play on a grid with an even number of dots on each side–eight by ten, say–so that there will be an odd number of boxes in the completed grid.

Mastermind

A Reasoning Game for Two

This game is marketed, although the principle is simple enough for you to make your own version. The basic idea is this: One player sets a problem by inserting five colored pegs, out of a possible eight colors, in a row. His pegs are then covered, and his opponent, the "mastermind," has to work out what the colors and their correct places are by forming trial rows. The problem setter indicates by the use of black and white pegs whether or not, first, the opponent has the right colored pegs and, second, they are in the right place.

The commercial board is made of plastic and has rows of five holes with a square grid at the end of each row. The version shown here has only four holes with a two-by-two square grid at the end of each row. A sample game will serve to indicate the rules and method of play. To simplify things, we will play with four colors and white only.

Suppose the first player puts up these four pegs: green (G), blue (B), red (R), and yellow (Y). He then covers them with a little hood, or *cloche*, so that his opponent cannot see the pegs. The opponent puts in the top row: red, green, white (W), and green. As the sketch shows, he has two colors, right, but they are not in the right place; to show this, the first player puts in two white pegs. The opponent's second try is the line green, blue, black (Bk), and white. Because this row has two colors *and* two places right—the green and the blue pegs—the first player puts in two black pegs. The opponent's third row is green, blue, white, and red, which has two colors in the right place (two black pegs) and one color right (red) but in the wrong place (one white peg). The game ends when he has formed a row exactly the same as the one originally set. The opponent works out by reasoning which pegs to change. The shorter the number of rows he can solve the problem in, the better he is at reasoning. The game can also be played on paper, with colored pencils or felt-tip pens substituting for pegs.

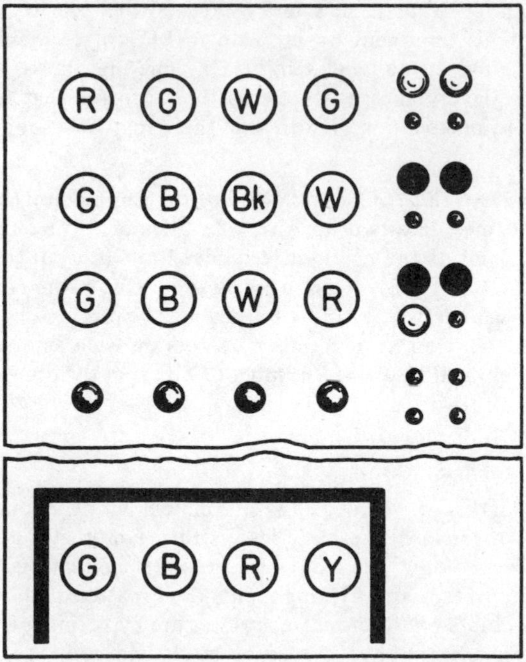

R G W G

G B Bk W

G B W R

G B R Y

Coincidences

A Word Game Any Number Can Play

This is a word game rather like "Mastermind" but played with letters instead of colored pegs. One player acts as the "accountant," who thinks of a five- or six-letter word. He notes this secretly on a sheet of paper, which he keeps. He calls out the number of letters it has. The other players try to discover his word by calling out a line of the same number of letters. The accountant then tells each player how many of the letters in his line match in position those in his word. Say the accountant's word is "CENTS" and a player calls "A-A-A-E-E"; then the accountant announces "None" because although the player has gotten one letter right (*E*), neither *E* is in the correct position. A good strategy for players is to call out all vowels, since most words contain them (*A, E, I, O, U*). If the accountant's word is discovered in fewer tries than there are letters in his word (four tries, say), then he scores nothing. He scores one point for every try over the number of letters in his word.

Here is how a sample game began. Accountant's word: SHIRT

Player's lines	*Accountant calls*
AAEEE	None
IIOOO	None
IIIOO	One
THITH	Two
THITT	Three
THILT	Three

To play well, one should know the letter frequences of English, as follows:

Single letters:	E, T, A, O, N, I, S, R, H, L, D, C, U
Two-letter groups:	TH, IN, ER, RE, AN, HE, AR, EN, TI, TE, AT, ON, HA
Three-letter groups:	THE, ING, AND, ION, ENT, FOR, TIO, ERE, HER, ATE, VER, TER, THA

Eleusis

A Reasoning Game for Four

Here is a game with a really novel twist, invented by a New Yorker, Robert Abbot (taken from *More Mathematical Puzzles and Diversions*, by Martin Gardner, New York: Penguin, 1961). He originally devised it as a card game, but it can also be played with paper and pencil. Its novel twist is this: Most games have rules you learn and use in order to decide your best move, but in Eleusis you play to discover the rule! The game is rather like discovering a scientific law, except that in science there is nobody to tell you if your law is the right one (or indeed if there even *is* such a law).

In Eleusis an "umpire" secretly sets the rule, which other players have to discover. There are several games based on Eleusis; ours is the paper-and-pencil version for four players—an umpire and players A, B, and C. (It could also be played by just two players.) Our game consists of four sets—one for each player. When everybody has had a go at being umpire, the game ends, and the player with the lowest number of penalty points is the winner.

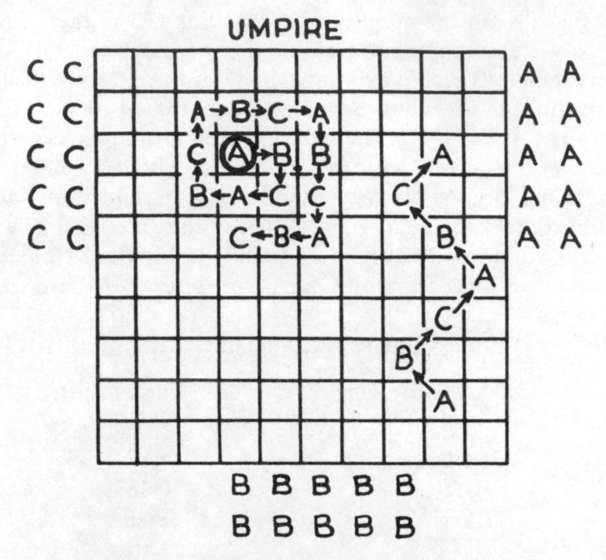

Two simple umpire's rules for the players to discover are shown in the picture of the board. On the left the rule is: The letters *A-B-C-A-B-C-A* . . . go in a spiral; the letters can move in any direction so long as their position is correct. On the right the rule is: The first letter *A* can go anywhere; the next letters must follow a "one square up, one square to the side" rule—that is, on the diagonal. The umpire keeps a drawing of his rule to show afterward in case of dispute.

Each player arms himself with a sheet of squared paper to keep a record of both his correct moves and incorrect attempts; about ten-by-ten squares should be big enough (see picture).

Player A sits on the umpire's left, then B, then C. Each player has ten of his own letters, which he tries to correctly place on the board. Player A takes a turn by pointing to an empty square and asking if he may write a letter *A* in it. If the umpire says yes, he puts an *A* in that square and crosses off one of the *A*'s on his side of the sheet. If the umpire says no, the turn passes to player B, and player A cannot cross out one of his letters. When A, B, and C have each had a turn, a round is completed; the next round begins when A takes his next turn.

The idea is that the umpire should set rules that are neither too easy nor too hard for the players to discover; ideally the players should be rid of their letters in the fifteenth round. The umpire is penalized if either his rule is so easy that the players are out before the fifteenth round or if the rule is so hard that the game continues after that round. The umpire keeps a tally of his "score" (penalty) by circling numbers on the tally card shown here, one number for each round:

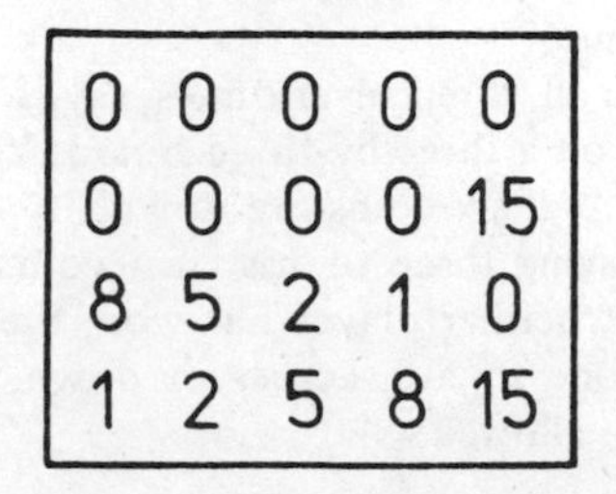

0	0	0	0	0
0	0	0	0	15
8	5	2	1	0
1	2	5	8	15

For the first nine rounds the umpire circles 0's and loses no points, since it would be impossible for the players to get rid of their letters before the tenth round. At the tenth round he is penalized 15 points; were the game to be over then, the players would have known the rules from the beginning. The penalty is progressively reduced until the fifteenth round, when it is again 0. After that round the penalty is progressively increased until the twentieth round, when it is back up to the maximum, 15.

Ticktactoe

A Game for Two

Ticktacktoe, or Noughts and Crosses, has to be the oldest battle of wits known to children and adults alike. The object is for one player to complete a line–horizontal, vertical, or diagonal–by himself. Any astute player will learn how to play to a draw in only a few hours' practice. The game must end in a draw unless one player makes a slip.

There are just three possible opening plays shown by the *X*'s in the picture–into a corner, the center, or a side box. The second player replies with O's. He can save himself from being trapped by one of the eight possible choices; he can mark the center. The side opening (third picture) offers traps to both players; it must be met by marking one of four cells.

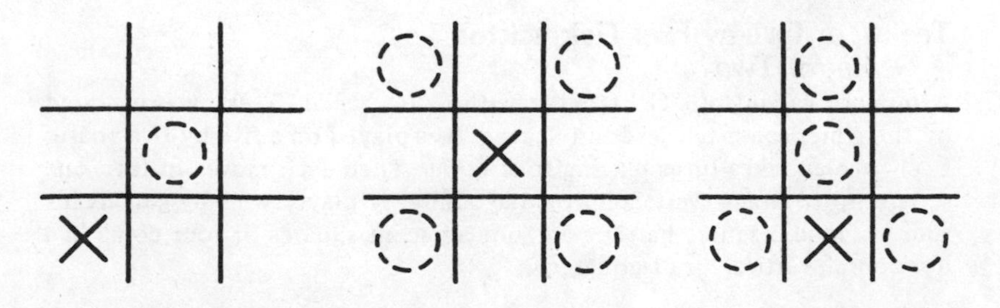

Ticktacktoe with Coins

A Game for Two

A more exciting variant of "Ticktacktoe" is where you play with coins or counters that can be moved after being placed. The game was played a lot in England in the 1300s, when it was called "Three Men's Morris," the forerunner of "Nine Men's Morris," page 75. It was also popular in ancient China, Greece, and Rome.

You use six coins in all, three silver dimes, say, for one player and three pennies for the other, on a three-by-three board. You take turns placing a coin on the board until all six coins are down. By this stage either player could have won by having three of his own coins in a row–horizontal, vertical, or diagonal. If neither player has won, they continue playing by moving a single coin one square, across or down, to any empty square. Diagonal *moves* are not allowed.

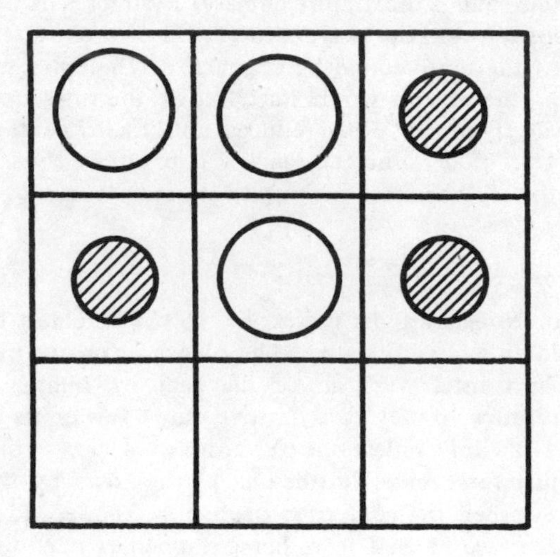

Teeko, or Five-by-Five Ticktacktoe

A Game for Two

A modern variant of "Ticktacktoe with Coins" called Teeko was invented by the American magician John Scarne. It is played on a five-by-five board. Each player takes turns placing four coins. Then each moves in turn one square horizontally, vertically, or diagonally. A player wins by getting his four coins in a square pattern on four adjacent squares or four coins in a horizontal, vertical, or diagonal row.

Nine Men's Morris

A Game for Two

This old English game was known to Shakespeare and has been played by young and old ever since. It is really a variant of "Ticktacktoe." It used to be played in the village green on a pattern like this one scratched in the earth. Nowadays it is played on a board. You can copy this diagram onto a sheet of stiff paper.

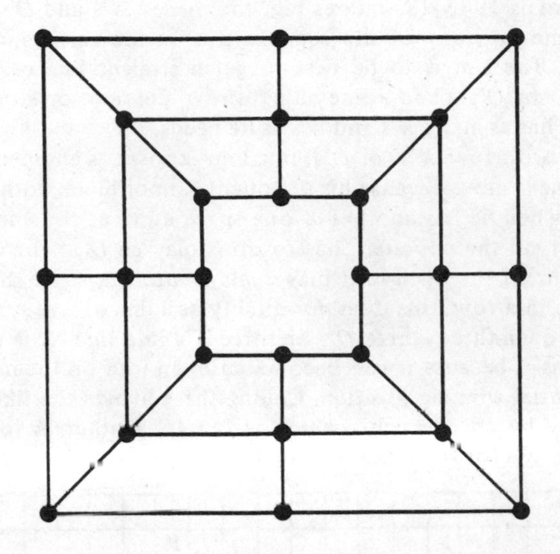

You need eighteen "men," nine black and nine white. Tiddledywink discs in any two colors will do well. Each player has his own color men. Each player in turn puts one man down on one of the 24 dots. He tries to form a three-in-a-row, or *mill* as it is called. A mill must be in a straight line; it cannot bend around a corner. This is a mill:

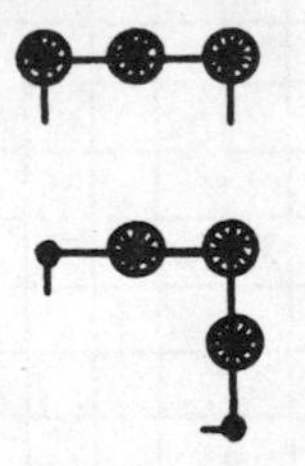

This is not a mill:

A player who has put down a mill can, on that move, remove an opposing man, providing it is not already part of a mill. The loser of the game is the player who loses all his men first. The shape I show here is the commonest form used; but other shapes are possible. In fact, why not invent one of your own?

Peggity

A Game for Two

This is an ancient game of position played on squared paper. It is also known as Peg Five and Spoil Five. Thousands of years ago in China the game went by the name of Go-Moku. It is like the famous Japanese game Go, except that Peggity does not involve capture of enemy pieces and so can be played on paper with pencil.

The board is 19-by-19 squares big; the pieces, *X*'s and *O*'s, are played one at a time into any of the sqaures (not on the corners, as in Go.) *X* moves first. The aim is to be first to get a straight line of exactly five adjacent *X*'s or *O*'s all in a line along a row, column, or either diagonal. Each player has as many *X*'s and *O*'s as he needs.

A player with four *X*'s (or *O*'s) in a line–known as an open-four–must win on his next move because his opponent cannot block both ends in one move. But when he has another *X* one space away at the end of the line (see picture), all the opponent has to do is play an *O* at the other end of the open-four. If the open-four player plays into the space, he gets a line with six *X*'s in a row; this does *not* qualify as a line of five symbols. After forming an open-three–three *O*'s or three *X*'s in a line–it is usual to call "three." This is because it can become an open-four on the next turn and thus a potential winning position. Calling three avoids the likelihood of a player losing by an oversight, which is fun for neither. A joined pair of lines of three *X*'s (or three *O*'s) is called a double-three (see picture).

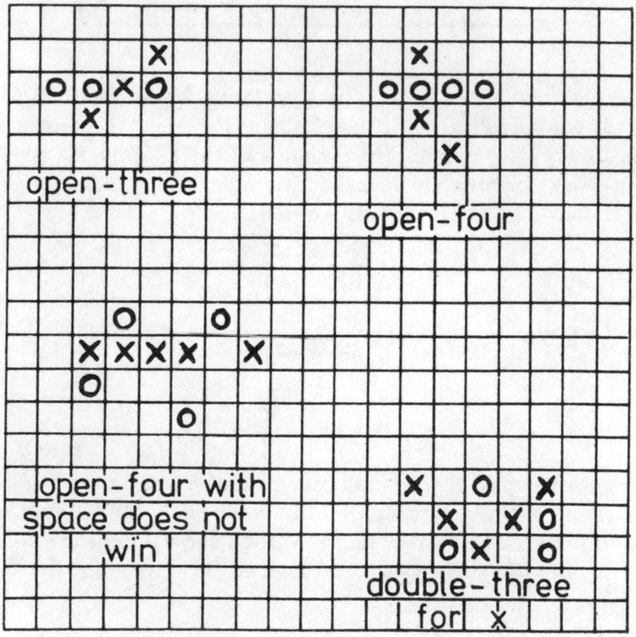

open-three

open-four

open-four with space does not win

double-three for x

Snake
A Game for Two

This game is played on a five-by-six board of dots, like this one. Players take turns at joining two dots by a line to make one long snake. No diagonal lines are allowed. You cannot leave any breaks in the snake. Each player adds to the snake at either end; a player can only add to his opponent's segment, not to his own. The first to make the snake *close* on itself loses. Here is an actual game. In it straight lines began and lost.

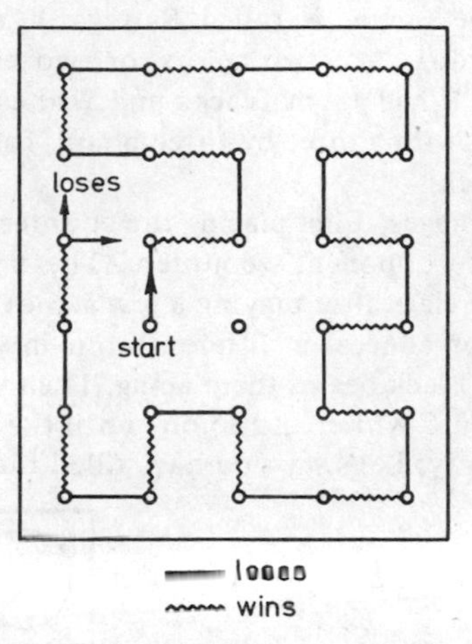

Daisy
A Game for Two

The two players take turns to pluck from the daisy either one petal or two adjacent petals. The player taking the last petal is the winner. This is a game invented by the great puzzlist Sam Loyd.

Make a daisy with 13 petals out of matches, like this. On a postcard mark little circles where the petals (matches) grow from. You need to know whether you have left a space between petals or whether petals are next to each other. The second player can always win—if he knows how. See the answer section for this winning strategy.

Remember you cannot take two petals if there is a space between them. That's why we recommend marking the petals' positions.

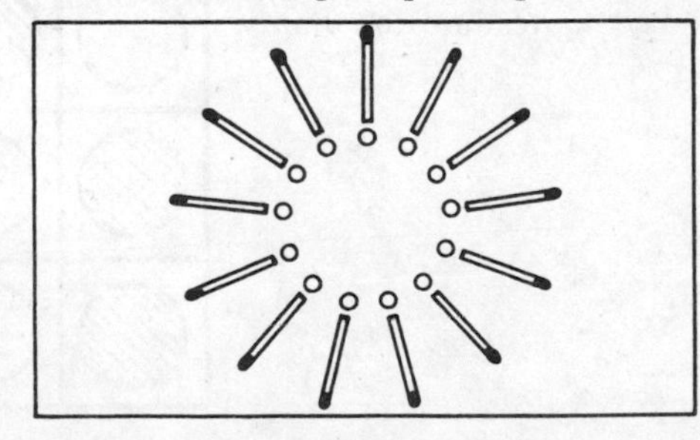

Sipu

A Game for Two

Sipu is an old folk game from the Sudan. It is like "Ticktacktoe," but it is different in two ways: It hasn't got an obvious strategy for not losing, and you can move your *X*'s and *O*'s as counters after they've been put down. It is played on a square board with any odd number of squares along each side; the odd number ensures that there is a center square. (Actually, Sipu is the name of the game played on a five-by-five board. The three-by-three board game, described here, is called Safragat.) You need counters or pebbles, known as "dogs," of two colors, or two kinds of coins (pennies and dimes, say). We'll call them Blacks and Whites. In order to see how play goes, we'll start with a three-by-three board, for which you need four Blacks and four Whites.

Play goes in two stages: First placing the counters and then making the moves and taking the opponent's counters. The best way to place your counters will become clear after playing a few games. To see who starts the placing, toss for it or conceal a different coin in each fist and let your opponent guess. Say Black begins the placing. Then you place the counters in turn—a Black, then a White, and so on—until the board is filled, leaving the center square empty. Let's say you have filled the board like this:

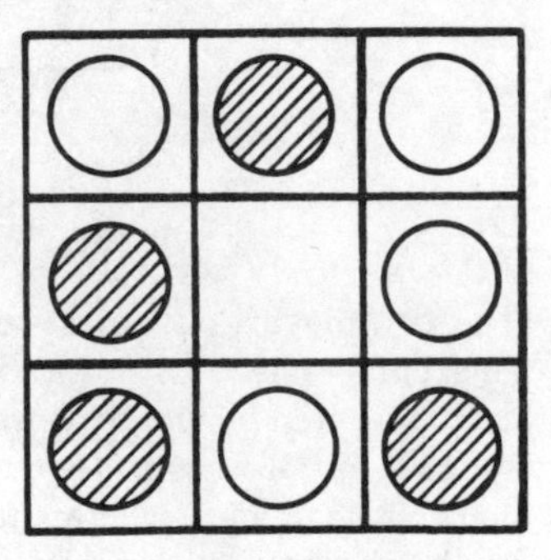

You are ready to begin moving counters. Toss to see who moves first. Let's say it is White's first move. Counters are moved either up or down or side to side, but *not* diagonally. They can only be moved into an empty square.

(1) White (we'll say) moves into the empty center square.

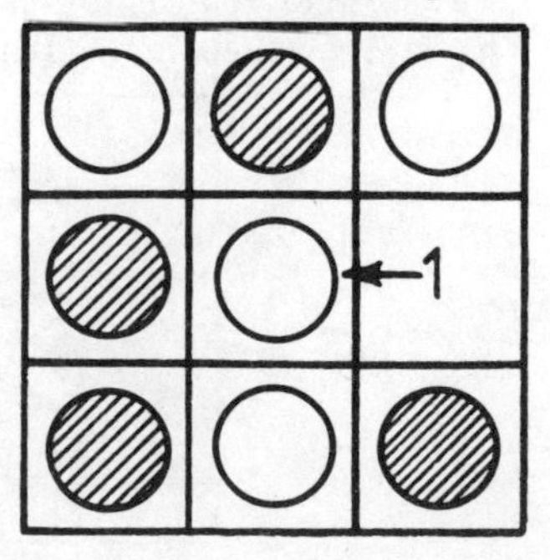

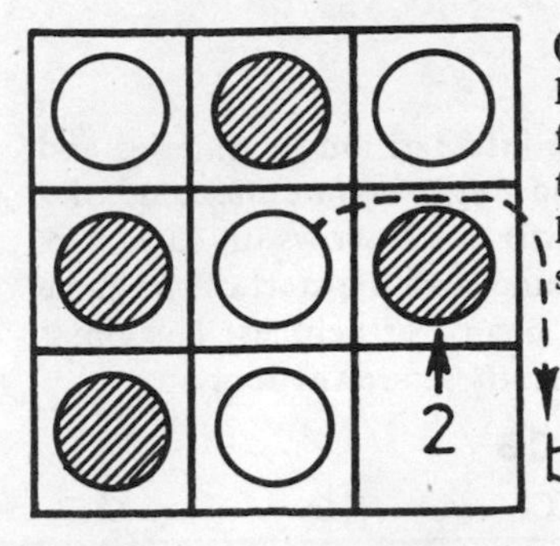

(2) Now Black moves up to the square White has just left empty. In moving, Black has flanked White's coin in a line "trap," along the middle row. Because he made the trap, he can take White's counter on the center square.

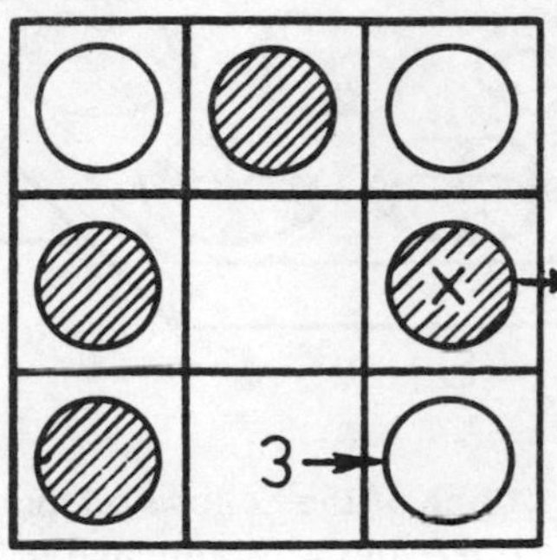

(3) White's next move forms another trap, which allows him to take Black's counter, marked *X* in the picture.

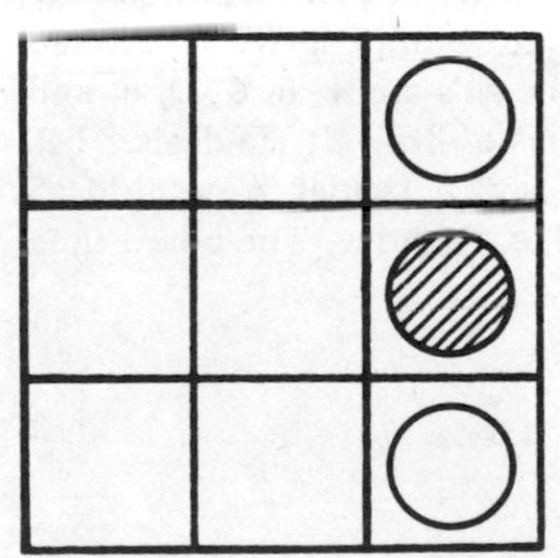

But suppose Black had moved into the trap himself like this: Then he could not have been taken because White hadn't made the trap by moving himself.

The player who traps the most coins is the winner of the game.

NOTE: Consider the starting positions on this board. White can move the center counter in the bottom row up, but Black still would have trapped him on the second move. In this starting position Black cannot move at all. Clearly, a position to be avoided!

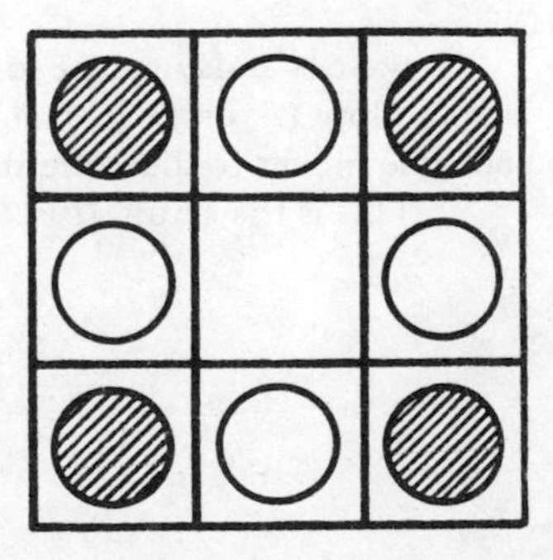

Longer-playing and harder games can be played on a five-by-five board (with 12 players apiece) or even a seven-by-seven board (with 24 players apiece). The same rules apply.

Mancala

A Game for Two

Mancala is an old African game now coming into fashion in America and Europe. Two players—we'll call them Al and Fey—sit on either side of a board, which is usually about a foot long with six hollows on each side. (The hollows can also be scratched in the ground.) At the start of the game each hollow is filled with four stones, balls, beads, or pebbles. The aim is for one player to capture all the others' stones; these are the loot.

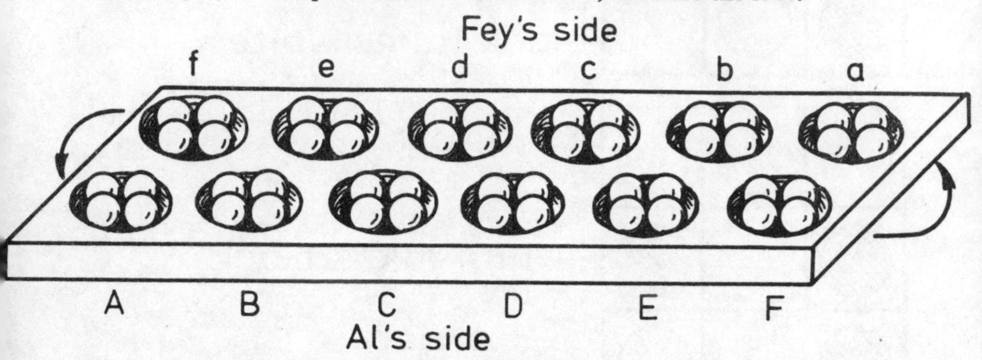

A player moves by taking all the stones out of one of the hollows on his own side and dealing them out in order, *counterclockwise* around the board, 1 stone into each hollow. The players move in turn. We've lettered the hollows simply to show how the game goes. Al's are *A, B, C, D, E,* and *F*; Fey's are *a, b, c, d, e,* and *f.* Say Al empties hollow *E*: He deals 1 ball each in *F, a, b,* and *c.* Then Fey empties, say, *b* (which now holds 5 stones). She deals them out into hollows *c, d, e, f,* and *A.* The board then looks like this:

f	*e*	*d*	*c*	*b*	*a*
5	5	5	6	0	5
5	4	4	4	0	5
A	*B*	*C*	*D*	*E*	*F*

How does a player take loot? By placing the last stone in his opponent's last hollow (*F* or *f*) so that there are 2 or 3 stones there. Here are three possible moves to illustrate the point.

1. This is the setup. It is Al's move.

f	*e*	*d*	*c*	*b*	*a*
1	2	2	3	1	2
0	0	0	0	0	6
A	*B*	*C*	*D*	*E*	*F*

Al moves all 6 stones from *F* (his only move), giving:

```
f e d c b a
2 3 3 4 2 3
0 0 0 0 0 0
A B C D E F
```

Al's last stone went into *f*, which now has 2 stones. He takes these, together with the 3 stones in hollow *e* and the 3 in *d*. His loot does not skip back over *c* to collect *b* and *a*. He wins a total of 8 stones.

2. Here's another setup. Again it is Al's move.

```
f e d c b a
0 2 3 0 3 1
1 0 0 0 7 8
A B C D E F
```

Moving from *F*, Al would win no loot, since his last stone would go in *B*, on his own side of the board. Moving from *E*, he also would win nothing; his last stone would go in *f*, which it must do to collect the loot, but does not result in 2 or 3 stones in that hollow.

3. Empty hollows aren't necessarily safe. Here all but one of the hollows on Al's side are empty. But the game still goes on.

```
 f e d c b a
18 0 0 0 1 0
 0 1 0 0 0 0
 A B C D E F
```

Fey deals from hollow *f*:

```
f e d c b a
0 1 1 1 2 2
2 3 2 2 2 2
A B C D E F
```

The last stone goes in *a*. She takes all the stones from Al's side. Why are there now no stones in *f*? Why didn't Fey put a stone in *f*? Because she took 12 or more stones out of it. When you take 12 or more stones out of a hollow, you skip that hollow when you come to it; thus the twelfth stone in Fey's hand goes in the next hollow. The game ends when the players agree there are not enough stones left to form loot or when a player cannot make a move.

The Crossword Game

A Game for Two to Five

This is such a popular game that though it is not a mathematical game, I have put it in. Each player has his own five-by-five grid. After it is decided who plays first, the first player calls out a letter and writes it in one of the 25 squares on his grid. Each of the other players writes the same letter in some square on his own grid. The next player then calls out a letter—the same or another one—which the other players enter on their grids. Each player must write his letter before the next letter is called. The aim is to form words reading across or down. If you cannot form a word, you can call an "unuseful" letter such as *Z* or *Q* so that nobody else is likely to be able to use it. Only words from an agreed-upon dictionary count, not proper names or slang words. When 25 letters have been called out and each player's grid is filled, scoring begins.

Two-letter words score 2; three-letter words score 3; four-letter, 4; and five-letter, 6 (an extra point). Totals for across and down are added together to get the final score. Highest score wins. Two words in the same row, or column, may not share the same letters. For example, the letters *H-E-A-R-T* score 6 points; whereas *H-E* scores 2 and *A-R-T* scores 3 points, totaling only 5 points. You could not add the two together to make 11. Also you could not score 2 for *H-E* as well as 4 for *H-E-A-R*.

Here is a complete grid with its scores and a grand total of 36.

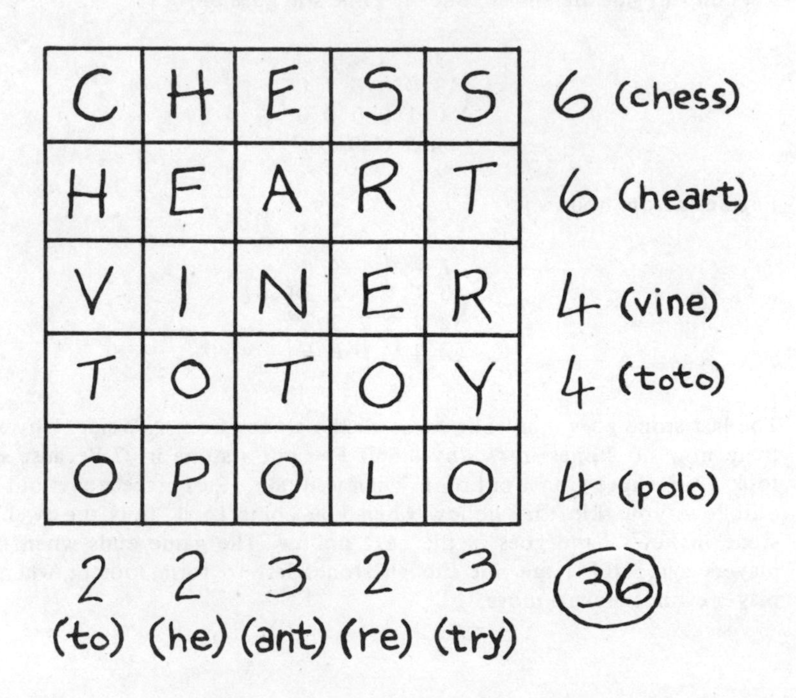

The Cop and the Robber

A Game for Two

Here is a single-board game for two. You can play on the city plan shown here or draw a larger version for yourself.

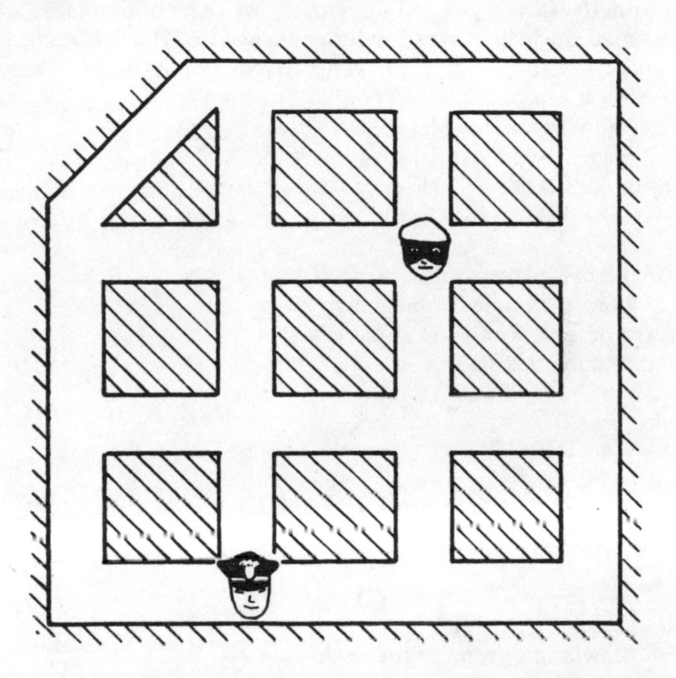

You need two coins, one for the cop, the other for the robber. Start with each coin on its picture. The rules are simple: The cop always moves first. After that, the players take turns to move. You move a coin one block only, left or right, up or down—that is, from one corner to the next. The aim is for the cop to catch the robber, which is done by the cop landing on the robber on his move. To make the game interesting, the cop must catch the robber in 20 moves, or he loses.

HINT: There *is* a way for the cop to nab the robber. The secret lies in the top left corner of the city plan.

Sprouts

A Game for Two

Sprouts is one of the best of the really new paper-and-pencil games. A Cambridge (England) mathematician invented it in the 1960s. Its name comes from the shapes you end up with. It is a game of *topology*, a branch of mathematics which is very briefly explained in "The Bridges of Königsberg" (page 25). Topology is the geometry of floppy rulers, wiggly lines, and stretchy sheets of paper!

This is how Sprouts is played. On a clean sheet of paper begin by drawing three or four spots. We'll work with three spots.

Each of the two players takes turns at joining the spots with lines, which can be as wiggly as you like. You must put a new spot somewhere along that line.

No lines may cross.

X NO

You can draw a line from a spot back onto itself to make a loop—with, of course, a new spot on it.

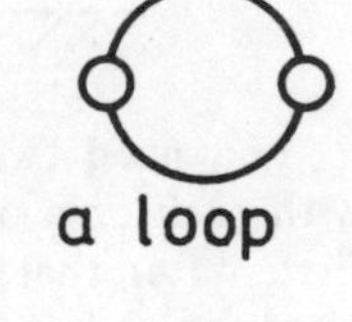

A spot is "dead" when it has three lines leading to it; no more lines can connect to it. To show it is dead, put a stroke through it or shade it in.

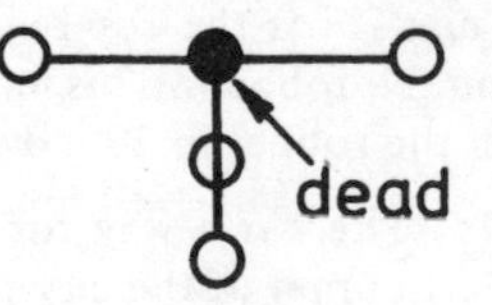

The winner is the one who draws the last line. A good way to win is to trap "live" spots inside loops so that your opponent cannot use them.

Mathematicians have worked out how many moves the game can go on for: The number lies between twice and 3 times the number of spots you start with. Starting with 3 spots, the game can go on for between 6 and 9 moves; with 4 starting spots, between 8 and 12 moves. And so on. But nobody has *proved* this yet!

Here is a sample game. In it player A wins in 7 moves.

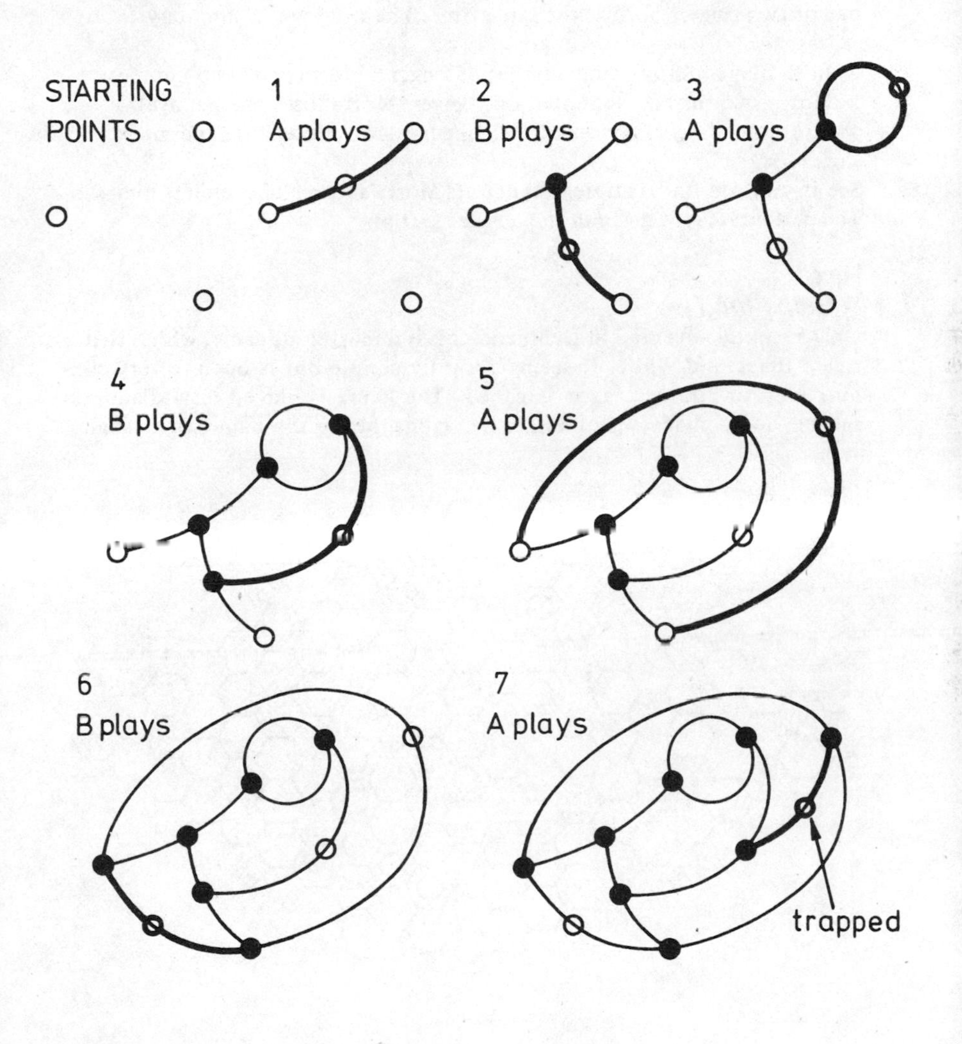

Morra

A Game for Two

This very old finger game comes from Italy. One player is called Morra. On a given signal—a nod of the head, for example—both players put up either one or two fingers both at the same time. The rules are in summary form:

Both players show same number of fingers: Morra wins two pennies
Morra two fingers, opponent one finger: Morra loses one penny
Morra one finger, opponent two fingers: Morra loses three pennies

See if you can find a strategy that cuts Morra's losses or even lets him win. The best strategy is given in the answer section.

Hex

A Game for Two

Only recently invented in Denmark, this is a marvelous game, which is also called Black and White. It seems absurdly simple but is open to very cunning play or *strategy*, as it is called. The game is played on a diamond-shaped board made up of either hexagons, hence the name, or triangles.

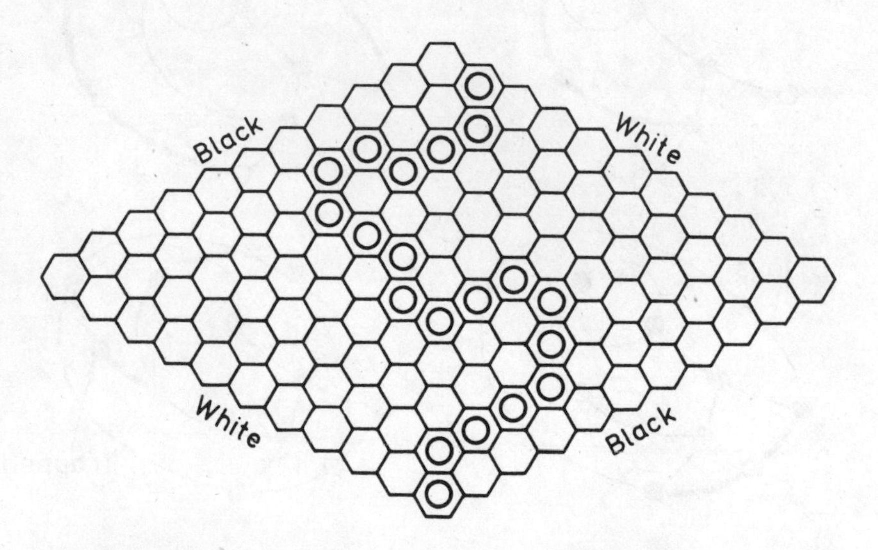

The board usually has 11 hexagons (or triangles) on each side. Two opposite sides of the diamond are Black's side; the other two are White's. The hexagons at the corner of the board belong to either player. The players take turns marking hexagons. White marks his point with a circle, Black with a heavy blob. The aim is to connect opposite sides of the board with an unbroken line of dots or blobs. (On the triangle paper, two dots are adjacent if there is a linking line between them.)

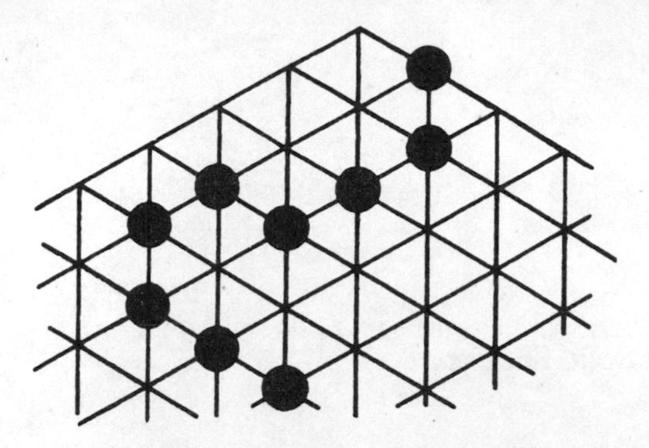

The first player to make an unbroken line is the winner. Two lines cannot cross, so there can never be a draw. Mathematicians have proved that the first player can always win, but they don't say how he is to do so! You can buy special printed paper with a grid of hexagons or triangles printed on it. If you draw up your own board, as here, do so in ink and play in pencil lightly so you can rub out the circles after each game.

To learn some of the strategies of Hex, play a game on a 2-by-2 board with just four hexagons. The player who makes the first move obviously wins. On a 3-by-3 board the first player wins by making his first move in the center of the board. This is because the first player has a double play on both sides of his opening cell, so his opponent has no way to keep him from winning in the next two moves. On a 4-by-4 board (see picture)

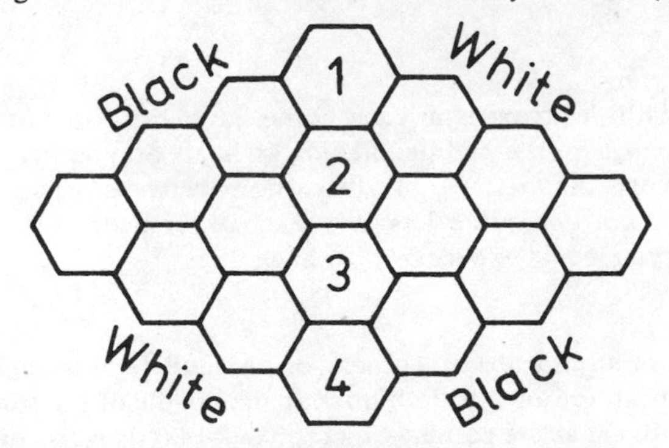

things are more complicated. The first player will win if he plays in one of the four numbered cells, but if he plays in any other cell, he can always be defeated. For an 11-by-11 board, as shown, the play is far too complicated to be analyzed.

ANSWERS

1. Flat and Solid Shapes

Real Estate!
The combined length of the two shorter sides of the triangular plot come to the same as the long side: 230 + 270 = 500. The plot is merely a straight line and covers no land!

Three-Piece Pie
Find the middle of the crustless triangle and make cuts from each corner of the pie to the middle. Otherwise, you could measure the angle of the slice and divide it by 3.

How Many Rectangles?
Nine.

Squaring Up
Seven squares.

Triangle Tripling
Counting the little triangles in each corner gives three lots of 13 plus the big black triangle in the middle, making 40 in all. So you have 1, 4, 13, 40 triangles. Note the pattern of differences between adjacent numbers (4 − 1 = 3, 13 − 4 = 9, 40 − 13 = 27). Each difference is 3 times the previous one—as you would expect from triangles!

The Four Shrubs
Plant three of the shrubs at corners of an equilateral triangle; plant the fourth shrub on top of a little hillock in the middle of the triangle so that all four shrubs are at the corners of a *tetrahedron* (triangular pyramid). See answer to "Triangle Quartet" (page 110).

Triangle Teaser
a. 13, *b.* 27.

Triangle Trickery

Fold the paper over as shown here. The folded flap (its underside showing uppermost) will conceal a third of the triangle's face-up area still flat on the table. It is now only two thirds of the original triangle's face-up area. So you have one third taken from two thirds, leaving one third of the original area. It therefore shows one third of the original triangle.

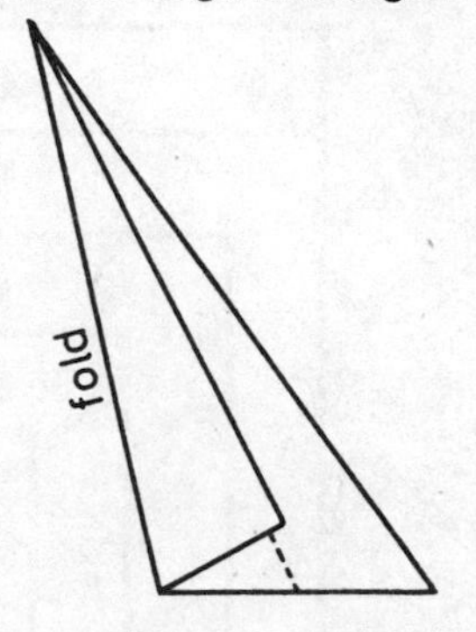

Fold 'n Cut

Two holes.

Four-Square Dance

Seven different ways.

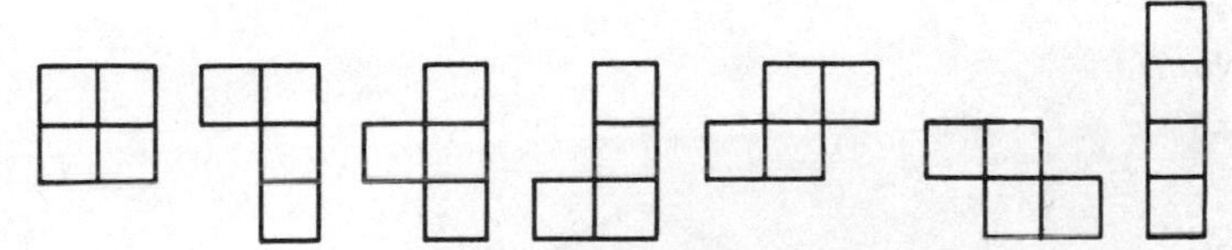

Net for a Cube

There are eleven nets that form a cube. The first six are, perhaps, fairly obvious; the other five you might not have thought of.

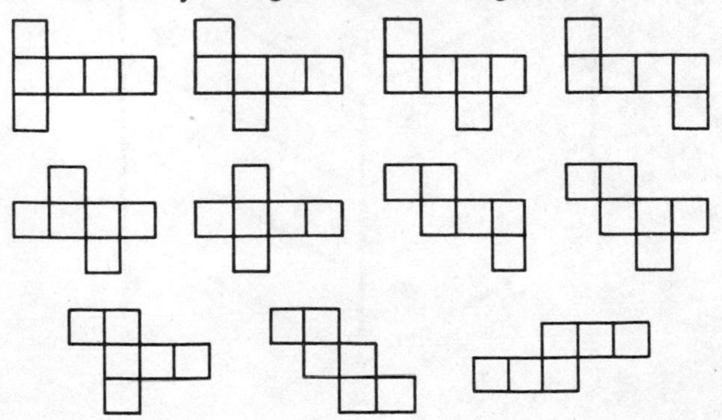

Stamp Stumper

The other ways are: 3 stamps joined side to side in a row, and three other L-shapes, like this ˥, ⌈, and ⌋.

The Four Oaks

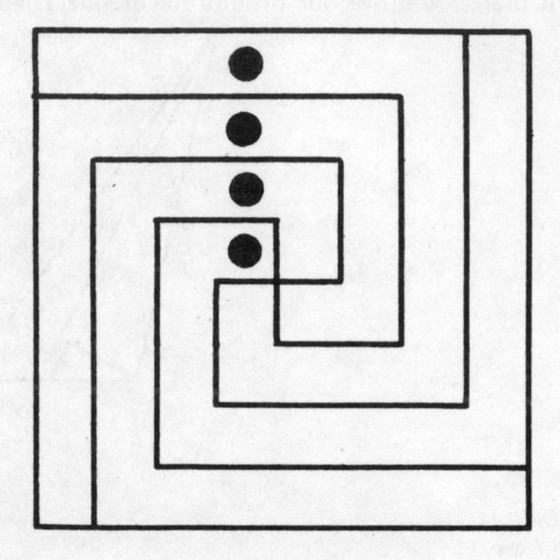

Box the Dots

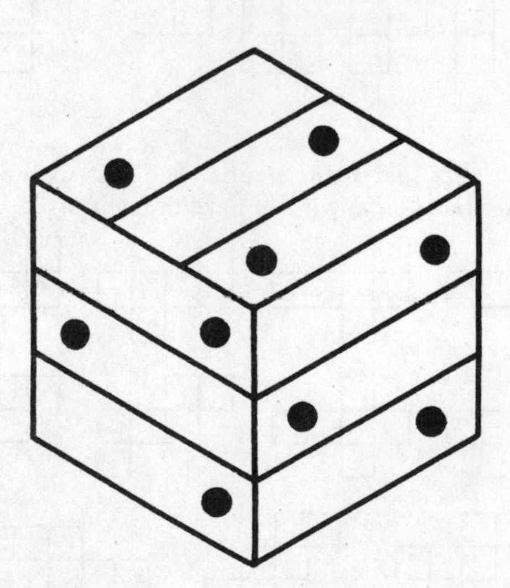

Cake Cutting

16 pieces. The rule is shown by the table. One cut plainly gives two pieces. For two cuts you add 2 to that number to make 4. For three cuts you add 3 to the 4 to make 7. For four cuts you add 4 to the 7 to make 11. When you draw the lines, the third line will cut two lines already drawn; the fourth line cuts three lines already drawn.

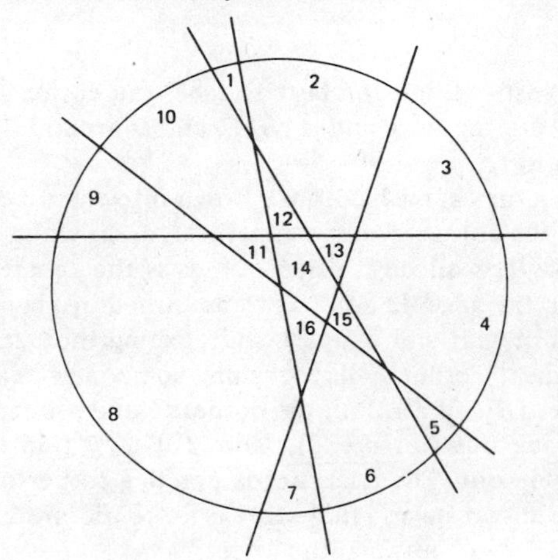

This table shows the number of pieces made by various numbers of cuts.

no. of cuts	no. of pieces
0	1
1	2
2	4
3	7
4	11
5	16

Four-Town Turnpike

The shortest network is made up of two diagonal turnpikes; each is $\sqrt{2}$ times 10 miles long, or 14.14 miles. So the total length of turnpike is 28.28 miles, or about 28.3 miles. The $\sqrt{2}$ comes from Pythagoras's theorem. It shows that with a right-angled triangle (two of which are produced by bisecting a square with a diagonal), where the shorter sides (the sides of the square) are each 1 unit long, the long side opposite the right angle (the diagonal) is $\sqrt{2}$ units long, or the square root of 2 units.

Obstinate Rectangles
In a six-by-seven rectangle, the diagonal cuts 12 squares. Rule: Add the length to the width and subtract 1.

One Over the Eight
1 + 8 jigs = 81. A jig must have 10 squares in it: 1 + (8 X 10) = 81.

Inside-out Collar
To follow these instructions, it's best to label the corner of the tube *a, b, c,* and *d* around the top edge and *A, B, C,* and *D* around the bottom edge, as shown in picture 1.

As shown in picture 2, push corner *c* down into the tube to meet corner *A*; this will pull the corners *b* and *d* together. As shown in black in picture 3, the square *CcdD* is already inside out, as is the square *CcbB.* The triangular part with the edge *Aa* still has to be turned inside out. This is done by pulling the corners *B* and *D* apart and pushing the peak (*a*) of the triangle down to meet corner *c*—like pushing someone's head (*a*) down between their knees (*B* and *D*). Pull the corners *b* and *d* outward to turn the "beak" *BCD* inside out (picture 3). You will now find that as the tube unfolds, it is inside out. The trick needs practice to perform it well: The secret is to do it in two stages—first stage is up to picture 2; second stage is pushing the peak down "between the knees."

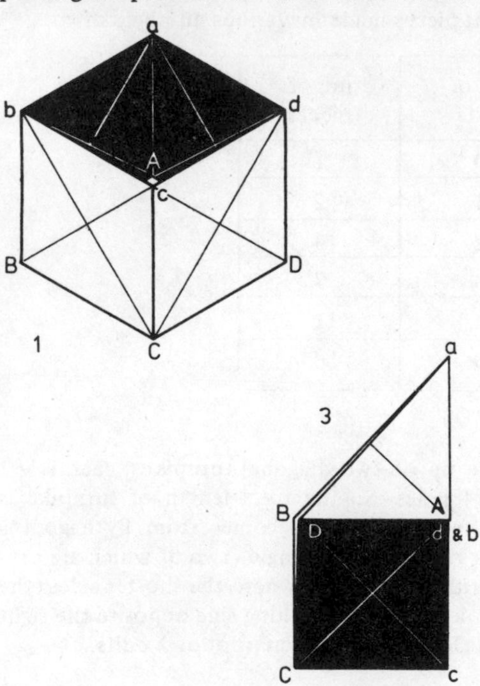

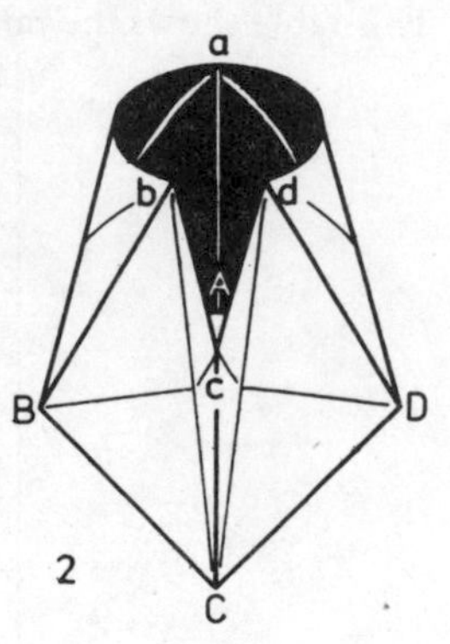

Cocktails for Seven

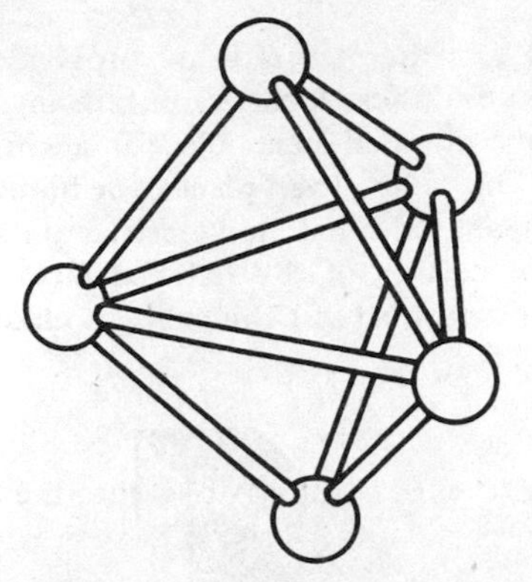

The Carpenter's Colored Cubes

He cut the cube into eight equal blocks, as shown.

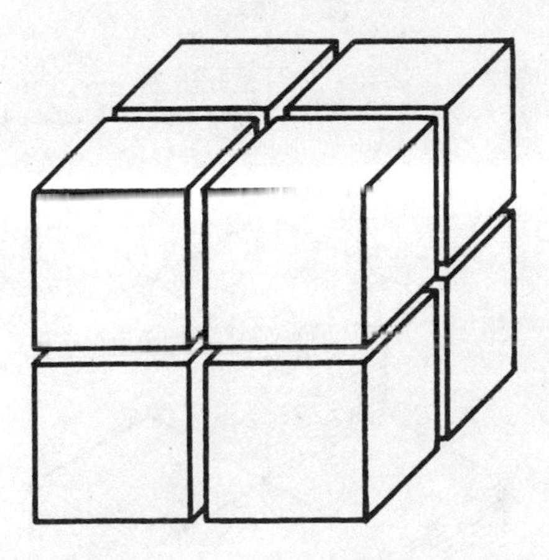

Painted Blocks

18 faces are painted, as shown.

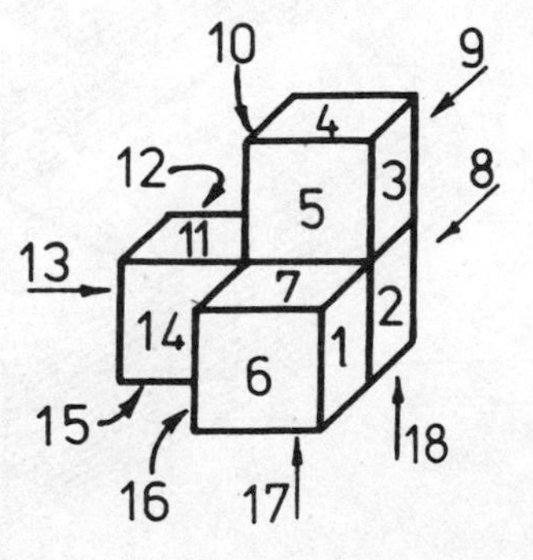

Instant Insanity

Take the cube marked 1 in the picture in the problem; it has three dotted faces. Place it so that two of these faces are not on any of the long sides of the rod. Next, take cube number 2 and place it so that the four different colors of it are on the long sides. Then place cube number 3 so that one of its white faces is hidden and both hatched faces are on the long sides. Place cube number 4 so that neither of the hatched faces appear on the long sides. All you have to do now is twist the cubes around the rod's axis until the solution shows up.

The Steinhaus Cube

Start building your cube by making this stepped shape. The rest should fit together easily.

How Large Is the Cube?

The surface area of the cube is 6 times the area of one of its six faces. Suppose the cube has an edge x inches. One of its faces has an area of x^2 square inches. So its total surface area is $6x^2$ square inches. But this must be equal in number to its volume or $x \times x \times x = x^3$ cubic inches. So $6x^2 = x^3$, which means $6 = x$. So the cube has a side of 6 inches.

If this reasoning is too hard to follow, go from the equation $6x^2 = x^3$ and then try $x = 1$, $x = 2$, and so on.

Plato's Cubes

The problem calls for a number which when multiplied by itself twice over gives a square number. This works with any number that is itself already a square. The smallest square (aside from 1) is 4; so the huge block might have $4 \times 4 \times 4$, or 64, cubes in it, and this would stand on a 8×8 square. The picture suggests that a side of the plaza is twice the extent of a side of the block. So this is the correct answer. The next size for the cube is $9 \times 9 \times 9 = 729$; this cube would be standing on a 27×27 square, which, according to the picture, is too large.

The Half-full Barrel

All they had to do was tilt the barrel on its bottom rim. Say the barrel was exactly half full. Then when the water is *just* about to pour out, the water level at the bottom of the barrel should just cover all the rim. That way half the barrel is full of water; the other half is air space.

Cake-Tin Puzzle

10 inches square—that is, twice the radius.

Animal Cubes

27 cubes in each animal. Both volumes are 27 cubic centimeters. Areas: dinosaur 90, gorilla 86.

Spider and Fly

Six shortest ways; each goes along only three sides. A typical way is shown by the solid lines on the cube here.

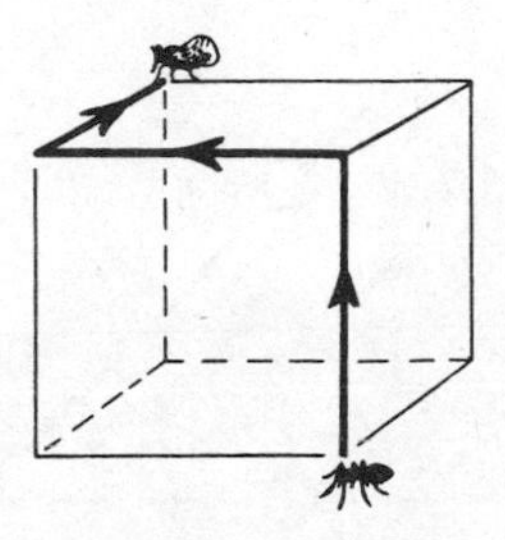

The Sly Slant Line
5 inches. The slant line must be the same length as the radius because it is one of the two equal diagonals in the rectangle.

2. Routes, Knots, and Topology

In-to-out Fly Paths
He can for shapes with an odd number of sides—the triangle, the pentagon, and the seven-sided shape (heptagon). As he begins inside, he has to cross an odd number of sides in order to end up outside.

In-to-in Fly Paths
He can for shapes with an even number of sides—the square, the hexagon, and so on.

ABC Maze
Out at *A* only, because an odd number of paths (5) lead to *A*. An even number of paths lead to *B*, or to *C*; so you cannot leave by them.

Eternal Triangle?

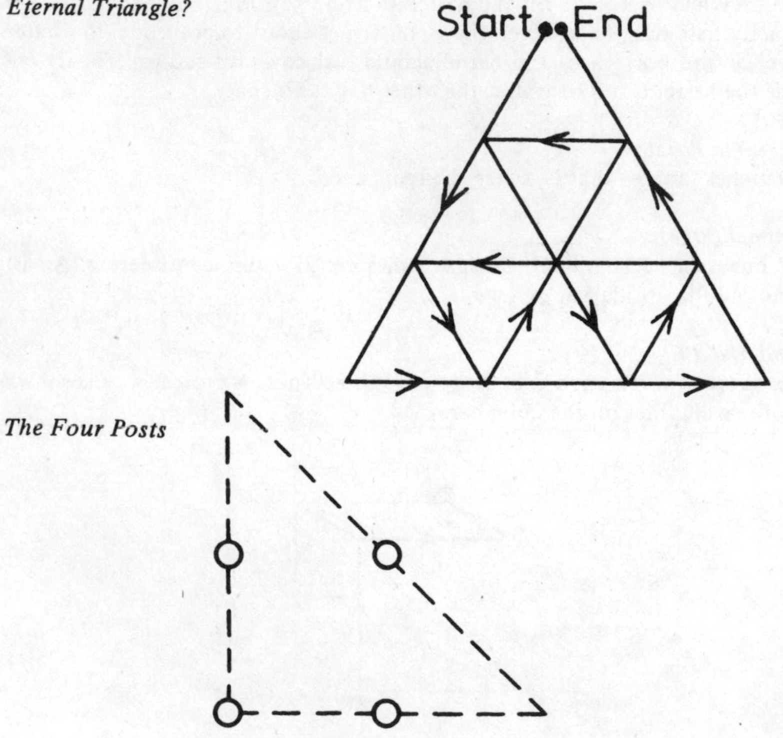

The Four Posts

The Nine Trees

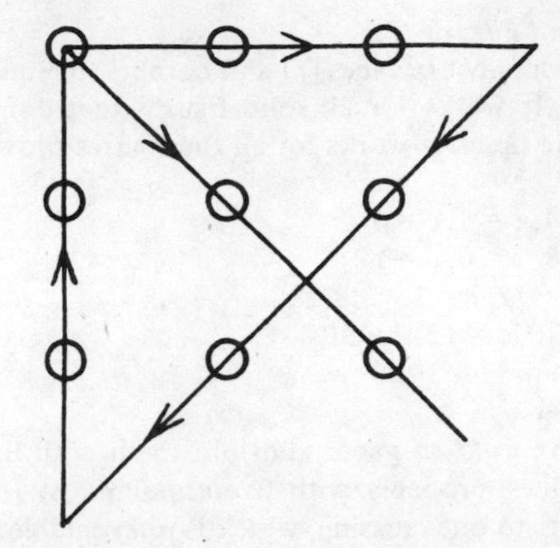

Salesman's Round Trip
Shortest route is *ACDBA*, which comes to 8 + 6 + 6 + 7 = 27 miles.

Swiss Race
Clear roadblock on road *AC*; then take route *ACDE*, which is 11 miles.

Get Through the Mozmaze
He can escape with 37 bites.

Space-Station Map
As Sam Loyd said, the more than fifty thousand readers who reported "there is no possible way" had all solved the puzzle! For that is the sentence that makes a round-trip tour of the space stations. (Actually Loyd used canals on Mars, not space stations.)

Round-Trip Flight
The sketch is:

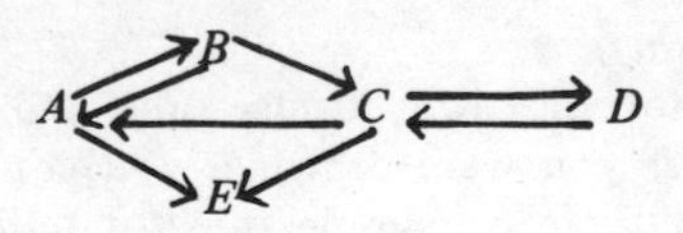

There is only one way from Albany (*A*) to Detroit (*D*) and return. El Paso is the "trap":

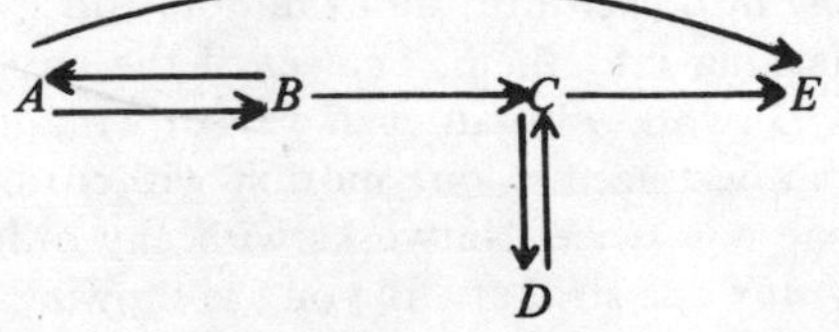

Faces, Corners, and Edges
Euler's rule is the number of faces (f) and corners (c) equals the number of edges (e) plus 2. It works for all solid figures that don't "bulge in" and don't have holes in them. It works for all the figures shown.

Tetrahedron: $f = 4, c = 4, e = 6$
Octahedron: $f = 8, c = 6, e = 12$
Dodecahedron: $f = 12, c = 18, e = 28$
Icosahedron: $f = 20, c = 12, e = 30$

Five City Freeways
Ten roads. Put five dots on paper and join them with lines for the roads. You'll need ten lines, probably with five crossings. By redrawing, you can reduce this number to one crossing, which is unavoidable.

The Bickering Neighbors

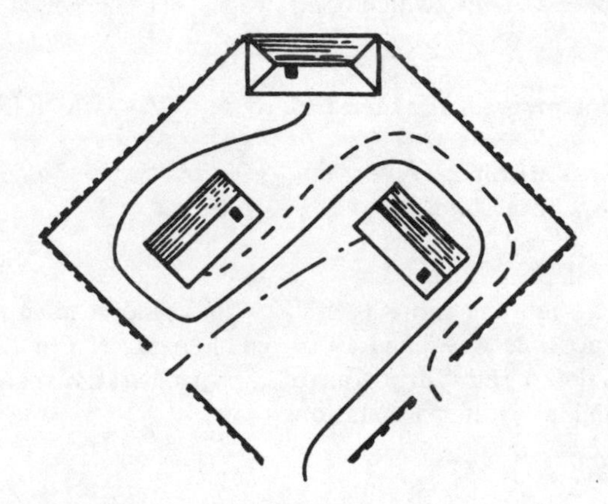

The Bridges of Königsberg
No, it is impossible to cross every bridge once and only once in a single stroll. Such a stroll, if you were drawing, you could call a *one-stroker.* Euler discovered that there's a simple rule for telling whether or not a route is a one-stroker. First draw the *network,* as he did for Königsberg; this cuts out all fiddly details that don't matter. Then count the number of roads (lines) leading into each dot. Call the dots *odd* if they have an odd number of lines leading into them, or *even* if the number is even. Euler found this rule: A network with all even dots or with just two odd dots is a one-stroker; it can be traced in one motion without lifting the pencil or going over the same line twice. Networks with any other number of odd dots are definitely *not* one-strokers. If you are showing somebody how to trace a network with two odd dots, be sure to begin at one of the odd dots.

Euler's Bridges

Odd number of bridges rule: The number of times you touch the north bank (call it N) equals half of 1 more than the number of bridges (b). Or in letters: $N = (b + 1)/2$.

Even number of bridges rule: Here the number of "norths" is 1 more than half the number of bridges, or $N = 1 + b/2$.

Mathematical note: To arrive at these formulas, you have to guess and juggle a bit. Note, however, that in the "odd" formula you halve (b + 1); in the "even" formula, on the other hand, you only halve b, which is obviously possible because b is even.

Möbius Band

Cut it down the middle and it falls into just *one* single band—an ordinary twisted collar. By cutting, you have added an edge and a face. Cut a third in, and you get one twisted collar and one smaller Möbius band linked to it.

Double Möbius Band

Open it out and you see it is actually one large band.

Release the Prisoners

You can get away from your friend by slipping the rope loop over one of your hands and then back under one of the loops around his wrist, as shown here.

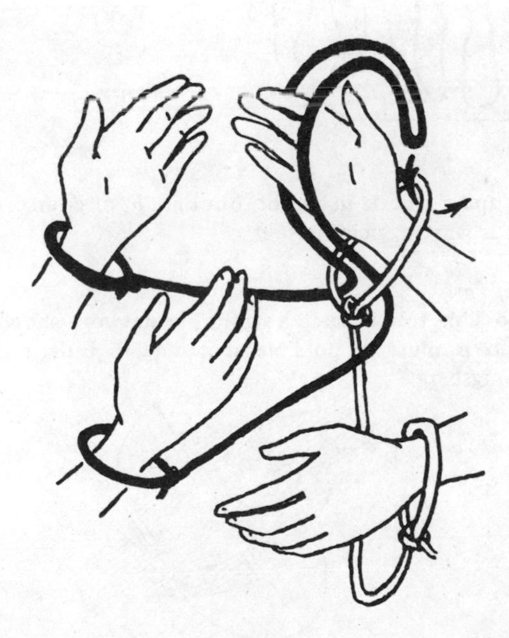

Three-Ring Rope Trick

Wedding Knots

Here are three different ways of joining the straws to make one single closed loop: There are many more ways.

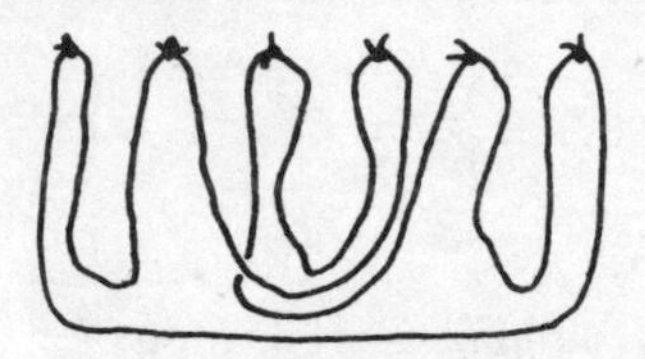

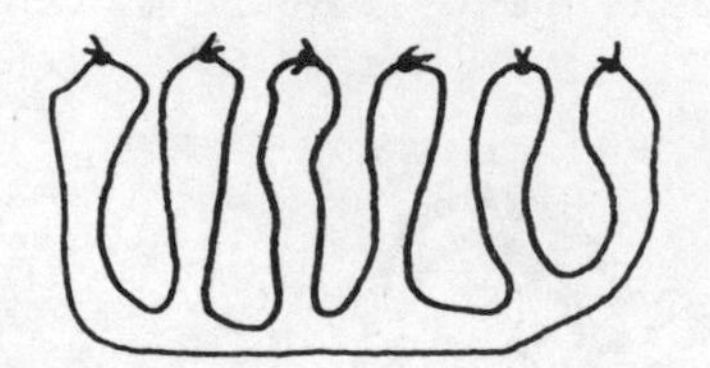

Tied in Knots?

Ropes *a, d, e,* and *g* will tie in a knot. But knot *h,* of course, does not tie in a knot, which is why magicians use it!

The Bridges of Paris

Yes, it was possible to take such a stroll. The network shown here has two odd points, so it must be possible according to Euler's rule. See "The Bridges of Königsberg."

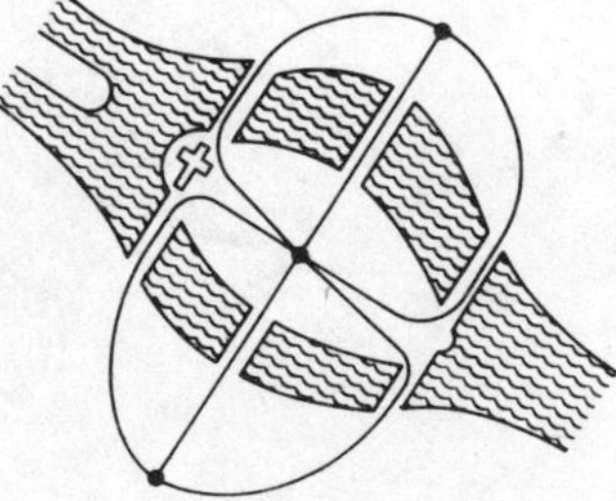

Tour of the Castle
These problems are obviously related to "Euler's Bridges." But to find a general rule is not so obvious! To find one, you have first to draw networks as Euler did in "The Bridges of Königsberg." The answers are: (*1a*) yes, (*1b*) no, (*1c*) yes, (*2a*) no, (*2b*) yes, (*2c*) no, and (*2d*) yes.

The Cuban Gunrunners Problem
Blow up bridges *a*, *c*, and *d*.

3. Vanishing-Line and Vanishing-Square Puzzles

Mr. Mad and the Mandarins
The oranges on the plate of the absent child "vanished." But, actually, each remaining plate of mandarins has gotten one more. It's just the same as saying four lots of three is the same as three lots of four. Or, as part of your multiplication tables, 4 X 3 = 3 X 4.

4. Match Puzzles

Squares from 24 Matches
(*a*) One extra square in two ways

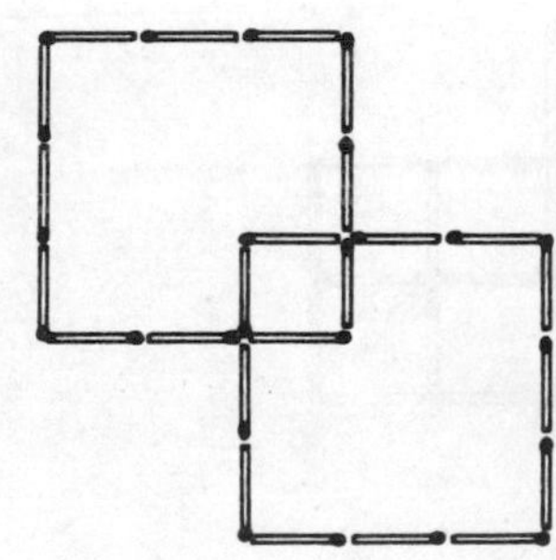

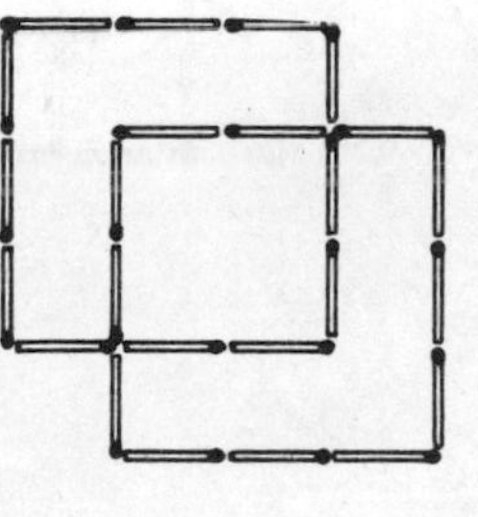

(*b*) Four extra squares–seven in all

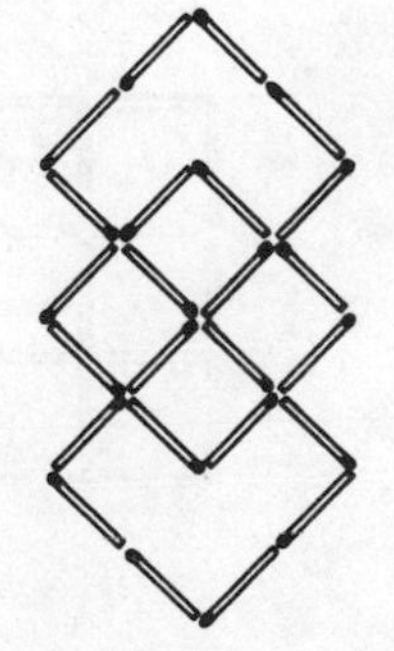

(*c*) Seven squares

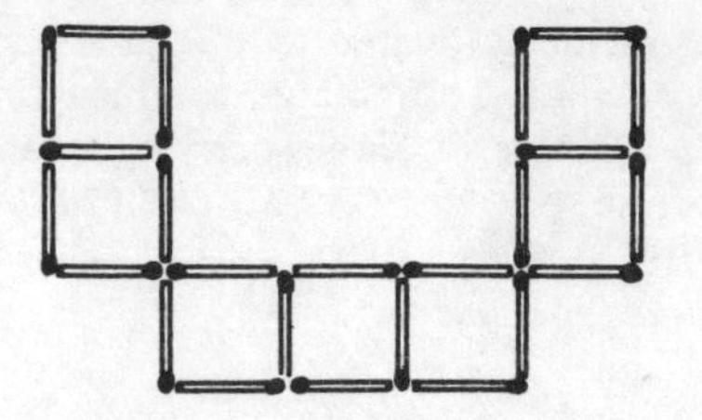

Eight squares with one extra, larger square

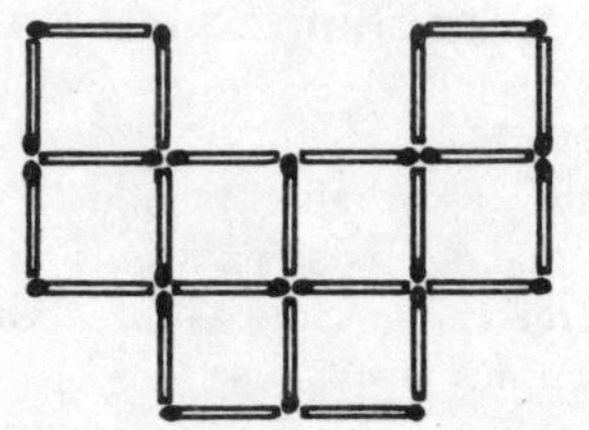

Eight squares with two extra, larger squares

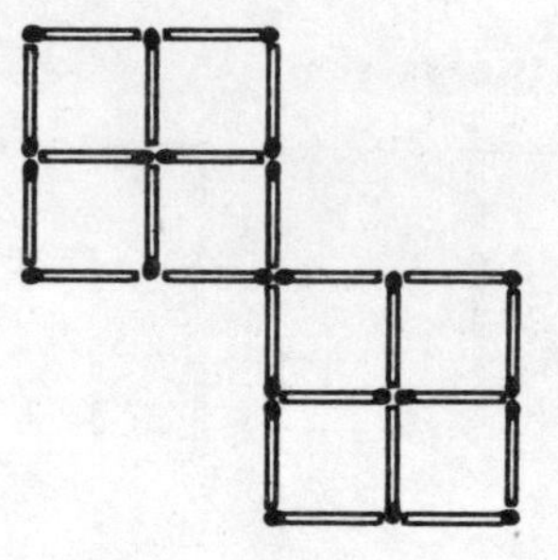

Nine squares with five extra squares

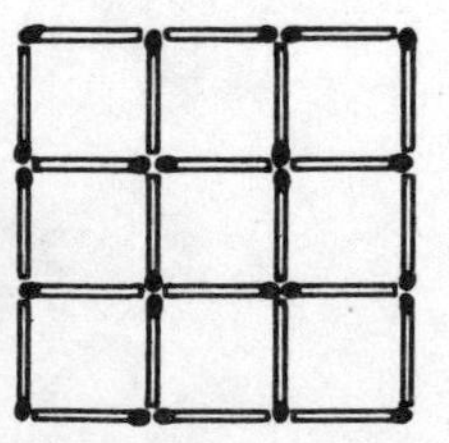

Half-Match Squares
Yes. Four larger squares.

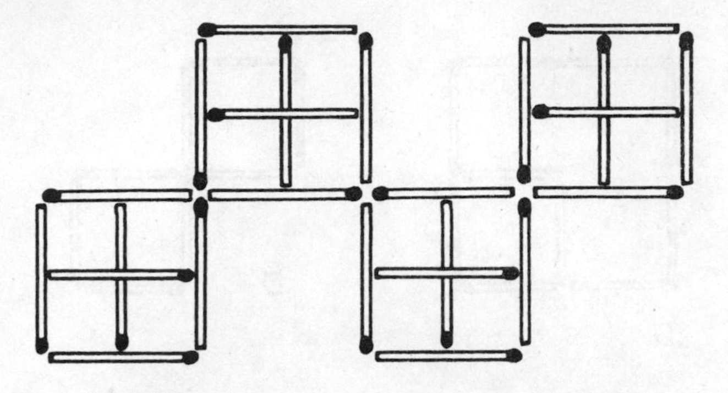

Third-Match Squares
Yes. Fifteen larger squares.

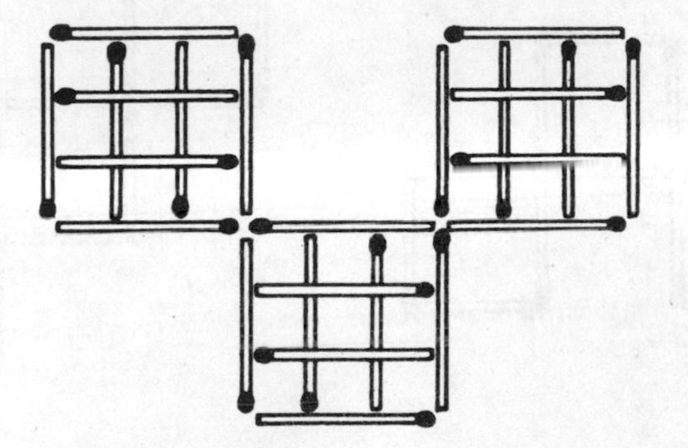

Fifth-Match Squares
Yes. 60 larger squares.

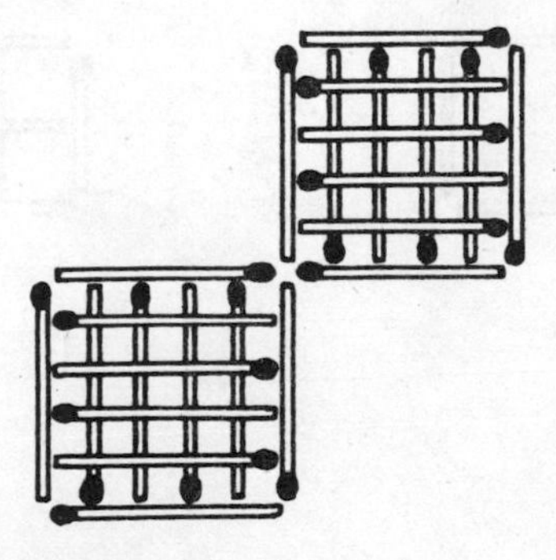

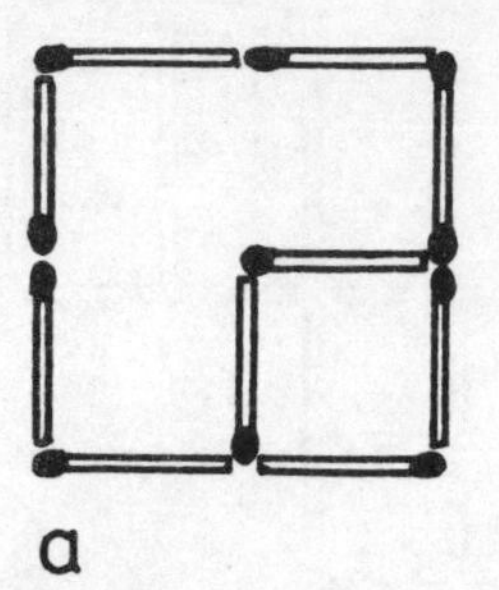

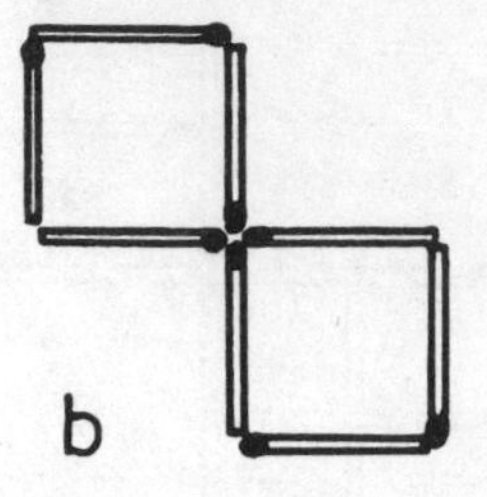

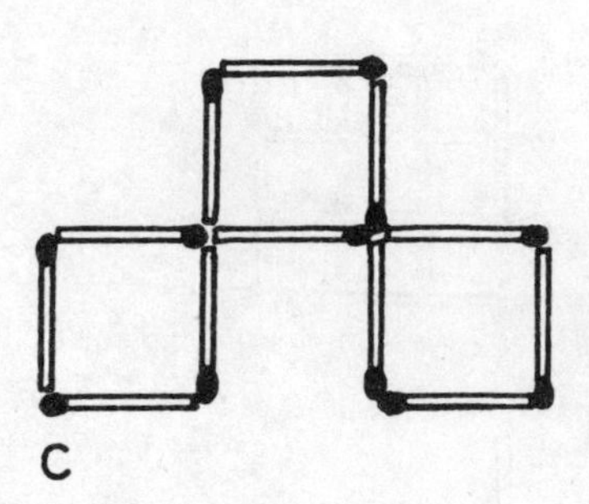

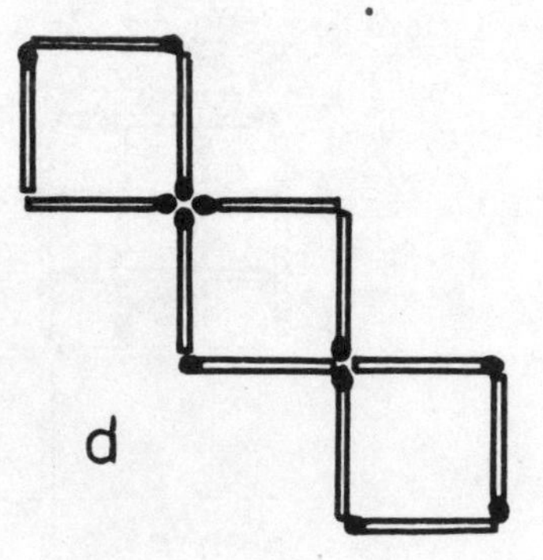

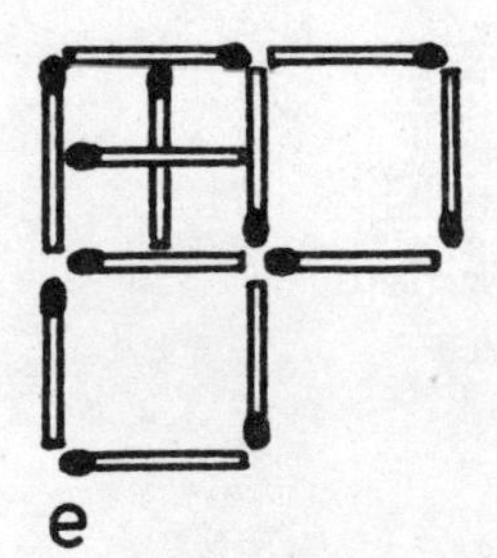

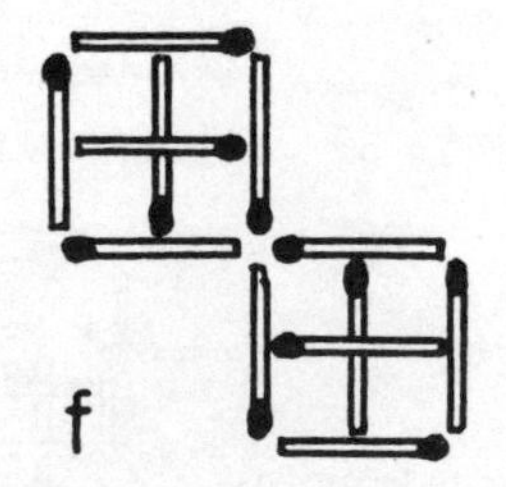

Move-or-Remove Puzzles II

(*a*) Remove the 12 matches inside the large square, and use them to make another large square.

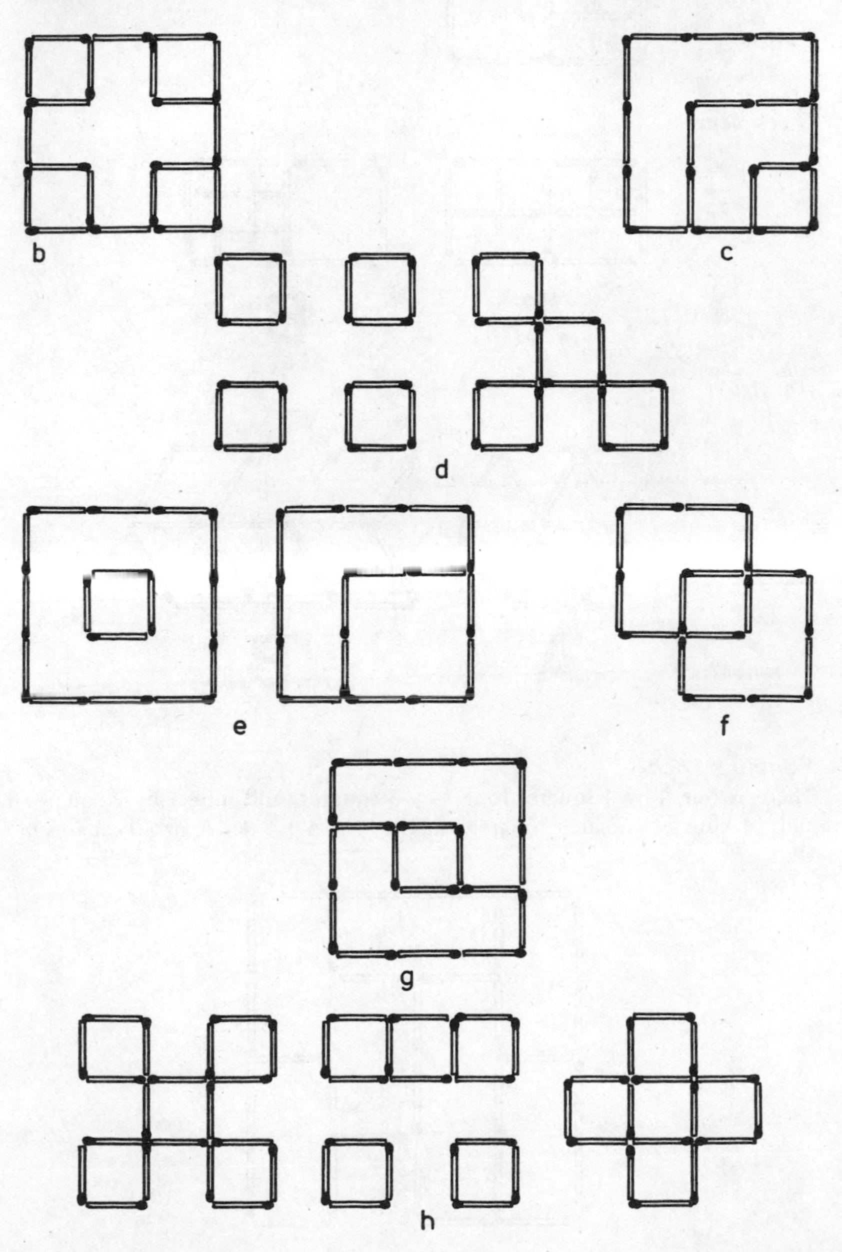

Windows

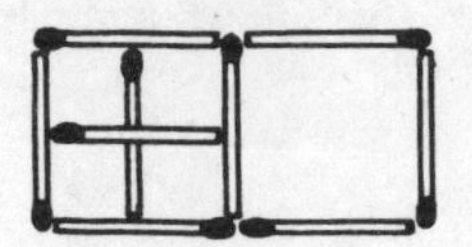

Greek Temple

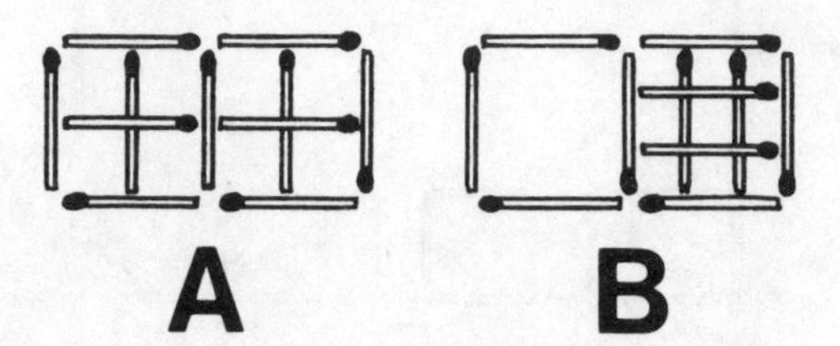

An Arrow

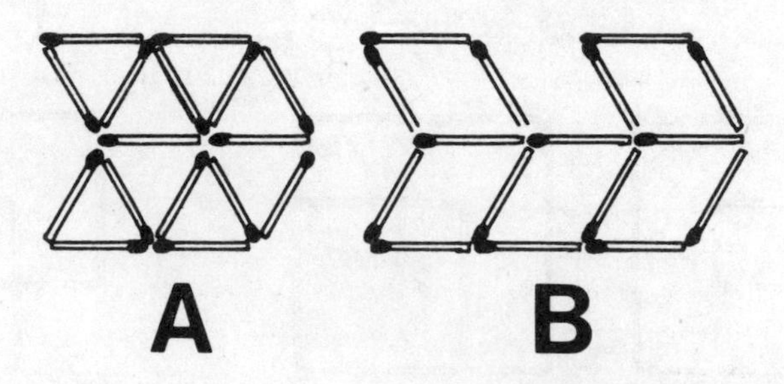

Vanishing Trick

There is one 4-by-4 square, four 3-by-3 squares, and nine 2-by-2 squares, and, of course, 16 small squares, making 1 + 4 + 9 + 16, or 30 squares in all.

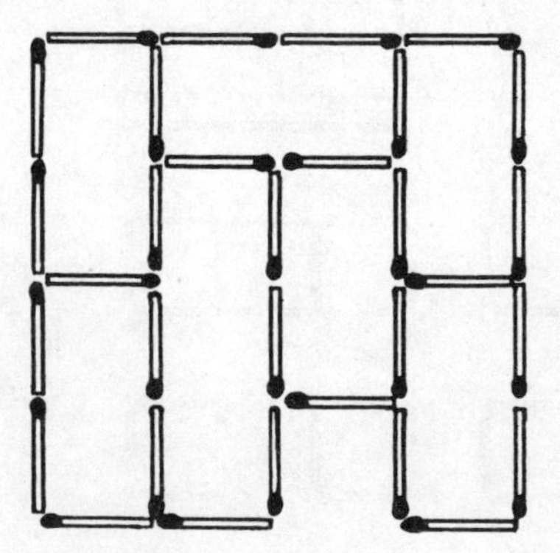

Take Two

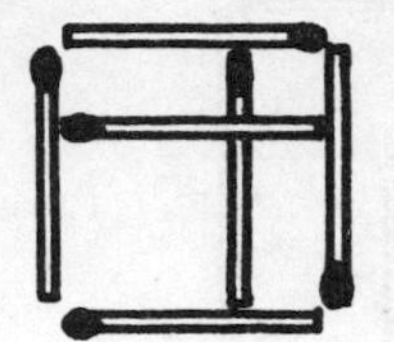

Six Triangles

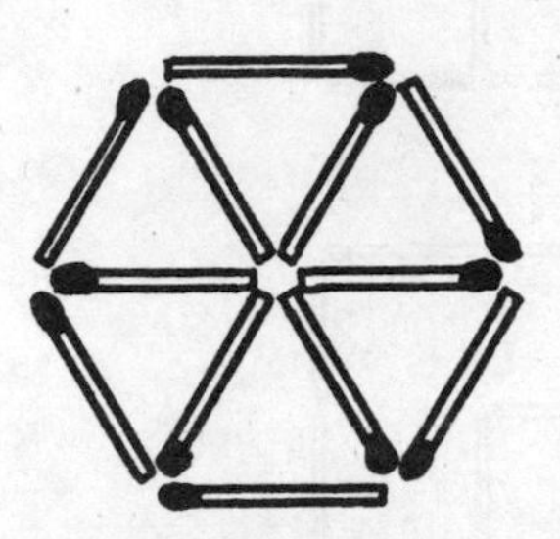

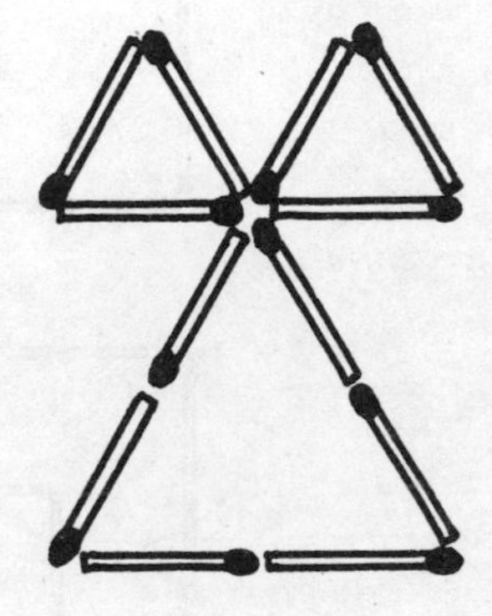

Squares and Diamonds

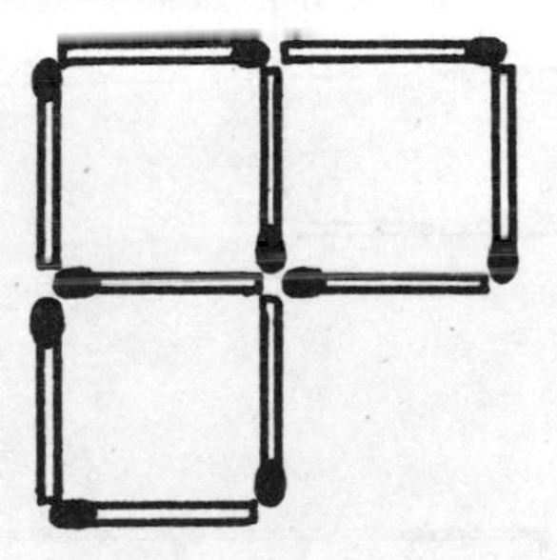

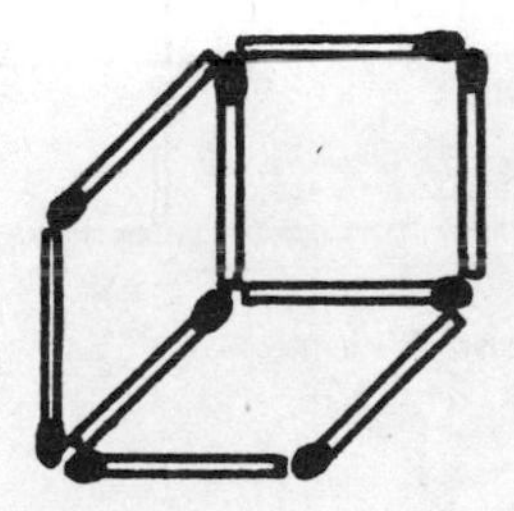

Stars and Squares

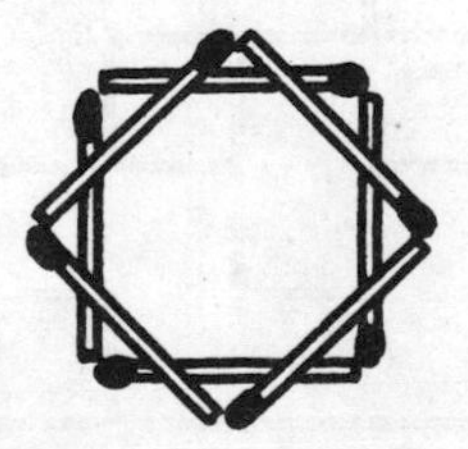

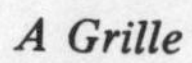
A Grille

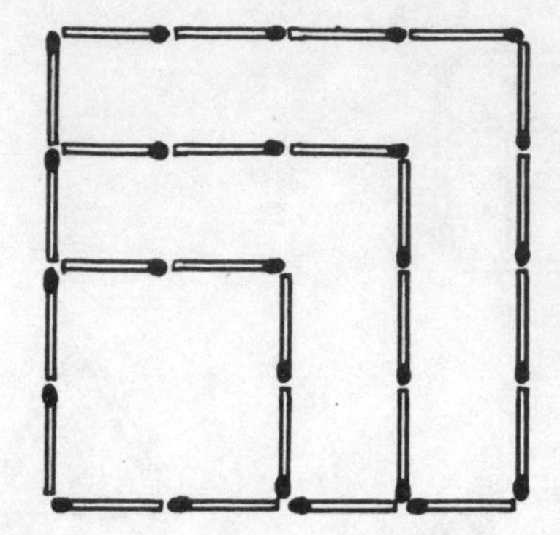

The Five Corrals

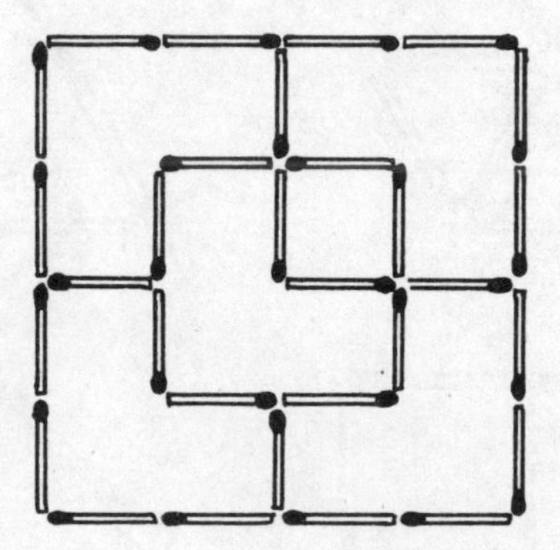

Patio and Well

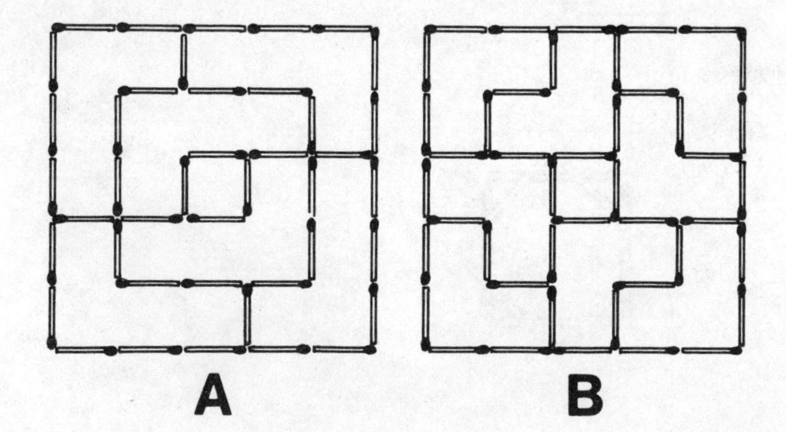

Four Equal Plots

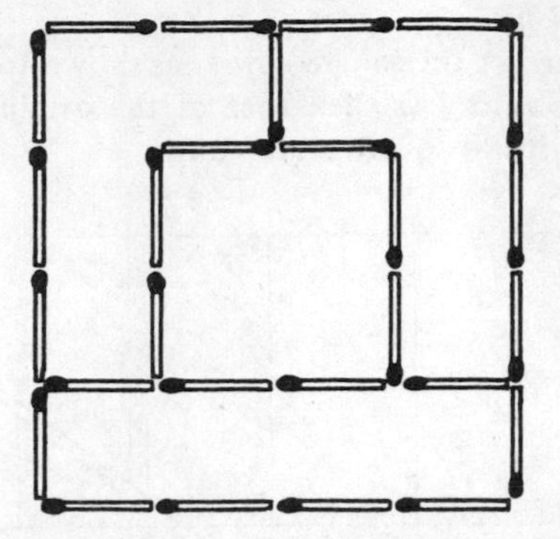

Get Across the Pool

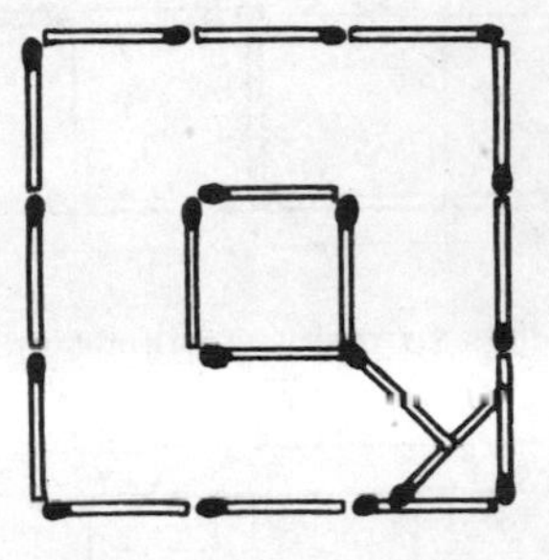

Spiral into Squares

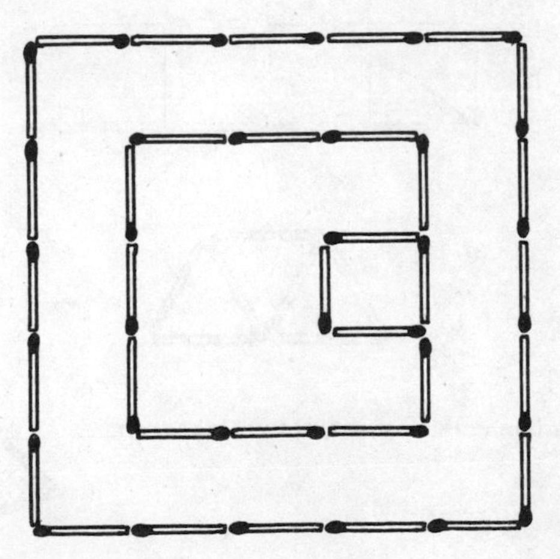

More Triangle Trickery

(*a*) Move 3 matches in the square corner as shown to form a step. Its area is 2 square match units less than that of the original triangle (6 square match units); thus, it is 4 square match units.

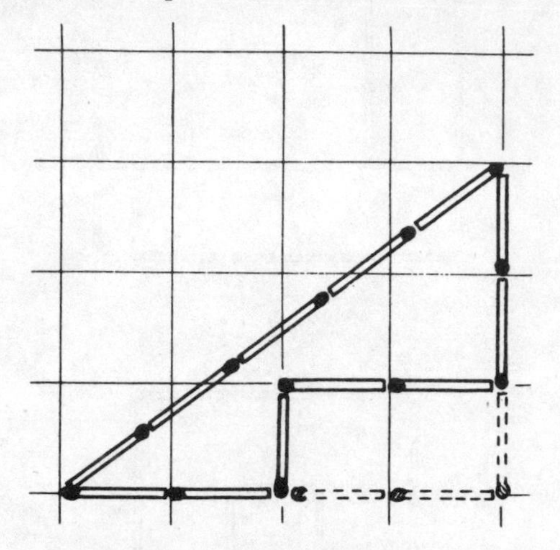

(*b*) Move 2 more matches to make another step. Its area is then 3 square match units less—that is, its area is 3 square match units.

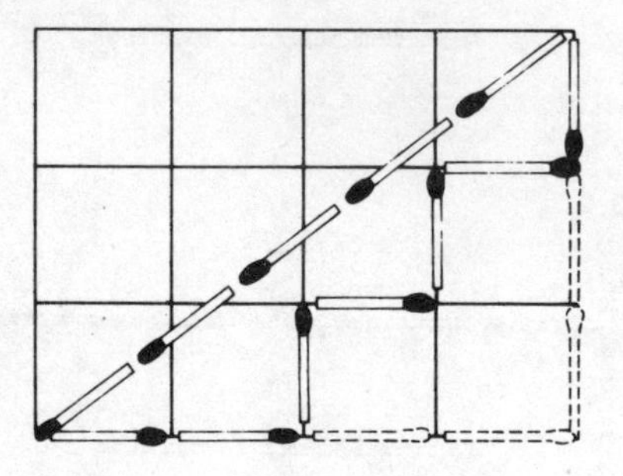

Triangle Trio

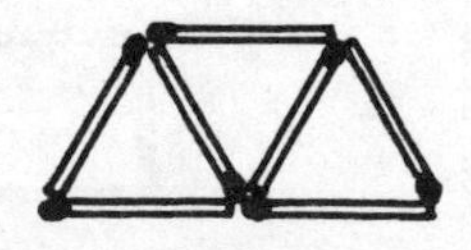

Triangle Quartet

The answer is a triangular pyramid, a *tetrahedron*.

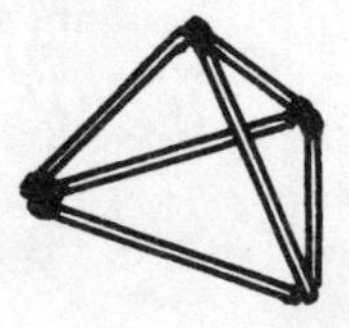

3 Times the Area

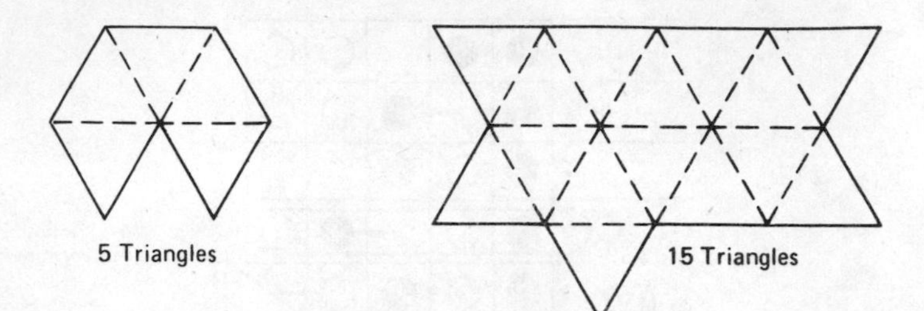

Cherry in the Glass
Slide one match across and move the other like this:

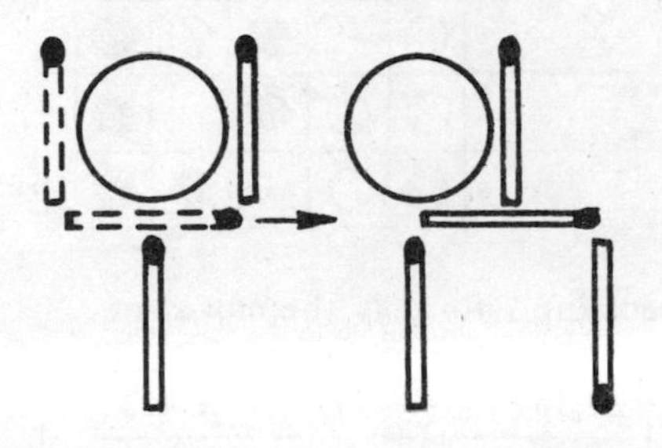

5. Coin and Shunting Problems

Coin Sorting in Pairs
We have numbered the coins to explain the answer. The coins can be regrouped in three moves: Move coins 1 and 2 two places to the left. Fill the gap by 4 and 5. Jump 5 and 3 over to the far left.

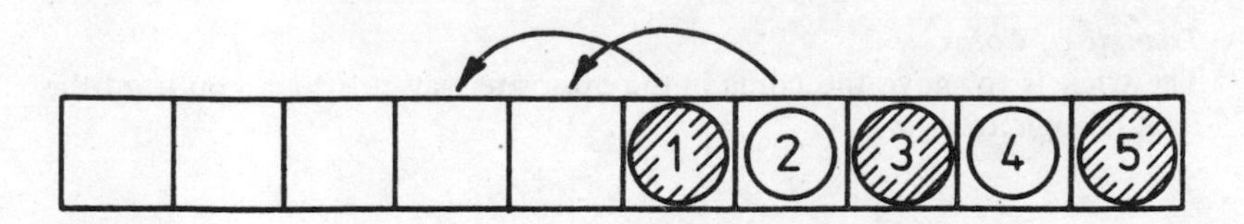

Rats in a Tunnel
The eight moves are as shown. There are two general rules: (1) Shift a coin forward into a free space, then jump another coin over the coin just shifted. (2) Always make shifts or jumps into the center of the tunnel first *before* making jumps or shifts away from it.

A wrong move 3 is shown to indicate how you can get blocked. The rats should end up exactly exchanged and not with two spaces between each of the black rats or each of the white ones.

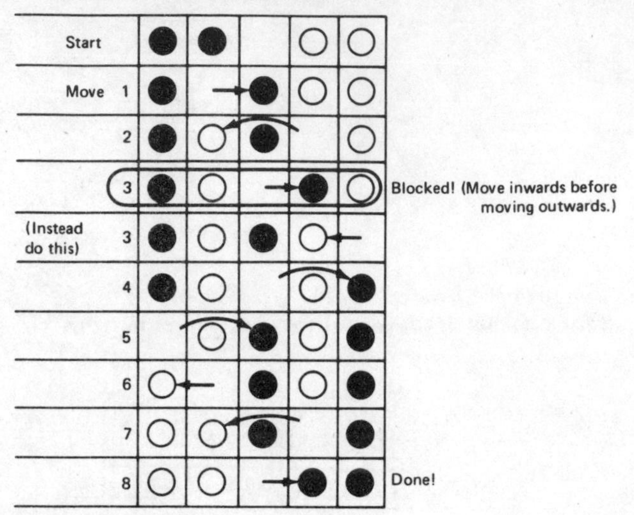

Three-Coin Trick

(*a*) Using *H* for heads and *T* for tails, the moves are:

Begin	*T*	*H*	*T*
Move 1	*H*	*T*	*T*
Move 2	*H*	*H*	*H*

Done!

(*b*) No, it cannot be done. Each move is not going to alter whether there is an even or an odd number of tails (or heads). As you see above, at each stage there is always an odd number of heads and an even number of tails. So you cannot get three tails because 3 is an odd number.

Triangle of Coins

The trick is to move the coins in the opposite way to which you want the final triangle to point.

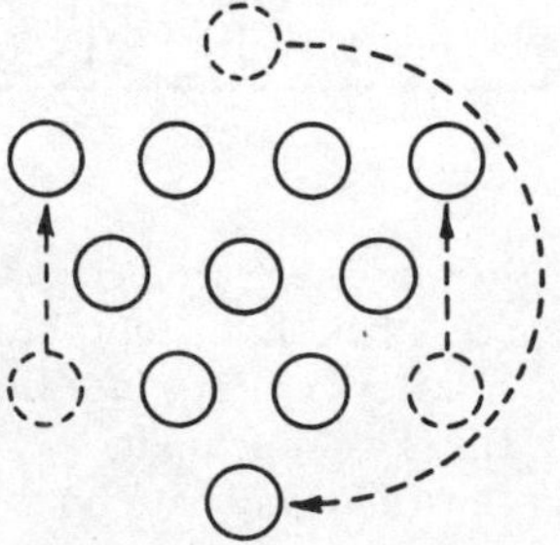

Five-Coin Trick

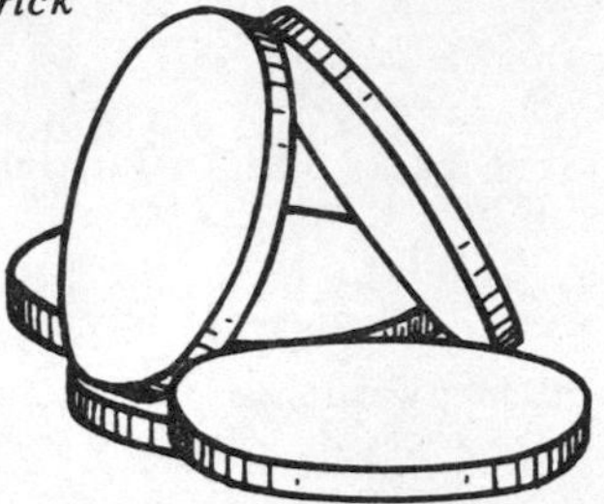

Five-Coin Puzzle

The general plan is as follows. You can shorten the number of moves but this description is easy to remember.

Slide all five coins around clockwise till the half-dollar is in the top right corner (picture 1). You note there is now a space between the half-dollar and the penny. Here we break the flow of coins. This is the cunning bit. Shift around *just* the penny, the dimes and the nickel in a clockwise direction until the penny is in the bottom left corner (picture 2). Shift around *just* the dime, the half-dollar, and the quarter in a counter-clockwise direction until the half-dollar is next to the penny (picture 3). All you have to do now is slide all five coins around clockwise until the penny is just above the half-dollar, on the left.

The trick was to split into two the flow of coins and reverse the direction of flow of three of them.

1

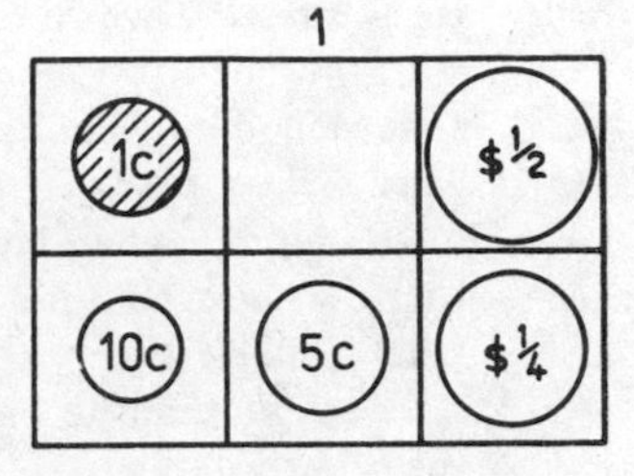

2

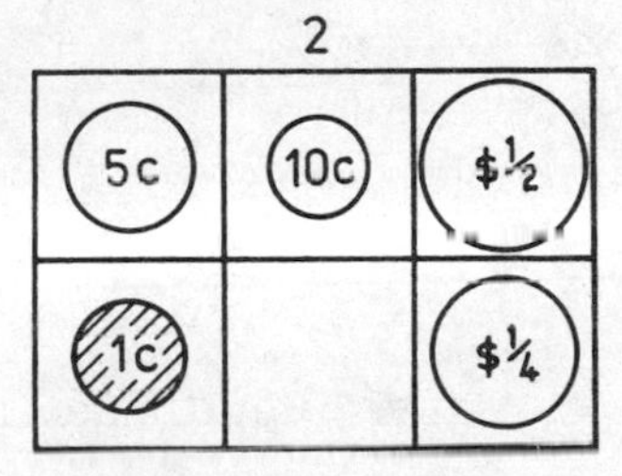

3

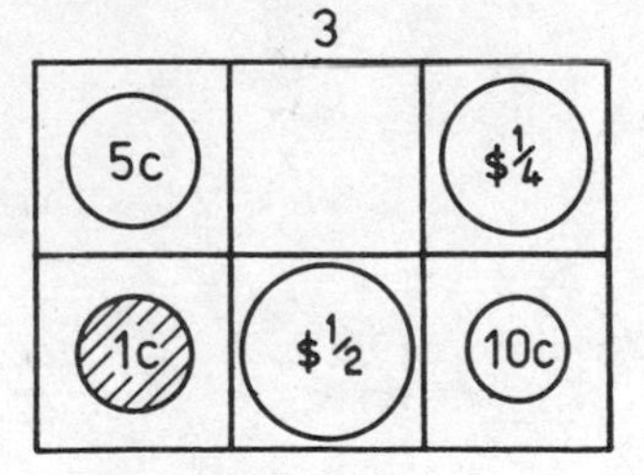

Coin Changeovers

The pennies and nickels *can* change places in both cases.

Mission Impossible?

Writing *F* for Dr. Fünf and *S* for Dr. Sieben, and *5* and *7* for the agents, here is one way of completing the mission. *F, 5, S,* and *7* start on the Slobodian bank. First, *F* and *5* row across the river; *F* stays on far bank. *5* rows back, picks up fellow agent *7* and rows him over, leaving *S* alone on the Slobodian bank. Then *7* rows back alone and picks up *S* and takes him across to join the other two. Mission *possible!*

Railroad Switch

Here are the six moves:

(1) The engine driver moves past *B*, backs up into *BC*, and couples on the black car.

(2) He pulls the black car past *B*, then he backs up into *AB* and uncouples the black car. Then he moves past *B* and backs into *BC* again.

(3) He backs past *C* and then shunts forward into *AC* and couples up the white car.

(4) He pushes the white car onto the main line out past *A*. Still coupled to it, he backs up along *AB* and couples on the black car; he is now sandwiched between the two cars.

(5) Sandwiched between the two cars, he backs down past *B*. Then he moves up *BC*, where he uncouples the white car.

(6) He now backs past *B* and then moves forward past *A*, still towing the black car. He then backs up *AC* and uncouples it. He moves out of *AC* past *A;* then he backs up into the stretch *AB*. He is now facing the other way.

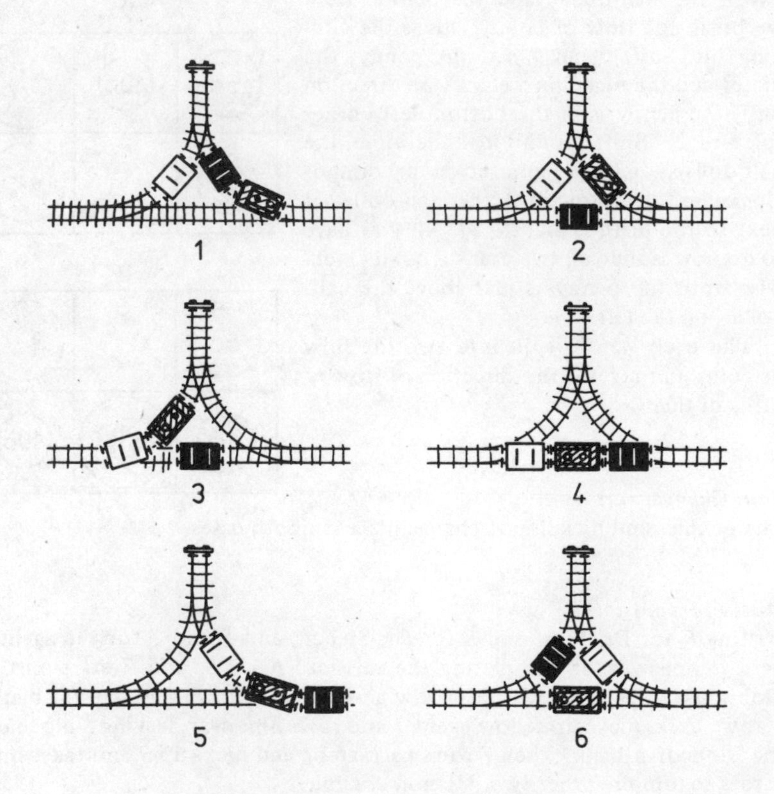

Restacking Coins

Just seven moves are needed, so they shouldn't have taken *too* long to do! Here is the relationship between the number of moves and the number of coins:

Coins	1	2	3	4	5
Moves	1	3	7	15	31

The number of moves is 2 times itself the same number of times as coins used, less 1. Thus for three coins, it is $(2 \times 2 \times 2) - 1$, or $8 - 1$ which is 7.

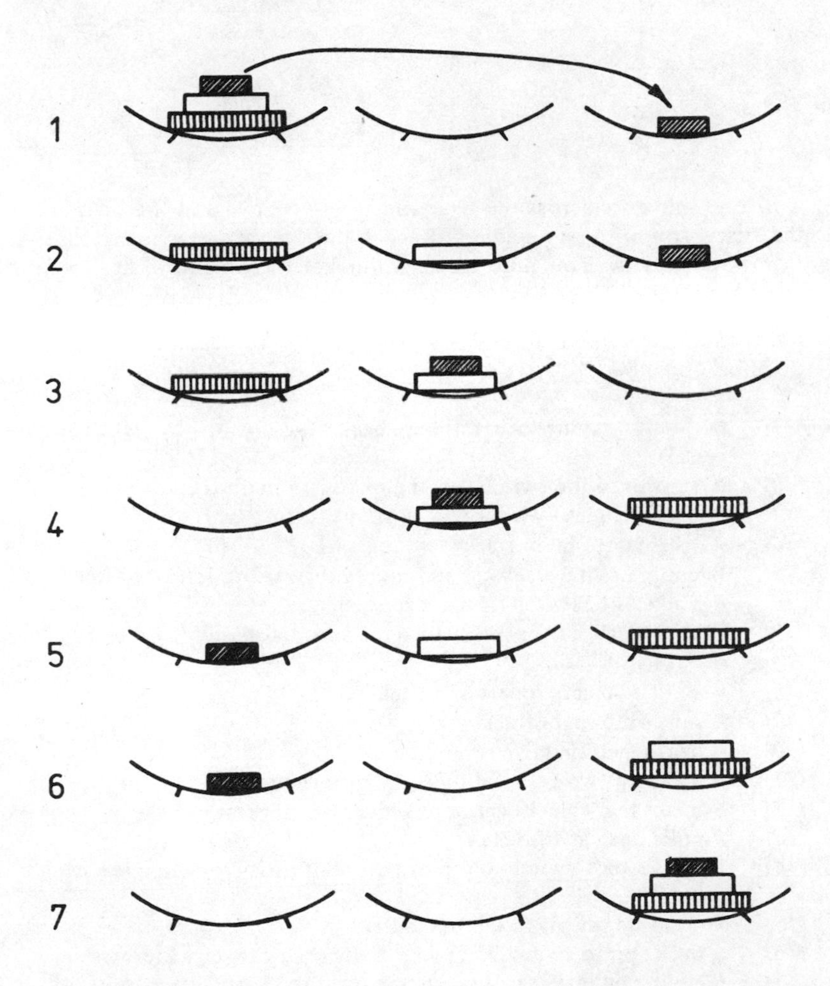

River Crossing

First, the two boys cross in the boat:

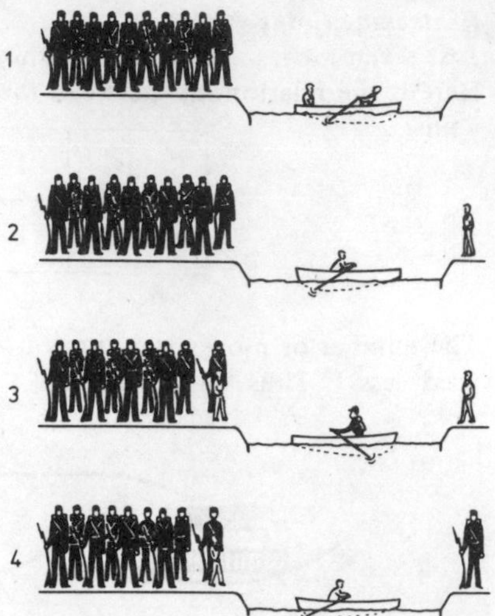

Now one soldier is across the river and the two boys and the boat are on the first bank with the soldiers. Repeat the operation as many times as there are soldiers! You note that the number of soldiers wasn't given; it doesn't matter.

Collision Course?

(1) *W* (white engine) with its car backs far out to the right (one reversal).
(2) *W* runs onto the switch, leaving its car on main track.
(3) *B* (black engine) with its car runs out to the right.
(4) *W* backs onto main track (two reversals).
(5) *W* couples with black car and moves forward to left of switch.
(6) *B* backs onto switch (three reversals).
(7) *W* and black car back off to right and couple with white car (four reversals).
(8) *W* pulls two cars to left of switch.
(9) *B* runs onto main track.
(10) *B* backs to train (five reversals).
(11) *B* picks up two cars and pulls them to right.
(12) *B* backs rear (black) car onto switch (six reversals).
(13) *B* pulls one car to right.
(14) *W* backs past switch and picks up white car from engine (seven reversals).
(15) *W* pulls its car off to left and away.
(16) *B* backs up to switch and picks up its own car (eight reversals).
(17) *B* engine pulls its car from switch onto track and goes on its way.

6. Reasoning and Logical Puzzles

Thinking Blocks

A.

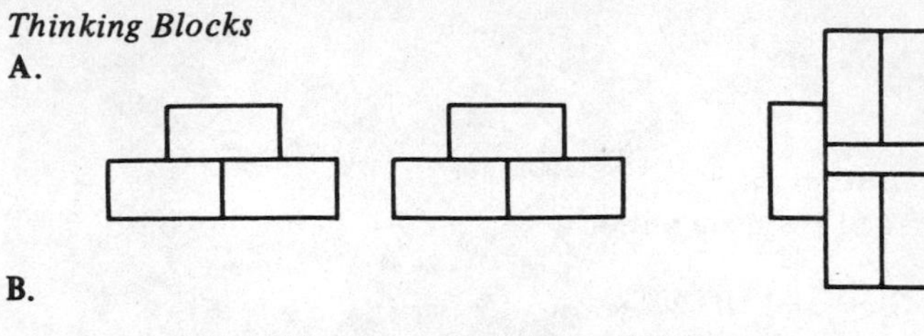

B.

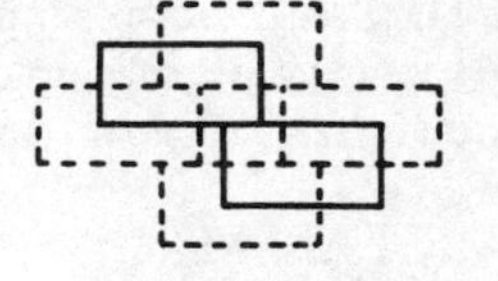

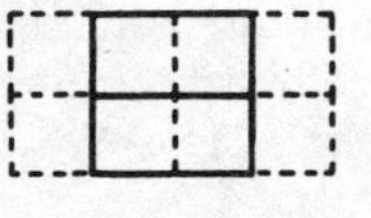

C.

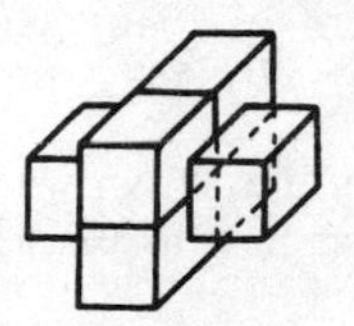

D.

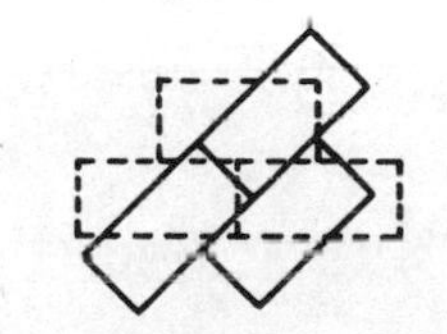

Martian Orders!
(*a*) Thalia, Zane, Xeron; (*b*) Sheree, Thalia, Zane, Xeron.

What Shape Next?
(*A*) Shape *c*, (*B*) shape *e*.

IQ Puzzle
Shape 3.

Odd Shape Out
a, 2; *b*, 3; *c*, 3; *d*, 1.

The Same Shape
(*A*) Shape *d*, (*B*) shape *c*.

Next Shape, Please

The Apt House
House 2.

Who Is Telling the Truth?
Con is.

The Colored Chemicals Puzzle
Orange, yellow, and green are poison.

Mr. Black, Mr. Gray, and Mr. White
The key is that the man in white is talking to Mr. Black and so cannot *be* him. Nor can he be Mr. White, since nobody is wearing his own color. So the man in white must be Mr. Gray. We can show what we know like this:

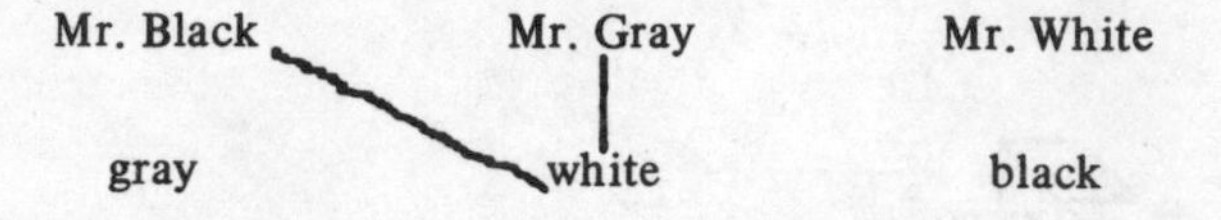

The straight line shows what must be true; the wiggly line shows what cannot be true. Mr White cannot be wearing white; so he's in black. That leaves Mr. Black wearing gray.

Hairdresser or Shop Assistant?
Amy and Babs are shop assistants; Carol is a hairdresser.

The Zookeeper's Puzzle
Art and Cora.

Who's Guilty?
Alf and Bert are guilty.

Who's in the Play?
Charles and Alice.

Tea, Coffee, or Malted Milk?
Malted milk.

Soda or Milkshake?
Suppose Alan has a soda. Then (*a*) says Bet has a milkshake. But (*c*) tells you Cis cannot then have a milkshake and must have a soda. But (*b*) says both Alan and Cis cannot both have a soda. Alan cannot have a soda; so Alan has a milkshake. From (*b*) that means Cis has a soda. Which, from (*c*), leaves Bet free to choose either a soda or a milkshake. Thus there are two possible orders: (1) Alan, milkshake; Cis, soda; and Bet, soda. (2) Alan, milkshake; Cis, soda; Bet, milkshake.

Newton's Kittens

Obviously the kittens could have gotten in and out by the same hole as the mother cat!

March Hare's Party

Sylvie had tea under the tree at table 1 because she wouldn't go near water. Al and Barbra sat at table 3: He couldn't take her in the boat to table 4. Gary joined them at 3, roller-skating over the bridge: He couldn't go to table 2 because of the "no boys" rule. That leaves Don, who wouldn't sit with Gary at table 3 and also couldn't take the path to table 2. Don rowed to table 4 and sat by himself.

Answer: table 1, Sylvie; 2, nobody; 3, Al, Barbra, and Gary; and 4, Don.

Marriage Mix-up

Ted is married to Barbra with daughter Ruth, Pete to Sue with daughter Wendy, and Charlie to Nicola with son Dick. The reasoning goes like this: Ted's daughter is not Wendy. So his daughter must be Ruth. So Pete is father of other girl, Wendy. Which means Charlie is father of Dick. So his wife cannot be Barbra because she has a daughter. (Assume a girl plays Annie and Ophelia!) His wife is not Sue, so his wife has to be Nicola. Now Pete's daughter is not Barbra's daughter because they have only one child each. So Pete cannot be married to Barbra. That means Ted is married to Barbra, and Pete therefore to Sue.

Who Does Which Job?

Orville is bartender and singer; Virgil is private eye and racing driver; Homer is jockey and cardsharp. This is how you get the answer. Draw a table to show the men and the jobs, and fill it in as follows:

Facts used		*Orville*	*Virgil*	*Homer*
3	Private eye			
1 2	Racing driver			X
2	Singer		X	X
3 4	Jockey	X	X	
4	Bartender			
1	Cardsharp			

First look at the *jobs*. Fact *1* tells us the bartender is not the same man as the racing driver. Put a *1* beside them (as shown). Similarly the racing driver (*2*) is not the singer (*2*). And so on. Now look at the *men*. Fact *2* tells us Homer is neither the racing driver nor the singer; so put an *X* in the table under *Homer* opposite those two jobs, as shown. Fact *5* says Virgil is not the singer; put an *X* under *Virgil* opposite *Singer.* Fact *6* tells you Homer is the jockey as Virgil and Orville are not; opposite *Jockey* put *X*'s under *V* and *O* and a check under *H.*

Now for the reasoning. Orville must be the singer—since neither Virgil nor Homer is—so put a check under *O* opposite *Singer.* Here is the table so far in brief:

	O	*V*	*H*
P			
R			X
S	√	X	X
J	X	X	√
B			
C			

To fill the *Singer* line put a check under Orville (*O*). Then in the *Jockey* line put a check under Homer (*H*). And so on.

Fact *2* tells us to put a cross under *H* opposite R. Fact *3* gives an *X* under *H* opposite P and B. That leaves only C for *H*'s second job: put a check there. The table looks like this:

	O	*V*	*H*
P			X
R			X
S	√	X	X
J	X	X	√
B			X
C			√

Now we can put a check under *V* opposite R. So Fact *1* gives an *X* under *V* opposite B—thus forcing a √ under *O* on that line (that is, Orville's second job is bartender). Finally, the bottom line with two *X*'s means Virgil's second job is P (private eye).

Birds and Insects
Answer *A* alone follows logically.

Wonderland Golf
Five shots: DDDSD or SDDSD. There *is* a pattern. To see it, turn back to the map of the golf course. Working backwards from hole 18, a D shot gets you back to hole 9, then an S shot to 8, followed by three D's to the first tee. (From 2 to 1 could be an S as well.) You can also work it out by arithmetic. Divide the hole number by 2 over and over again, noting if there is a remainder of 1. For 18 you get:

18
9
4 *r* 1
2
1

Count up the number of answers and remainders: 9, 4, 1, 2, 1, which makes five numbers; that's how many shots it takes. This rule works for *any* hole.

Mad Hatter's Tea Party
Set *G* to table 1, *M* to 3, and *B* to 4. Table 2 stays empty.

7. Mathematical Games

Nim
The way to calculate a winning position is best shown with the starting position of Nim. It has 3, 4, and 5 matches. We rewrite the rows in binary—that is, in powers of 2, or in "doublings." The numbers 100, 10, and 1 in binary are 4, 2, and 1 in everyday numbers. While *11* in usual counting numbers means 1 ten and 1 one, in binary it means 1 two and 1 one. We can make 3 out of 2 + 1 and in binary write it as 11. Then 4 in binary is 100, meaning 1 four and no twos and no ones, and 5 in binary is 101, meaning 1 four, no twos and 1 one. We set the rows out in binary as follows:

	Matches	Fours	Twos	Ones
Top row	3		1	1
Middle row	4	1	0	0
Bottom row	5	1	0	1
Totals		2	1	2

As you see, we added each column up in ordinary numbers; but we did not "carry" numbers over from one column to the next. Two column totals are even, and one, the middle column, is odd. To make the position safe for yourself, all you do is make the totals of each column *even.* So your first move is to take 2 matches from the top row, as explained. This changes the top binary number to 1. The columns then become:

	Matches	Fours	Twos	Ones
Top row	1			1
Middle row	4	1	0	0
Bottom row	5	1	0	1
Totals		2	0	2

Now each column adds up to an even number. The position is safe.

Daisy
Here is the second player's winning strategy: Say the first player takes one petal; then the second player takes two petals, which must be next to each other, directly opposite the one taken by the first player. If the first player takes two adjacent petals, the second player takes one petal, again directly opposite. Either way this leaves two sets of five petals, symmetrically arranged about the two spaces. All the second player has to do now is to keep the pattern symmetrical, taking special note of the spaces.

The Cop and the Robber
The cop has first to go around the triangular block at the top left corner. Then he is an odd number of corners away from the robber and can catch him–provided the robber does not go around the triangle! Remember, there are only three corners in the triangular block, and you can get right around it in three moves.

Morra

Morra's Winnings

		Other shows	
		1 finger	2 fingers
Morra shows	1 finger	+ 2	− 3
	2 fingers	− 1	+ 2

Morra's best strategy, to reduce his losses, is to show two fingers all the time; then he never loses more than one penny.